Power of the Invisible

The *quantessence* of reality

Sander Bais

Amsterdam University Press

Publication of this book has been made possible by the
financial support of generous individuals as well as the
following organizations and institutions:
Lorentz Fonds
Stichting Physica
Institute of Physics, University of Amsterdam
Delta ITP (NL)
Qusoft
Nikhef
Commenius Leergangen

Cover design: bij Barbara
Lay-out and illustrations: Sander Bais
This book has been typeset in Latex

ISBN   9789048562879 (cassette)
ISBN   9789048565306 (Volume I)
ISBN   9789048565313 (Volume II)
ISBN   9789048565320 (Volume III)
e-ISBN 9789048562886 (pdf)
DOI   10.5117/9789048562879
BISAC   SCI057000

If quantum mechanics hasn't profoundly shocked you, you haven't understood it yet.

Niels Bohr

Whether we like it or not, modern ways are going to alter and in part destroy traditional customs and values.

Werner Heisenberg,
Physics and Philosophy:
The Revolution in Modern Science

Contents

II Quantessence:
how quantum theory works

Contents   5

III   Hierarchies:
the emergence of diversity

Contents   5

Some like it hot!

I assume that readers share a curiosity about quantum things, but they may have different levels of mathematical proficiency, if any. Therefore, I have put warning symbols next to the section headings. Some people like it hot & spicy and they presumably feel attracted to the sections that are marked with three hot peppers. The book is conceived such that the quite hot 2- and 3-pepper sections can be left aside without corrupting the main line of argument. *Bon appetit*!

A preface of prefaces

> We all agree that your theory is crazy. The question which divides us is whether it is crazy enough to have a chance of being correct.
>
> Niels Bohr (addressing Wolfgang Pauli)

The title *Power of the invisible* could cover a lot of possible subjects, ranging from ordinary gossip to the most elevated of spiritual teachings, as well as from the Earth's magnetic field to the invisible microcosmos. It underscores the plain fact that most things are actually invisible, unseen by the naked eye. The subtitle of this trilogy *The quantessence of reality* makes clear that in this book we limit ourselves to a world that is inaccessible to the human eye in a physical sense: A world that was only made visible hundreds of thousands of years after human history started through the development of science and technology. Humans have always been aware of the sky and the heavens, but only relatively late did they realize that there was a universe as vast, diverse and mysterious on the inside of things. The title mainly refers to the power of that hidden microcosmos, and the tremendous forces that are at work within it.

The word *quantessence* is a neologism which means 'the quintessence of quantum,' referring to phenomena that can only be explained in terms of quantum theory. A theory is a model, a symbolic representation of (a part of) the world and supposedly explains in a logically coherent way how that works. In that sense it is a visualization, an abstract reconstruction of that invisible microcosmos in terms of mathematical symbols and equations. And this is what most scientific explanations in the end tend to boil down to. And it is also this underlying network of relations and fundamental principles which govern reality that represents the power of the invisible.

The path towards such a model has been provided by an incredible interplay between science and technology, where ever more refined instruments were conceived and constructed to make discernible what was invisible before. In this way humankind has for millennia managed to push the boundaries of what is observable forward in an objective sense. And that process has fundamentally changed the nature of human existence. That is how we became aware of the tremendous *power of the invisible* and *the quantessence of reality*. The beautiful phrase 'Humans became aware, or learned about, or understood,' covers up the sobering fact that the lucky humans who are referred to unfortunately form a tiny fraction of humankind: a nerdy caste of scientist, as high priests of scientific knowledge. They are a tiny fraction in spite of the fact that everybody is invited to come and share their collective wisdom by reading books or engaging otherwise. And that turns out to be not so easy.

Scientific textbooks take pride in being as impersonal as a brick. It provides them with an aura of objectivity. Question: what do *Bethe, Baym, Bohm, Davies, Dirac, Feynman, Greiner, Griffiths, Gottfried, Kemble, Kramers, Landau, Leblond, Levy, Lipkin, Mandl, Martin, Matthews, Merzbacher, Messiah, Mott, Omnès, Pauling, Schiff, Sakurai, Shankar, Tannoudji en Weyl* have in common? Indeed, each of them has (co-)authored a textbook or two on quantum mechanics. Let me tell you how this works. If you have to teach a course on quantum theory, you can choose from more than fifty textbooks: an impressive oeuvre that bears witness to a profound love for our deepest knowledge. It doesn't stop many a teacher from adding their own little masterpiece to it. For students it is often a great relief to discover that the overlap between these books is so immense, that complete bookcases in the library effectively shrink to a tiny pile of classics. *If you've read one, you've read many.*

The personal view of the author usually becomes clear in their limited choice of subjects, and if everything is well, they should apologize for that in the Preface. That by itself is not so exciting, in spite of being universal. Sometimes however – and that is what concerns us here – the Preface has far more to say. It appears to be the only place where the author is allowed to make their personal views known, and indeed I must admit that those are harder to embed in a treatment of, say, *angular momentum*. In the preface the author may bare their soul. It may articulate the *zeitgeist* and even deteriorate into a manifesto of principles. The innocent looking preface may actually just be a hidden persuader for personal prejudices: a *mission statement*, which might amount to little more than the scientific equivalent of what politicians call *corridor talk*. Actually, it is a place where scientist publicly tell each other the truth. Therefore this 'preface of prefaces' is a virtual quantum dialog between some of the masters which is concocted from their outspoken prefaces. This is a small quantum correction to the immaculate status of some of our quantum classics.

In 1924 the first version appeared of the standard work *Methoden der Mathematische Physik* by Courant and Hilbert (this book evolved into the monumental work in two parts that was printed in 1938). It appeared in the German university city of Göttingen at the time when the mental landslide that quantum mechanics was took place. As a matter of fact the books covered classical mathematical physics but treated the subject of differential equations and in particular eigenvalue problems in great detail, which then played a central role in solving for example the Schrödinger equation. After Courant fled Germany, long before the Second World War, the Nazi's blocked distribution of the book (as you may read in the preface to the 1953 edition). Let me share a somber quote from the original 1924 version:

> So kommt es dass viele Vertreter der Analysis das Bewusstsein der Zusammengehörigkeit ihrer Wissenschaft mit der Physik und anderen Gebieten verloren haben, während auf die andere Seite oft den Physikern das Verständnis für die Probleme and Methoden der Mathematiker, ja sogar für deren ganze Interessensphäre und Sprache abhanden gekommen ist. Ohne Zweifel liegt in dieser Tendenz eine Bedrohung für die ganze Wissenschaft überhaupt; der Strom der wissentschaftlichen Entwicklung ist in Gefahr, sich weiter und weiter zu verästeln, zu versickern und auszutrocknen.[1]

Courant therefore had no lack of drive to write a beautiful book. Another early classic (but in many ways modern) about quantum theory is *The Principles of Quantum Mechanics* by Paul Dirac (first edition in 1930). He was well-known to be a man of few words:

> Mathematics is the tool especially suited for dealing with abstract concepts of any kind and there is no limit to its power in this field. For this reason a book on the new physics, if not purely descriptive of experimental work, must be essentially mathematical.

The book then continues to present quantum theory in a form that he referred to as the 'symbolic method', a method used all over the place today:

> ...I have chosen the symbolic method, introducing the representatives later merely as an aid to practical calculation. This has necessitated a complete break from the historical line of development, but this break is an advantage through enabling the approach to the new

---

[1]As a result, many practitioners of mathematical analysis have lost the awareness of their science's affiliation with physics and other fields, while on the other hand, physicists often have lost the understanding of the problems and methods of mathematicians, and indeed of their whole sphere of interest and language. There is no doubt that this trend poses a threat to the whole of science; the stream of scientific development is in danger of becoming more and more branched out, to seep away and to become dehydrated.

ideas to be made as direct as possible.

The physicists who were of the opinion that Dirac's approach was too mathematical were silenced by the quite outspoken preface of the *Mathematische Grundlagen der Quantenmechanik* by John von Neumann (1932). The opening line makes it unambiguously clear what the goals are and what the standards to be maintained throughout:[2]

> Der Gegenstand dieses Buches ist die einheitliche, und, soweit als möglich und angebracht, mathematisch einwandfreie Darstellung der neuen Quantenmechanik,...

And later on he even makes a compliment:

> Eine an Kürze und Eleganz kaum zu überbietende Darstellung der Quantenmechanik, die ebenfalls von invariantem Character ist, hat Dirac in mehreren Abhandlungen sowie in seinem kürzlich erschienenen Buche gegeben.[3]

that turns out to be a prelude to a less generous passage:

> Die erwähnte, infolge ihrer Durchsichtigkeit und Eleganz heute in einen grossen Teil der quantenmechanische Literatur übergegangene Methodik von Dirac wird den Anforderungen der mathematische Strenge in keiner Weise gerecht – auch dann nicht, wenn diese natürlicher- und billigerweise auf das sonst in der theoretischen Physik

übliche Mass reduziert werden.[4]

Kramers in his *Quantum Mechanics* from 1937 holds a view rather orthogonal to Von Neuman's, where he returns to the more heuristic, physically oriented approach of Bohr:

> The apparent lack of mathematical morals which is contritely pointed out repeatedly in the text is not exclusively due to the incompetence of the author. Physical morals, even (or rather especially) in their purest form, that is, unencumbered by pedagogic afterthoughts, do not live happily together with their mathematical relations in the restricted mansion of the human mind – and neither in the restricted volume of a monograph.

The famous Russian physicists Landau and Lifschitz set their own magnificent standard in their course on Theoretical Physics, which consists of more than ten volumes. These are the books from which our Russian colleagues loved to recite. If you got into a heavy-duty technical argument with them, they would exclaim: 'But don't you know this? Is well-known exercise in the chapter five, of the volume eight of the Landau Lifschitz!' Little less than the Soviet equivalent of a bible, it managed quite well to spread its profound physics wisdom. The first edition dates back to 1947. In the preface to volume three, *Quantummechanik* the authors note the following:[5]

---

[2]The subject of this book is the unified, and as far as possible and appropriate, mathematically rigorously correct representation of the new quantum mechanics.

[3]An account of quantum mechanics, which can hardly be surpassed in brevity and elegance, and which is also of an invariant character, has been given by Dirac in several papers as well as in his recently published book.

[4]The methodology of Dirac mentioned above, which, owing to its transparency and elegance, has today been carried over to a large part of the quantum mechanical literature, does in no way justice to the requirements of mathematical rigor, even if the standard is lowered to the more natural and reasonable one typical for theoretical physics.

[5]I apologize for quoting the German version which was for sale for a dollar or less in the former Soviet Union, at least on the rare occasions that it was not sold out. No easy reading because the formulas were set in *Fraktur* - the old German alphabet.

Man kann nicht umhin festzustellen, dass die Darstellung in vielen Lehrbüchern der Quantenmechanik komplizierter als in den Originalarbeiten ist. Obwohl eine solche Darstellung gewöhnlich mit grösserer Allgemeinheit und Strenge begründet wird, ist jedoch bei aufmerksamer Betrachtung leicht zu erkennen, dass sowohl das eine wie die andere tatsächlich oft illusorisch sind, was sogar soweit geht, dass sich ein beträchtlicher Teil der 'strengen' Sätze alsxfx fehlerhaft erweisst. Da uns eine solche komplizierte Darstellung völlig ungerechtfertigt erscheint, haben wir uns umgekehrt um denkbar mögliche Einfachheit bemüht und haben vielfach auf die Originalarbeiten zurückgegriffen.[6]

David Bohm also regrets in the preface to his *Quantum Theory* from 1951 the loss of qualitative, imaginable physical concepts. Bohm was well aware of the subtleties and essential role of the measurement process in quantum mechanics. And it should be said that the whole arsenal of rather puzzling, if not controversial, *Gedanken Experimente* which have in the meantime descended into the blood, sweat and tears in the lab, form a vindication of his cry to further elucidate the fundamental concepts underlying the theory:

> So strong is this contrast [between classical and quantum physics] that an appreciable number of physicists were led to the conclusion that the quantum properties of matter imply a renunciation of the possibility of their being understood in the customary imaginative sense,

and that instead, there remains only a self-consistent mathematical formalism which can, in some mysterious way, predict the numerical results of actual experiments. Nevertheless, . . . , it finally became possible to express the results of the quantum theory in terms of comparitively qualitative and imaginative concepts, which are, however of a totally different nature from those appearing in the classical theory.

In this anthology we have to include the celebrated *Feynman Lectures*, as they form a most original and inspiring treatment of the theoretical basis of the physics curriculum.[7] To my knowledge it is also the first book written in first person reflecting his outspoken aversion to formality and distance. Therefore in his *Lectures* you will find regularly statements that are unmistakably Mr. Feynman like (from Part III, Chapter 1: *Quantum behavior*):

> This would mean, if it were true, that physics has given up on the problem of trying to predict exactly what will happen in a definite circumstance. Yes! Physics *has* given up.

In the preface the legendary teacher shows himself accountable for his pedagogical adventures (no need for the evaluation jungle that tends to stifle modern educational institutions):

> The question, of course, is how well this experiment succeeded. My own point of view – which, however, does not seem to be shared by most of the people who worked with the students – is pessimistic. I don't think I did well by the students. When I look at the way the

---

[6]One cannot help but notice that the presentation in many textbooks of quantum mechanics is more complicated than in the original works. Although such a statement is usually justified by greater generality and rigor, it is easy to see, after careful consideration, that both are often illusory, and this even goes so far as to state that a considerable part of the 'rigorous' statements prove to be faulty. As in our view such a complicated presentation appears to be completely unjustified, we have, conversely, tried to stay as simple as possible and have often resorted to the original works.

[7]The quite accessible first chapter of his book with Hibbs about *Quantum mechanics and path integrals* and his popular booklet called *QED* are also a must.

majority of the students handled the problems on the examinations, I think that the system is a failure. . . . But then, 'The power of instruction is seldom of much efficacy except in those happy circumstances where it is almost superfluous.' (Gibbons)

There are more recent attempts to pick up the innovative approach in the presentation of quantum mechanics, for example in the book *Quantics* of Lévy-Leblond and Balibar. The term 'quantique' is apparently slang for 'quantum mechanics' used by French students. The English version 'quantics' has not seen a similar popularity among the youth educated in English, and if it is used, it is rather in in the world of data analysis and consultancy. There is a species of whizzkids called 'quants', who make money in investment banking. No quantum theory required. Yet.

Nobody really dares to base an entire course in the spirit of these textbooks [the Feynman and Berkeley series], and often they are only used to breathe an extra bit of spirit (in some physical sense, let us say) into the traditional abstract and scholastic way of teaching. The teaching method of Feynman and Wichman is not, after all, taken seriously.

Further on in the preface we read:

One often hears research workers expressing the desire to widen their professional culture, to deepen or rejuvenate their primary education. Such an aspiration does not come from an abstract desire to become generally cultured. Rather, it reflects the desire to increase their ability to picture, interpret and understand physics – *their* physics. To satisfy this need, these researchers all too often have at their disposal daunting and sophisticated treatises, which they find intimidating, since they

have the impression that they would only find abstract answers to their concrete questions.

It was this exploration of prefaces that provided me with one of the principle motivations for writing this book. In theoretical physics and quantum theory in particular, there is always a tension between mathematical rigor and physical understanding, between formal arguments and intuition, between abstract representations and physical reality. If we look back at the development of quantum theory, we see from observational evidence that classical physics was failing us; we had to first develop a mathematical framework for the quantum world. The physical intuitions, of which the physicists were so proud, were so deeply rooted in the classical experience that they led them completely astray in the quantum world and made the development of a suitable theory very hard.

Today however, we are armed with the outcomes of a broad spectrum of real lab experiments that in the early quantum days only could be dreamt of as far-out *gedanken* experiments. There is a wide variety of quantum phenomena we have in the meantime become so 'familiar' with, that practitioners have developed a sort of *quantum intuition* – in the sense of adaption, being a healthy blend of experience and common sense. And, with that, a 'quantum heuristics' came into being – where whatever was considered esoteric speculation before, kind of turned into a bunch of 'no brainers'. This 'quantum heuristics' has at least informally gained some respectability and legitimacy. It is not quite so visible in textbooks but it is certainly predominantly present when physicists argue in front of their blackboards. I expect that this perspective will percolate through in future quantum books. One might object that this may introduce even more quantum vagueness in our quantum conversations. Apparently quantum uncertainties have made it all the way up to the heart of our ontology and epistemology, a remarkable recursion indeed.

This being said, you now know where I found the courage to produce yet another semi-popular book on quantum physics and information. You need no longer ask: 'Who ordered that?'.[8]

This book aims to demonstrate the 'Power of the invisible,' where that power refers to the 'essence' or better the 'quintessence' of quantum. This assumes that we, after more than a century of study, do know what the essence of quantum is. What we know for sure is that it is extremely powerful, in spite of being to a large extent concerned with the 'invisible.'

Talking about the essence of something requires a certain depth, not just conveying facts, but creating the appropriate reference frames and language. This *quantessential* perspective will be presented in the following Introductory chapter which also provides a roadmap to this book.

Further reading.
Some of the classics mentioned in this chapter:

— *Methods of Mathematical Physics*
  D. Hilbert and R. Courant
  Wiley-VCH; 2 Volumes (1989)

— *The Principles of Quantum Mechanics*
  P.A.M. Dirac
  Oxford University Press; 4th edition (1961)

— *Mathematical Foundations of Quantum Mechanics:*
  J. von Neumann
  Princeton Univers. Press; New edition (2018)

— *Quantum Mechanics*
  H.A. Kramers
  Dover Publications (1964)

— *Quantum Mechanics (Non-Relativistic Theory)*
  L.D. Landau, E.M. Lifshitz
  Pergamon Press; 3rd edition (1981)

— *Quantum Theory*
  D. Bohm
  Dover Publications Inc (1989)

— *The Feynman Lectures on Physics*
  R.P. Feynman (Author), R.B. Leighton (Contributor), M. Sands (Contributor)
  Pearson P T R; (3 Volume Set) 1st edition (1970)

— *Quantics: Rudiments of Quantum Physics*
  J-M. Levy-Leblond F. Balibar
  North Holland (1990)

Complementary reading:

— *The Quantum Physicists*
  W.H. Cropper
  Oxford University. Press (1970)

---

[8]This is what Nobel laureate Isodor Rabi quipped in the mid-thirties, when informed about the discovery of the *muon* particle, a heavy brother of the electron that at that time seemed to have no purpose, and no reason to exist.

Introduction

When it comes to atoms, language can be used only as in poetry. The poet, too, is not nearly so concerned with describing facts as with creating images.

Niels Bohr, 'Atomic Physics and the Description of Nature' (1934)

In this introduction we show how the book is structured and give some advice on how to read it.

Mathematics as a language of Nature. Quantum theory is known to be a difficult subject and becomes completely unfathomable if you have to rely entirely on our feeble natural language to describe it. Therefore I hope that you will not be scared away by the book's rather mathematical appearance, particularly the second volume which looks as if it is full of equations. Don't put the book aside just because of its intimidating appearance. Natural language is not the optimal means precisely because in quantum theory we enter realms of reality that are quite remote from our everyday experiences and preconceptions. Our cherished 'common sense' appeared to be of limited use and easily led us astray. Some call the quantum world mysterious or alien, while others see iut as elusive or unfathomable; indeed one may easily get drowned if the message is communicated to you in words only.

Mathematics is here to rescue us; it allows us to construct smart and elegant notions that perfectly fit nature's needs it comes with a beautifully efficient notation. The lengthy descriptions one would need in natural language to convey the essentials of quantum reality would too easily clut-

The quantum leap. This art work called 'The running knot' is located in the city park of Kanazawa, Japan. (Source: Eryn Vorn, FLICKR)

ter the mind and lead to the utmost confusion, as I have seen happening in quite a few 'no formula' expositions of the quantum world to the layperson. So there are ample reasons to be courageous and go 'symbolic.'

Great narratives choose their own language. The heart of music is in the sound and a verbal substitute would not do. And as we all know, it takes guidance to learn how to hear what it expresses. The same is true for the visual arts. It is hard to imagine a book about Picasso without pictures. And this is what Sagredo in the *Dialogos* of Galileo confided: 'If I were again beginning my studies, I would follow the advice of Plato and start with mathematics.' Yes, the narrative of Nature expresses itself most eloquently in mathematics. So, we take Sagredo's advice to heart and will gently introduce some of the *quantessential* mathematical concepts along the way, but always in a rather pedestrian way[9]. Math, as a language of nature, as a means for understanding, but not as a purpose on its own. To that end I have included several so-called *Math Excursions* at the end of the third volume. These excursions explain in a user-friendly way what the math in the main text is about and will tell you all you need – but maybe never wanted – to know about matters like functions, complex numbers, matrices, algebras or vectors. Checking out these excursions will help you to get more out of this book.

The best part of climbing a mountain is often the splendid view from the top. In a similar way we work our way up to some of the quantessential equations, not in praise of rigor, but in praise of clarity and beauty. I tell my students that equations love people and they better do because they owe their existence to them. Bearing that in mind, isn't it amazing that this man-made language of mathematics turns out to be the most 'natural' after all? This fascinating fact inspired the famous mathematical physicist Eugene Wigner to write an interesting essay about this paradox titled: 'The unreasonable effectiveness of mathematics in the natural sciences.' And as I intend to remain your traveling companion all along the winding road to the quantum world, I hope that you will be patient with some of the math that we will encounter along the way. Think of it as the poetry of reality: a sublime shorthand endowed with a built-in integrity. A minimal yet powerful representation of reality. There is some truth in what John von Neumann, as keynote speaker at the first national meeting of the Association for Computing Machinery in 1947, quipped: 'If people do not believe that mathematics is simple, it is only

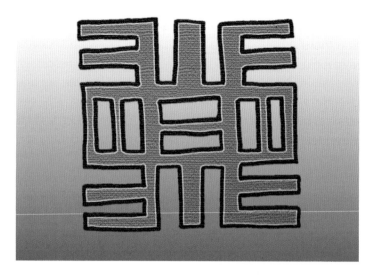

Figure 1: *Adinkra symbol.* Adinkras are symbols of the people of the Ashanti Kingdom in West Africa (Ghana) that represent concepts or wise sayings (aphorisms). This adinkra is called 'nea onnim no sua a, ohu,' which translates as 'he/she who does not know can become knowledgeable through learning.' I happen to see many interlocked copies of the letter 'E' , from Education, a striking coincidence!

S. James Gates, *Complex ideas, complex shapes* (2012)

because they do not realize how complicated life is.'

To whom am I talking? One of the first questions a potential publisher will throw at you as potential author is about who your perceived audience is. Who is going to read (or rather, buy) this book? So many pages, so many topics, so many equations, who the hell do you think....*If you cannot kill your darlings they will kill you!* My answer is encrypted in the symbolic aphorism depicted in Figure 1 saying: *'he/she who does not know can become knowledgeable through learning'.* Keeping in mind that this holds true for basically everybody, it stands for the notion of *education permanente*, which advocates a broader spectrum of conceivable audiences for books on knowledge. There is the questionable dichotomy that books about science have, for some reason, to belong to either the categories 'popular' or

---

[9]As we will indeed encounter many of the fundamental equations of physics along the way, the interested reader who is not at all versed in these equations may want to look at my popular science book entitled *The Equations: icons of knowledge* (Harvard University Press, 2005).

'textbook', with basically nothing in between. From my experience of teaching science to all kinds of people, I know that there are many diverse audiences between those of laypeople and Harvard graduates. And these present us with a need for books that try to bridge the intellectual pseudo gap I just mentioned. And with the availability of internet sources like Wikipedia and Youtube there is still a clear need for in-between books that give a broad coherent account with some theoretical depth. My hope is that this book provides an example thereof. So who are the would-be members in this perceived audience: students of various backgrounds and disciplines, from motivated high school whizzkids to multidisciplinary college students, as well as their teachers. I think of students in the disciplines neighbouring physics in the natural sciences, as well as engineering, mathematics and information science. I think of journalists and of the growing group of seniors who finally have time to get to grips with some of the deep scientific subjects that over the last century through technological developments have so radically transformed the world around them. I dedicate this work to the bright young people throughout the world who share that insatiable hunger for true knowledge and I hope that it will inspire their honorable quest. Students tend to be overwhelmed by the 'how to' questions, which means that the 'why' and 'what does it mean' questions are neglected. Let me close this little pitch with a quote from the early muslim polymath Al Kindi[10], who lived around 850 AD:

> We should not be ashamed of recognizing truth and assimilating it from whatever source it may reach us, even though it might come from earlier generations or foreign peoples. For him who seeks truth there is nothing of more value than truth itself. It never cheapens or abases him who searches for it, but ennobles and honors him.

---

[10]Al Kindi wrote more then 250 books. His Manuscript on Deciphering Cryptographic Messages, in which he laid the foundation of crypto-analysis using statistical interference and frequency analysis, is remarkable.

Nature is quantized

Quantum theory is not a theory of one particular system like the atom; it is a set of universal principles that applies to all of nature.
We present an overview of how this elaborate field is structured as a whole and thereby motivate the lay out of the book.

Quantum theory is based on a set of fundamental principles that nature appears to obey at basically all scales and therefore underlies all of physics, and more indirectly also all of chemistry and biology. The dictum is 'One Nature, One Science'. Deep down all physical theories have to behave according to the quantum rules and therefore all our theories have to be 'quantized,' somewhat like kids have to be potty-trained, and dogs have to go to obedience school to learn not to bark. The quantum postulates forced us to reinvent the whole of fundamental physics from a new conceptual basis. We have quite successfully quantized particles and mechanics, electrodynamics including optics, and liquids, solids and other condensed forms of matter. But also unified theories describing subnuclear physics have been successfully quantized and led to the celebrated *Standard Model*. And finally, not so long ago, we realized that even information should be quantized. This ongoing quantization process has led to a much deeper understanding of the fundamental structure of nature, but also to a huge number of breathtaking applications and quantum technologies that have only just started to take off. Indeed, technologies involving quantum information processing are expected to generate a highly disruptive transition with a huge socio-economic impact. Yet, this having been said, there are still many fundamental challenges, like the quantum interpretation of gravity, the oldest known force, which are required to be tackled in order to understand the origins of the universe or how black holes work.

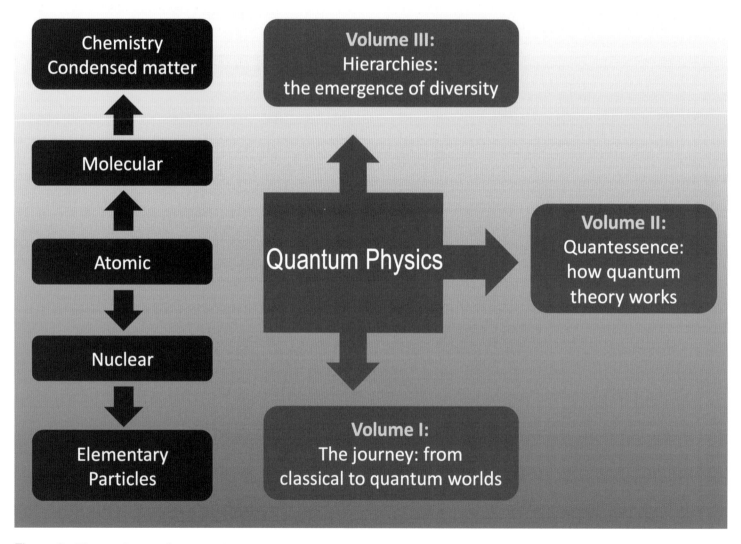

Figure 2: *Three volumes.* Quantum theory was introduced to physics at the atomic level. From there it started spreading into the other levels of physics, at both larger and smaller scales.

Three volumes. Quantum theory basically originated at the level of the atom, and by modern standards that is an intermediate length scale. From there the applications of the basic theory developed in two opposite directions, as indicated in the left column of Figure 2. On the one hand to ever smaller distances, all the way down to modern particle physics, and on the other hand to ever larger distances, moving up all the way to modern (bio)chemistry and condensed matter physics. The arrows pointing upward underscore the basic fact that quantum effects are by no means restricted to the microscopic domain. There are many research fields devoted to the study of quantum principles on macroscopic scales, which amounts to applying quantum theory to collective phenomena. In that sense every cell phone is full of quantum.

Even though I will restrict myself to the 'quantessentials', the subject is so vast that the book is divided into three parts, i.e. volumes, which – as also indicated in Figure 2 – can be characterized as follows.

The first volume of the book, called *The journey: from classical to quantum worlds*, starts with the highlights of classical physics and informatics after which it descends into the quantum world. It is the narrative guided by man's passionate quest for the most basic building blocks of nature and their interactions. We start with marbles and end up with quarks and even superstrings.

In the second volume of the book, called *Quantessence: how quantum theory works*, we delve deeper into the structure of the theory and present some of its mathematical representations. And we will talk about the conceptual issues concerning quantum states, observables and measurements that we encounter along the way. There we will be concerned extensively with mind-boggling notions like entanglement, particle interference and quantum teleportation.

In the third and final volume called *Hierarchies: the emer-*

gence of diversity, we discuss quantum theory as it applies to the structural hierarchy of matter from the atomic level to chemistry and the quantum physics of condensed states of matter. We not only consider the hierarchy in a spatial sense but also how that hierarchy arose in a temporal sense during the early stages of cosmic evolution. It closes with a chapter on *scaling*, discussing notions such as self-similarity, scale invariance and renormalization of theories in order to understand their asymptotic behavior if one imagines the behavior of theories as models of nature, at ever smaller or larger scales. We conclude this quantum trilogy by offering a concluding chapter with a more general science-driven perspective.

Physics, mathematics and concepts

If you look long enough, anything becomes abstract
Diane Arbus

This section presents a meta-perspective on how to read this quantessential book. The quantum world can be traversed in many ways, all pertaining to a certain 'logic'. Taking a single path will enlighten certain aspects but may obscure others. Therefore it is better to combine different paths to get an optimal feeling for the quantum landscape. To get to the quantessence, one would have to add up the contributions of all the different paths[11].

Once a field of science (like physics) has matured sufficiently, one can learn something interesting about the structure of scientific knowledge in general. This is indicated in the layered structure of quantum knowledge in the scheme of Figure 3, in which the three columns refer to the three layers of knowledge that I like to distinguish between and which will be explained shortly.

---

[11] In a symbolic – if not ironic – sense, you could call this a 'path integral approach to the understanding of quantum theory.'

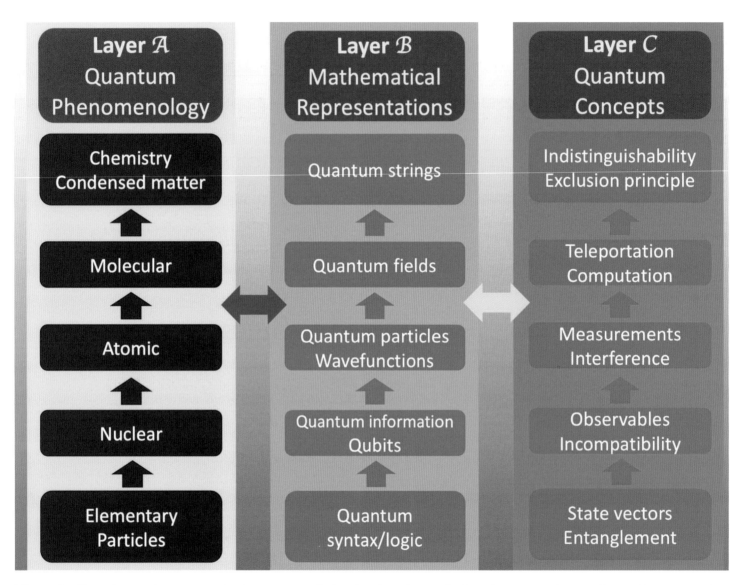

Figure 3: *Three layers.* In quantum physics one may distinguish three layers displayed here as columns. From left to right, ($\mathcal{A}$) is about the phenomenology of systems in which quantum theory manifests itself, ($\mathcal{B}$) is the layer of mathematical representations or realizations and ($\mathcal{C}$) is the layer of quantum concepts and principles. Note that the layers are coupled together as a whole, not via their individual components.

Theoretical physics is basically about constructing optimal mathematical models of reality. It usually starts by effectively describing certain regularities apparent in some observed physical phenomena. The next step – if possible – is to relate *different* phenomena through the model. This amounts to reducing the number of independent parameters in the models. Finally, one hopes that it will make predictions and suggestions as to where to look for unique signatures of new phenomena. Over time this modelling has been done in an ever more sophisticated way, exploiting existing as well as developing new mathematical and computational tools.

A first step in modelling a physical system is to just identify which degrees of freedom are relevant to the phenomena one wants to study and understand. A second crucial step is to identify what the relevant interactions between these basic degrees of freedom are. For the moment these are just words referring to basic notions, which have to find their way into some symbolic representation or mathematical framework. We may, in the end, have to extend our set of basic concepts and rules, our grammar so to speak, in order to accommodate new phenomena and new underlying principles.

In the development of quantum theory over the past century, this is exactly what happened. It turned out that we needed new mathematical realizations and ever more sophisticated representations of the material world. It is a multitude of unfolding insights intertwined with the dramatic growth of our experimental means to probe physical reality that marked the advances in theory over the last century. And finally, once the mathematical, maybe somewhat pragmatic modeling has advanced sufficiently, one should try to come to a more fundamental insight as to what these models imply for the logical structure of the underlying physical reality. Here we enter a realm with philosophical ramifications, where we move from the syntax anchored in the mathematical consistency of the model, to its semantics and interpretation. We can pose ontological questions about what is 'to be and/or not to be', as well as questions about the epistemology and about what is 'knowable'. We enter the territories of *beables* and *knowables*: in short, the realm of *meaning*.

Three layers. Quantum theory at large comprises a huge body of knowledge I like to think of as consisting of three layers as depicted in the columns of Figure 3. The $\mathcal{A}$-layer comprises the physical realizations and manifestations of quantum matter, the $\mathcal{B}$-layer is about mathematical representations and realizations, and finally the $\mathcal{C}$-layer concerns underlying concepts and principles, and their logical structure and interpretation. Indeed it is only after one has a mathematically consistent formulation of the theory that conceptual questions force themselves on us in a way that we can make sense out of them. Yet, one cannot avoid switching between the layers if one is to give a coherent account of the subject as a whole.

The first layer $\mathcal{A}$ refers to quantum phenomenology, the body of observational evidence concerning the broad spectrum of quantum phenomena that we will consider in this book. It is in fact the same as the first column in Figure 2, but note that the other columns of the two Figures refer to qualitatively entirely different things.

The second layer $\mathcal{B}$ refers to mathematical representations or models. This is already more abstract, as we ascend to the mathematical modeling of the observed phenomena. One might for example think of quantum states being elements of some vector space referred to as the Hilbert space, or of the mathematics of a qubit, or of a wave function. Or consider physical observables as represented by operators that act on that Hilbert space, like matrices or differential operators. And we may think of the dynamics of the quantum system described by famous differential equations, such as the Schrödinger, Heisenberg and Dirac equations.

And indeed, in the middle column from bottom to top we

see increasingly complex realizations of the same quantum principles, which are stated in the first step at the bottom. It is a hierarchy of degrees of freedom. We start with the discrete case of qubits and 'qubit mechanics', and move one step up to the simple continuous case of a single quantum particle. In the next step we face the problems of many particles of one single type or species, and the interactions between these species, which leads us to the theory of quantum fields. This level includes multi-particle states, and the creation and annihilation of particles; furthermore the forces are included and quantized. We finally end up with theories (and so far only theories) that attempt to combine all types of fields (or particle species) in the spectrum of a unique quantum (super)string. At this level space-time is included and quantized. So what we have indicated in the second column is the idea that states representing the physics at one given level form a small subspace of the set of states in the next step. It represents a modelling hierarchy.

We have mapped the system onto a mathematical model that allows us to make calculations and predictions, but models also pose new challenges for finding out what the essential concepts are that underlie all those quantum phenomena. We like to understand what the generic features are that set the quantum world apart from what we were used to in classical physics. That is what the next layer is about.

The third layer $\mathcal{C}$ is concerned with the conceptual implications of the mathematical framework, where we are required to interpret the basic mathematical entities back into physical terms. You may compare this to coming home from an exciting journey to some unknown country, and being forced to describe to your colleagues what the exquisite, extremely exotic food tasted like. You may think of mathematical models that manage to successfully describe and predict measurement outcomes, but at the same time force us to reinterpret what the very nature of physical reality is. There is the saying cherished by many theorists that 'equations speak for themselves', but that is often not the case. For example, you may know that the mathematics of special relativity is surprisingly simple, but its physical ramifications are certainly *not*; it forced us to fundamentally redefine our concepts of space and time. Something similar happened in the realm of quantum theory with respect to the true nature of what we, for convenience, call 'matter', or 'radiation', or 'energy', or 'information'. Here we encounter the necessary consequences of the Hilbert space formalism, such as the existence of quantum entanglement and quantum interference. And we have to cope with non-commuting observables leading to fundamental uncertainties in measurement outcomes. These unambiguous consequences of the mathematical formalism, which by itself is clear cut, will, as we will show, pose quite formidable epistemological and philosophical questions. It suffices to refer to the infamous Einstein, Podolsky, Rosen (EPR) paradox, which lies at the heart of the well-known Einstein–Bohr debate about how quantum theory defines what we call 'reality.' This debate has been going on for three quarters of a century and only now appears about to be settled.

Going from left to right in Figure 3 is, in some sense, a perspective marked by experimental discoveries and as such a rather historical perspective. Going from left to right is therefore hard because it is erratic, and it moves slowly except for sudden jumps. It is highly unpredictable because it basically lacks internal logic: there is no strictly logical path from classical to quantum physics. The path from left to right is the historic one, and therefore bumpy, but also paved with would-be miracles and intriguing misconceptions, which indeed make a wonderful narrative with ample heroism and drama.

But once the subject has matured, there is the other possibility, namely to start on the right with the concepts and a logical, abstract framework, and from there move back to the left. A theorist like myself naturally prefers a presentation from right to left, which in a sense is highly anti-chronological, but would be more comprehensive because it has an internal logic and systematics. I believe that once things are understood, going from right to left is *easy*. Moreover, it would give the author the freedom to limit himself to the *quantessence* of a coherent body of knowledge.

Yet, in spite of this argument, it would be a bad idea to really treat the three layers sequentially from right to left, because you need the stuff on the left to appreciate the content of the right column. This suggests the option of a left-right compromise, or left-right coalition, just like that is often the case in the politics of healthy democracies.

Combining parts and layers: the outline. After some reflections on the general structure of the book, let me now just give a more detailed description of the layout of the chapters. As mentioned, I have divided the book in three parts or volumes, as indicated in Figure 2. Volumes I and III are primarily descriptive and do not require much math, since they are phenomenologically-oriented. So in the context of the layers, Volumes I and III mainly deals with $\mathcal{A}$ with some attention to layer $\mathcal{B}$. Volume II, with a title that refers to the 'quantessence', focusses more on the mathematical and conceptual structure of the theory, and covers the layers $\mathcal{B}$ and $\mathcal{C}$. As a matter of fact, quantum lovers with an outspoken fear of formulas may prefer to read only Volumes I and III as a single coherent descriptive account of what quantum theory has achieved. The following preview may help you to make up your mind.

Volume I talks about *The journey*, where we follow a path starting at the level of atoms, and descending deeper into matter to the worlds of nuclei and elementary particles and their interactions. This part is so to speak *inward bound*. But before we embark on this descent in Chapter I.4, we give a review of what classical physics is about in Chapter I.1. Chapter I.2 deals with the very breakdown of classical physics, from which crises the theories of relativity and quantum emerged. Here we also included a section

on the physics of geometry and a section on the notions of information and computation, highlighting another fundamental turning point in twentieth century science and technology. In Chapter I.3, on units, scales and universal constants, we obtain surprisingly deep insights in the domains of validity of our cherished theories by applying what we call 'dimensional analysis.' It provides us with a heuristic quantitative sense of what the characteristic scales in nature are, and why. In Chapter I.4 we describe the quest for the basic building blocks of matter all the way from atoms down to the most fundamental constituents of matter and radiation.

In Volume II – called *Quantessence: how quantum theory works* – we give an accessible introduction to the mathematical modelling tools and representations that comprise quantum theory, including those which led to a number of remarkable conceptual and semantic puzzles. This part emphasizes the two deeper layers I alluded to before, i.e. the layers $\mathcal{B}$ and $\mathcal{C}$ of Figure 3.

This second part also leads us deeper into the subjects of quantum information and computing. To that end we first have to contrast the setting of quantum theory with its classical counterpart. In Chapter II.1, the first of Volume II, we start by introducing quantum states as vectors in Hilbert space. I discuss the structure of Hilbert space for qubits and quantum information in quite a lot of detail. In the second Chapter II.2, I discuss the quantessence of observables, why we think of them as operators acting on Hilbert space, and what it means to make a quantum measurement. In this chapter the Heisenberg uncertainty relations are also introduced. In Chapter II.3 I talk about the measurement process more extensively with a particular focus on quantum interference phenomena. Chapter II.4 examines quantum entanglement and some of the modern experiments addressing the profound questions of cloning, Schrödinger's cat, hidden variables, as well as quantum teleportation and computation. In Chapter II.5 I explain the concepts of quantum particles, fields and strings. There, the famous equations of Schrödinger, Heisenberg and Dirac that describe the time evolution of states and observables, will be introduced. I also explain properties like quantum spin, quantum statistics and their relationships. In Chapter II.6, the final chapter of Volume II, we introduce the notions of symmetry and symmetry breaking which play a central role in all of modern physics. The notion of symmetry served as a powerful guiding principle in our quest to understand nature.

In the third and final Volume of the series we return to model physical reality but we now move upwards from the atomic scale. In Chapter III.1 we discuss how matter sequentially evolved in the very early universe, from quarks, to nucleons, to atoms, and from simple molecules to the basic (bio)chemistry concerning the molecules of life.

Chapter III.2 and III.3 are devoted to the splendid diversity of quantum phenomena in the physics of many body systems that are manifest in gaseous, liquid as well as solid phases. Where in Chapter III.2 we consider the atomic and nuclear lattices and to what extent these are ordered, the focus in chapter III.3 is on the electronic behavior in solids and the quantum phenomena they display.

In Chapter III.4, we touch upon the quite advanced notions of scale dependence and renormalization. Part III could well be called *outward bound*, certainly if reasoned from the atomic scale where quantum theory made its first appearance. The criteria of inward and outward bound refer to the arrows in the left column of Figure 2.

In the concluding Chapter III.5, we zoom out and look at the meaning and impact of quantum in the broader context of science, technology and society.

After the concluding chapter you find a set of *Math Excursions,* appendices in which we offer rather minimal but tailor-made introductions to the mathematics used throughout the book.

Choosing the structure of a three-volume book means that we couple together the layers of Figure 3 so as to enable a coherent presentation of the quantessence as a whole, which is accessible without being too superficial. What you see is that quantum theory, even when you restrict yourself to the *quantessence*, is a huge field. and that is why I divided the book up in three volumes.

As you may be aware, an impressive number of Nobel prizes have been awarded in the course of the past century to quantum discoveries in physics and chemistry. We list most of them in an appendix (on page 644) at the end of the final volume. There we also provide some of the chronology, and list the names of many of the influential thinkers who made seminal contributions to the field. It may also help you to follow up specific topics that have caught your interest while reading.

I like to think of the three parts of the book as a kind of a triptych, where the central panel covers the deeper quantum scenery, while the side panels are more descriptive and discuss lots of real physics, from quarks all the way up to bio-chemistry and the splendid diversity we encounter in the condensed states of matter.

Volume I

The journey:
from classical to quantum worlds

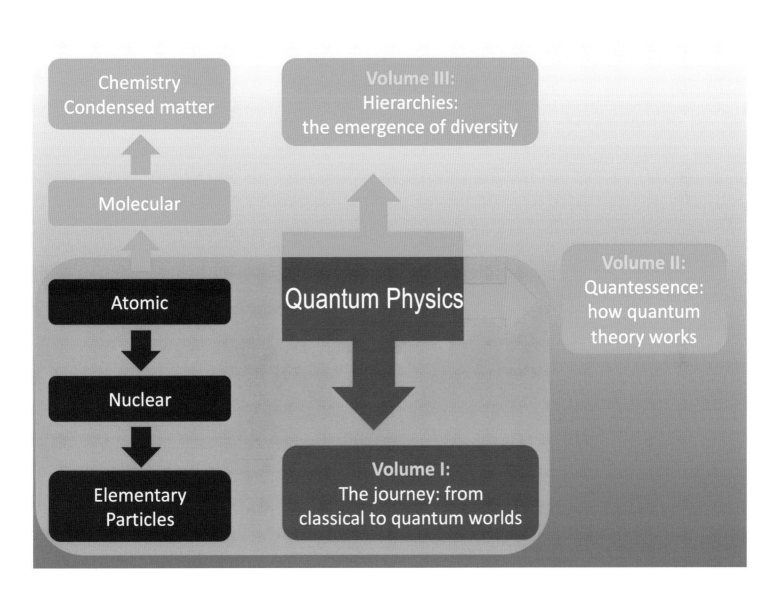

Chapter I.1

The gems of classical physics

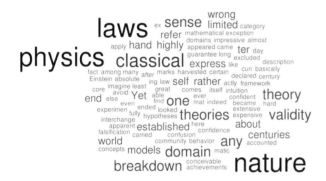

Mission almost completed

'Don't laugh! There is a special section in purgatory for professors of quantum theory, where they will be obliged to listen to lectures on classical physics ten hours every day.'

Paul Ehrenfest (in a 1927 note to Einstein)

In this chapter we recall the great theories of classical physics with an emphasis on their underlying principles. You could call them 'classessential.' One by one they represented turning points in our understanding of Nature. First there are the four fundamental laws of Newtonian mechanics and gravity, which open the door tto the precise description and modeling of general dynamical systems through systems of differential equations. The sec-

ond pillar corresponds to Maxwell's four laws of electromagnetism, describing all classical electromagnetic phenomena including those of light and radiation. The third component consists of the macroscopic laws of thermodynamics and how they are explained from the underlying microscopic dynamics by the theory of statistical mechanics. It is here that the notion of entropy emerges as a measure of information or disorder.

Towards the end of the nineteenth century, physics almost came to an end. The physics community seemed optimistic and self-confident. Most of the observed natural phenomena appeared to be accounted for in the established framework of classical physics, at least in principle. It was hard to imagine what else could present itself to their curious minds. And indeed, after many centuries of scientific research, there had been not only highly impressive technical achievements, but fundamental laws of nature had also been established.

I like to warn agains the sloppy use of terminology when it comes to words like 'models,' 'theories' and even 'laws of nature.' It is rule rather than exception among scientists to treat these concepts as basically interchangeable. We refer to the theories of Newton and Einstein, by which we mean the mathematical description of certain theoretical models of nature's behavior, which in fact have been so successful that they are often also referred to as 'laws of nature.' Yet they are not true in any absolute sense, there is no guarantee that we will not one day find that nature violates such a law of nature in a domain of reality that we cannot yet observe. So, on the one hand, one might as well put these cherished 'laws' in the category of 'working hypotheses' in view of the fact that we can never fully exclude the possibility that they are conceivably false. On the other hand, the 'laws' have proven to be remarkable robust quantitative statements on the workings of nature that have survived centuries of ever more extensive (and expensive) experimental tests. In that sense they express some of the core messages carried by nature about our world, about what and who we are, and how things ended up this way. They may not tell us *why* we are here but at least *how* we got here. It appears that modern science in many ways liberates us from the narrow anthropocentric views that are as dominant as they are questionable in the debate of what the place and future of humankind in this universe may be.

When I talk about the breakdown of classical physics, I refer precisely to the type of breakdown where the declared universality of laws turned out to primarily express our overconfidence. The term breakdown here is not as much a matter of whether a theory is right or wrong, but rather marks the limited domain of validity of any particular theory. In any pragmatic sense there is nothing wrong with classical physics as long as you apply it to problems within its domain of validity. You may compare it to the situation in biological evolution where it is evident that we have passed beyond the stage of bacteria, but that doesn't stop them from being around and still playing a crucial role.

What the notion of classical physics refers to depends on the context in which it is discussed. Often 'classical' is contrasted with 'quantum', and in that case we can consider the theory of relativity to be part of classical physics. We could however also contrast 'classical' with 'modern', and in that case we can draw the line at the end of the nineteenth century and count both relativity and quantum

Figure I.1.2: *Newtonia: Composition with bound orbits.* (Image constructed using visualization & graphics tools of the Mathematica package.)

theory as parts of 'modern' physics. It is this latter distinction that we will make in this chapter. The use of the word 'modern' will strike you remarkably inappropriate because this 'modern' physics was to a large extent formulated a century ago; 'modern' in this context clearly does not mean contemporary. Modern theory in this context apparently just means that we have not yet encountered the limits of its domain of validity. In this chapter we start by briefly recalling the core messages of the classical theories of mechanics and the gravitational force, of the theory of electromagnetism and light, and of the theories of thermodynamics and statistical physics.

In the next chapter we briefly summarize how certain crises in classical physics seeded two fundamental turning points in our thinking about nature: relativity and quantum physics. In that chapter we also introduce the basic concepts of information theory, as this branch of science is now also heading towards a quantum revolution.

In the third chapter we delve deeper into the notion of the domain of validity of a model and discuss how the particular values of the universal constants that appear as parameters in physical models basically set the scale of our universe.

The fourth chapter gives an account of our progressive insights in what the basic building blocks of nature are, from the atomic level all the way down to superstrings.

Newtonian mechanics and gravity

Newton's work lead to the unified description of terrestrial and heavenly mechanics and involved the creation of the mathematics of change, called differential calculus, which in turn gave rise to the birth of the general theory of dynamical systems.

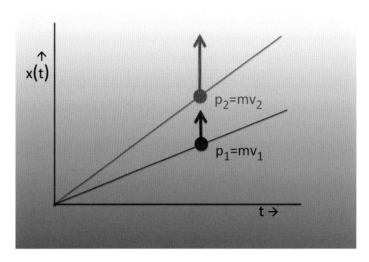

Figure I.1.3: *Newton's first law.* In the absence of a force a body will move at a constant velocity and momentum. In the figure the distance traveled as a function of time $x(t)$ for a body of mass is plotted for two constant momenta p_1 and p_2, corresponding to the two arrows.

Four laws only

Back to the achievements of classical physics. Firstly there are Newton's four laws described in his genial *Principia Mathematica* published in 1667. Three of those laws constituted the foundations of mechanics: (i) the law of inertia, (ii) the force law and (iii) the the law of action and reaction. The fourth law is the law that defines the gravitational force between two masses.

The first law: the law of inertia. The law of inertia postulates that if a body is at rest or moving at a constant speed in a straight line, it will remain at rest or keep moving in a straight line at constant speed unless it is acted upon by a force. This property is called *inertia*. We have illustrated the distance traveled $x(t)$ for a body of some mass m, for two constant velocities $v_1 < v_2$ in Figure I.1.3. In the absence of a force the distance traveled is proportional to the elapsed time, in other words: $x(t) = vt$.[1] The *first law* led

to the fundamental notion of momentum, where the *momentum* **p** of an object is defined as the product of its mass m and its velocity, $\mathbf{p} = m\mathbf{v}$. This linear relation between momentum and velocity is depicted in Figure I.1.4 , where the slope of the line by definition equals the mass. Momentum is also referred to as the 'amount of motion,' and if you don't have a feeling for it, think of it as impact. If somebody throws a large brick to you the impact will be much larger than when that same person would have thrown a piece of foam of the same shape with the same velocity. The first law states that in the absence of a net force on an object its momentum will not change. Zero force means that momentum is conserved, and this implies that the velocity is constant.

The second law: the force law. The *second law*, called the *force law*, is the well-known relation between the force **F** applied to a body, and the resulting acceleration **a** , given

---

[1]We adopt the notational convention where symbols denoting vector-like quantities like position, velocity, momentum and force are given in bold except when we are dealing with one spatial dimension. For the length and the length squared of a vector we write $|\mathbf{v}| \equiv v$ and $\mathbf{v} \cdot \mathbf{v} \equiv |\mathbf{v}|^2 \equiv v^2$. Scalar quantities like mass are set in the default typeface.

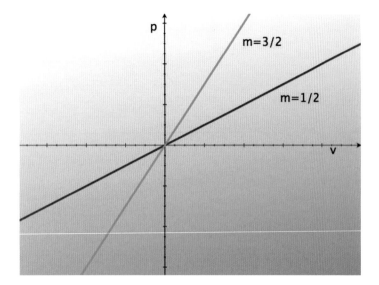

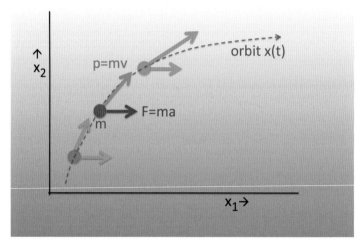

Figure I.1.4: *Definition of momentum.* Newton defined momentum as the 'quantity of motion' directly proportional to the velocity of the object, the proportionality constant equals the mass m of the object.

Figure I.1.5: *Newton's second law.* We have drawn a segment of the orbit in 2 dimensions of a particle with mass m under a constant force $\mathbf{F}$ in the x_1-direction. This could be a particle with charge q in a constant electric field $\mathbf{E}$ exerting a force $\mathbf{F} = q\mathbf{E}$. Note that the momentum $\mathbf{p}$ at time t points along the slope of the particle's trajectory $\mathbf{x}(t)$. Because the force $\mathbf{F}$ points in the x_1-direction, only the component p_1- will increase while p_2 remains constant.

by the fomula $\mathbf{F} = m\mathbf{a}$.[2] As acceleration is the rate of change in velocity, the force is then equal to the rate of change in momentum. A brilliant aspect of this equation is that at first glance it doesn't seem to hold. I remember as a kid pulling other kids on a sled through the snow: yes I had to pull to get the sled moving but if I stopped pulling it did not keep moving with constant velocity as I thought should be concluded from the law. No force, no change in momentum. But the sled immediately came to a halt after I stopped pulling it. I had to conclude that there should be another force in action, and indeed there was, it was the resistive force of the snow. Now that is a funny force that opposes motion, the greater the velocity, the greater the force in the opposite direction. It is as subtle as the workings of the opposition in parliament. But postulating

a force with such a subtle adaptive power, is that not just postulating what you see, postulating the facts you wished to explain? Well don't put the book aside yet, there is more to come.

The third law: action is reaction. A simple example of the law of 'action is reaction' is provided by a book at rest on a table as depicted on the left in Figure I.1.6. Gravity pulls the book down (light blue arrow) attached to centre of mass pointing down), it equals the force of the book on the table (dark blue arrow pointing down) and indeed, the book would fall down were it not for the table exerting an equal but upward directed *normal* force on the book It is this balance of forces that act on an object, which is the main topic of *statics*. It means that the net force, but also the net torque, on an object should be zero and that does

---

[2]Actually it should be written as $\mathbf{F} = d\mathbf{p}/dt$, where strictly speaking there is an extra contribution because $d\mathbf{p}/dt = \mathbf{v}\,dm/dt + m\,d\mathbf{v}/dt$. The first term proportional to the change in mass is considered to be zero because for a single particle one assumes a constant mass. But for a rocket burning its fuel this is no longer true.

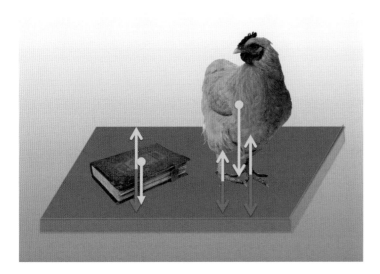

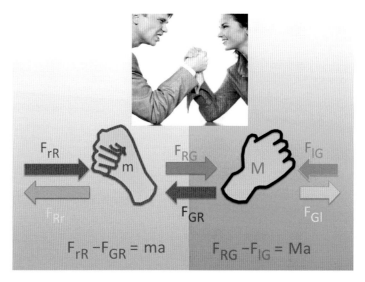

Figure I.1.6: *Newton's third law.* The third law *Action = Reaction* applies to a chicken at rest on a table. The downward gravitational force can be represented by the large light blue arrow attached to its centre of mass. Through its legs it exerts in two places a force on the table, and the table exerts a *reaction force* exactly equal and opposite at the points of contact. The net force, which is the sum of the light and dark blue arrows on the chicken, is zero and its change in momentum will be zero so it doesn't move. But why are the forces of the two legs unequal? That is to make sure that the chicken doesn't fall over sideways. This requires that the *torque* on the chicken has to be zero as well, so that its angular momentum does not change.

not only explain the stability of architectural structures like bridges, arches or cathedrals, but also the stability of the chicken at rest on the table at the right-hand side of the figure.

A more subtle example of the *third law* is provided by a game called 'arm wrestling.' Two individuals (still mostly men) sit at opposite sides of the table and fix their elbows on the table and try to push each other's hand towards the table. For quite some time nothing seems to happen, in spite of the fact that both individuals do their utmost best to get the fists moving. As long as nothing happens the net forces of the hands are in perfect balance, a situation that

Figure I.1.7: *Newton's third law.* The third law *Action = Reaction* applies to arm wrestling, also when the balance of power is broken and the 'red' force is larger than the 'grey' force. An explanation is given in the text.

is called a static equilibrium. This lasts until the balance is broken, leading to a net force in one direction causing both fists to start moving, until one hand is forced on the table and somebody has to order a round of beer.

The question you may wrestle with is whether in such a dynamic situation the action-is-reaction-law still holds. So, let us look more closely at how to apply the fundamental action-is-reaction-law in such a dynamic setting. This is explained in Figure I.1.7, where we give a schematic of the forces involved. We identify three different instances where the third law can be applied. Firstly, on the left side we have the force of the red arm r on the 'red' hand R (denoted by F_{rR}), which indeed equals the opposite force of the red hand on the red arm (F_{Rr}). In the middle we have the force of the red hand on the grey hand (F_{RG}), and the force of the grey on the red hand (F_{GR}), these have to be equal because of the third law applied at the interface between the hands. On the right side we have the force of the grey arm (F_{lG}) on the grey hand and the equal and oppo-

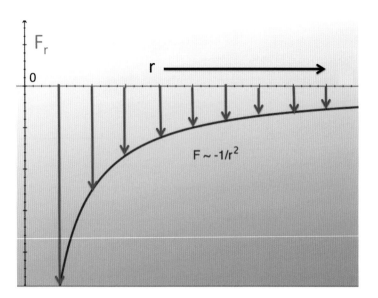

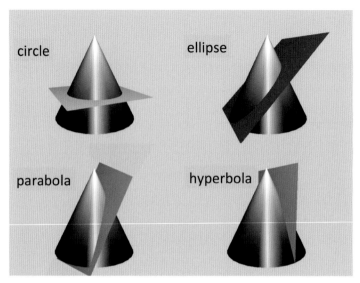

Figure I.1.8: *Newton's fourth law*. This is Newton's famous 'inverse square law' for the gravitational force between two massive objects as a function of their distance r. The force only has a radial component, which is negative meaning that the force is attractive.

Figure I.1.9: *Conic sections*. The general solution for the orbits of a planetary object around a star can be obtained by inserting the gravitational force in the second law. The resulting orbits correspond to the conic sections depicted above.

site force (F_{Gl}). So we see that the third law should be applied three times referring to three different forces. If both hands move with an acceleration a we can firstly apply the force law to the red hand telling us that the net force on it is $F_{rR} - F_{GR} = ma$, applying it to the grey hand it yields $F_{RG} - F_{lG} = Ma$. Next we use the result that $F_{RG} = F_{GR}$ to ascertain that the net force $F_{rR} - F_{lG} = (m + M)a$, which is the force law applied to the system of both hands. This argument shows that the hands can be in accelerated motion, not in spite of, but rather thanks to the fact that the law of 'action is reaction' remains valid all along. It illustrates the important fact that 'action is reaction' is a general law, that is applicable as long as the objects exerting force on each other stay in contact.

The fourth law: the law of gravitation. Newton's *fourth law* is his celebrated *universal law of gravitation*,

$$F_r = -\frac{G_N m_1 m_2}{r^2}, \qquad (I.1.1)$$

expressing the attractive gravitational force between two masses m_1 and m_2 as proportional to the inverse square of their distance r. The force as a function of the distance, is depicted in Figure I.1.8. Note that here the principle of 'action is reaction' is indeed respected implicitly, because it is the force 'between' two objects, they experience an equal force in opposite directions. Indeed it is so universal that it applies with the same constant G_N equally well to a pencil dropping on the floor (the earth) as to the motions in the solar system or to the motion of stars in the Milky Way. It was justly said that Newton with this law unified celestial and terrestrial mechanics. Substituting this gravitational force in the second law, one can solve the system for general planetary orbits around a star. They correspond to the well-known *conic sections* depicted in Figure I.1.9, where the top two are the bound circular or elliptic orbits, and the bottom two are the unbound parabolic and hyperbolic orbits.

Dynamical systems

Let me say a little more on how these laws of Newtonian mechanics furnished a first and powerful description of what nowadays is called a *dynamical system*, a system described by a set of variables whose values change over time. Thinking about mechanics that way, one would rewrite the laws in a different way that illuminates the dynamical system's perspective.

Phase space. First we say that if we look at a particle as a system, then it has at any instant in time a state that is labeled by two variables, its position x and its momentum p. So, we may think of the state of the system as corresponding to a point in (x, p)-space. This space is usually called the *phase space* $\mathcal{P}_{ph}$ of the system. For a particle moving in ordinary space $\mathcal{P}_{ph}$ is six-dimensional, because we have to specify the three components of its position and the three components of its momentum. The dynamics of the system can be envisaged as a trajectory $(x(t), p(t))$ of the point that represents the state of the system, through $\mathcal{P}_{ph}$. This trajectory is then specified by giving the rule which tells you where the system goes if you give the point at some initial time t_0.

Differential equations. This rule is like an incremental prescription, it specifies an infinitesimal change by using the notion of a (time) *derivative* (d/dt) as a measure of change:

$$\frac{d\,\textbf{Something}}{dt}\bigg|_{t_0} = \left\{ \begin{array}{l} change\ of\ that\ '\textbf{Something}' \\ per\ unit\ time\ at\ t = t_0. \end{array} \right.$$

Equations involving this (time) differential are called *differential equations*, to contrast them with algebraic equations – like the quadratic equation $ax^2 + bx + c = 0$ – in which algebraic expressions in the variables appear but no derivatives. If the equations involve time derivatives, we speak of the *equations of motion*. If the system is *closed*, the change will depend only on the state of the system at earlier times. In the quite common case that the system

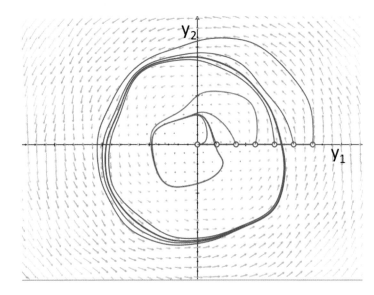

Figure I.1.10: *Dynamical system.* We display the vector field corresponding to a particular example of (I.1.2). This means that in each point (y_1, y_2) we plot the vector (arrow) with components $dy_1/dt = -y_2 + \cos 2y_1$ and $dy_2/dt = y_1 + \sin 2y_2$. Solutions of the system correspond to trajectories that start from a given point in (y_1, y_2)-space, following the arrows. In this case we give some trajectories starting on the y_1 axis that converge either to the blue or the red limit cycle.

has no memory – like the system of the sun and the earth in the Newtonian picture – the change at some particular time t only depends on the state of the system at time t. It is generally agreed upon that sun and earth do not wrestle with sleepless nights caused by bad memories. So the dynamical system with a set of N independent variables $\{y_i\}$ with $i = 1, \ldots, N$ would look like a set of N coupled equations describing the change of the system by specifying the N components f_i of the change vector, each of which may in turn depend on the set of all variables $\{y_j\}$:

$$\frac{dy_i}{dt} = f_i(\{y_j\}). \tag{I.1.2}$$

The functions $f_i(y_j)$ encode the interactions between the different variables, In other words, these variables include their mutual dependence and of course a number of external parameters which typically appear as the coefficients of the terms specifying the interactions. The $f_i(y_j)$ correspond to the components of the 'change vector' at any point in phase space, which means that they define a *vector field* over the configuration or ($\{y_i\}$) space. This vector field forms a powerful mathematical representation of the dynamical system as a whole. It depicts the phase space as a fluid flow. If we drop autumn leaves into the flow, they will start to move, following the particular flow lines which correspond to the particular solutions of the dynamical system. We have depicted a particular vector field in Figure I.1.10 , which also shows two sets of trajectories described by solutions of the dynamical system for different starting points on the y_1-axis. The trajectories are obtained by locally following the direction of the vector field. The dictum is indeed: 'go with the flow.' The orbits are seen to converge on one of two different closed limit cycles.

Yet another way to look at a dynamical system is that it represents an algorithm that takes input information, the vector defining the initial point in phase space and moves or 'processes' it, to some final state.

Writing Newtonian mechanics in this format the first and second laws look like,

$$\frac{d\mathbf{x}}{dt} = \mathbf{p}/m,$$
$$\frac{d\mathbf{p}}{dt} = \mathbf{F}. \tag{I.1.3}$$

They completely specify the motion of the point in phase space, where the force $\mathbf{F} = \mathbf{F}(\mathbf{x}, \mathbf{p})$ may in general depend on the position and velocity of the particle. It is customary to treat the earth-sun system by keeping the sun fixed in the origin (a good approximation because the sun has a huge mass) and let the earth move through the gravitational force (the fourth law) that only depends on the length of the position vector $r = |\mathbf{x}|$. The third law is basically a *constraint* on the system: if we had included the position and momentum of the sun as independent variables, then the third law would require that the same force

$\mathbf{F}$ would appear with the opposite sign in the equations for the sun and for the earth respectively. From this example it is also clear that the functions on the right-hand side of the equations do not only depend on the variables, but also on certain parameters that set the strength of the couplings or interactions. These parameters, like the masses or the Newton's gravitational constant, are supposed to be constant but must of course be varied to find the best fit to the experimental data. They are the input parameters of the model. It is here that *Occam's razor* – the principle of rational minimalism – applies, decreeing that if two models perform equally well, the one with the fewest parameters is to be preferred.

Conservation laws

> The tears of the world are a constant quantity. For each one who begins to weep, somewhere else someone stops. The same is true for laugh.
> *Samuel Becket – Waiting for Godot*

Note that with the dynamical laws for the fundamental variables, one can also calculate the time evolution of other ($\mathbf{x}-$ and $\mathbf{p}-$dependent) dynamical variables. One such variable is the energy, often called the Hamiltonian and denoted as H. It should be thought of as a function $H = H(\mathbf{x}, \mathbf{p})$ of the basic state variables $\mathbf{x}$ and $\mathbf{p}$. Another such variable is the angular momentum $\mathbf{L} = \mathbf{x} \times \mathbf{p}$, which is basically the amount of rotational motion, or the rotational momentum. We will return to these quantities shortly.

Under certain circumstances it may happen that some dynamical variables are *conserved*, meaning that they do not change over time. These are often called *constants of the motion*. For example in Newtonian mechanics, if there is no force, that is we have that $\mathbf{F} = 0$, then the equation (I.1.3) tells us immediately that the momentum does not change, it stays constant and is thus 'conserved.' On the other hand, if the force only depends on the distance and not on the direction (as is the case in Newton's gravitational force), then the angular momentum will be conserved as we will explain shortly. So, if the time derivative of some physical quantity Q equals zero:

$$\frac{dQ}{dt} = 0, \qquad (I.1.4)$$

we call the equation a *conservation law* for Q, because the amount of Q is constant in time.

Energy conservation. Of special interest is the case of energy conservation because it is of general validity and applies to basically all observed processes in nature that are physically based. Let us for convenience restrict ourselves to a (one-dimensional) situation which is simple but also surprisingly common, where the energy H consists of two parts, a *kinetic energy* part $U(p)$ which only depends on the momentum, and a *potential energy* part $V(x)$ that only depends on position:

$$H(x, p) = U(p) + V(x). \qquad (I.1.5)$$

Then its time derivative can be calculated:[3]

$$\frac{dH}{dt} = \frac{dU}{dt} + \frac{dV}{dt} = \frac{dU}{dp}\frac{dp}{dt} + \frac{dV}{dx}\frac{dx}{dt} = F\frac{dU}{dp} + \frac{p}{m}\frac{dV}{dx}.$$

We see that the energy will be conserved if the terms on the right-hand side cancel each other. This requires that the following equalities have to hold:

$$\frac{dU}{dp} = p/m, \qquad (I.1.6a)$$

$$\frac{dV}{dx} = -F. \qquad (I.1.6b)$$

---

[3]The second equal sign involves the use of a mathematical identity called the *chain rule* which says that if $U(p)$ depends on t only through its dependence on $p(t)$, the time change can be found by first calculating the change in U because of a change in momentum, multiplied by the change in time of the momentum. It roughly means that one may cross out the dp factors of the numerator and denominator.

The first condition leads to the well-known expression $U = p^2/2m$ while the second restricts the force in that it has to be equal to minus the spatial change of some potential energy function V. Such a force field is not surprisingly called *conservative*, exactly because its action 'conserves' the total energy of the system. Whereas a 'conservative force' is standard physics jargon, I have never come across terms such as 'liberal' or 'progressive' forces, though if we get to the strong nuclear force, other evocative terms will surface, like 'asymptotic freedom' and 'infrared slavery.'

Applying a (net) force means doing work. If we apply a force F to a mass m, the mass will accelerate and over time its kinetic energy will change. If we push a stroller, we do work by applying a force on it. If we put a charge in an electric field, the charge will start moving because it is the field that exerts a force that causes the motion and it is the field that does the work. The change in kinetic energy ΔU by definition equals the amount of work ΔW that the force has done. If the force is constant, this means that $\Delta W = F \cdot \Delta \mathbf{x}$. If the mass moves through a conservative force field $F(\mathbf{x})$ and it moves along a certain path γ from $\mathbf{x}_0$ to $\mathbf{x}_1$, we know from conservation of the total energy that $\Delta E = 0$, and thus $\Delta U = -\Delta V = V(\mathbf{x}_0) - V(\mathbf{x}_1)$. The amount of work in an arbitrary force field can be expressed as the *line integral* of the force field along a path of motion γ :

$$W = \int_{x_0}^{x_1} \mathbf{F}(\mathbf{x}) \cdot \mathbf{dl},$$

where the line element $\mathbf{dl}$ is the infinitesimal vector tangent to the path γ in the point $\mathbf{x}$. For a conservative force field we get,

$$W = -\int_{x_0}^{x_1} \nabla V(\mathbf{x}) \cdot \mathbf{dx} = V(\mathbf{x}_0) - V(\mathbf{x}_1),$$

and we see that the change in potential energy equals the difference of the potential energies at the endpoints of the path, consistent with the conservation of total energy E. The fact that the difference only depends on the endpoints means that the increase of energy is *not* dependent on the

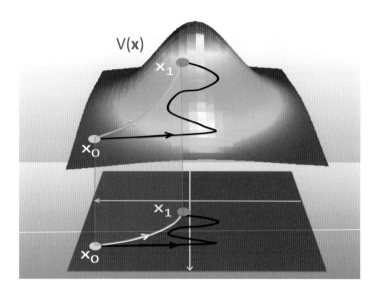

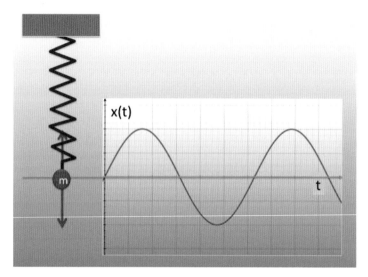

Figure I.1.11: *A line integral.* In the upper picture we give a two-dimensional potential surface $V(\mathbf{x})$. The force field is defined as $\mathbf{F}(\mathbf{x}) = -\boldsymbol{\nabla}V(\mathbf{x})$. If we choose a path from point $\mathbf{x}_0$ to $\mathbf{x}_1$, we can integrate $\mathbf{F}$ along that path. This means that we need to integrate the component that is tangential to the path. This line integral yields the value $W = V(\mathbf{x}_0) - V(\mathbf{x}_1)$ which equals the work performed by the force, which in this case is negative. We had to perform a force to go uphill and therefore the potential energy was increased. Note that the outcome is *independent* of the path chosen.

Figure I.1.12: *The oscillating mass*. A model system consisting of a mass m attached to a spring. The inset shows the oscillatory motion of the mass in configuration (x, t)-space.

particular path chosen. If you want to climb to the top of a mountain, you can choose between a path that is long and not so steep or a very short, very steep path, in either case you would have to deliver the same amount of work.

The harmonic oscillator. A simple example of a conservative force is the one-dimensional elastic force, applied to a mass m hanging on a spring attached to a beam as depicted in Figure I.1.12,

$$F = -kx,\qquad (\text{I.1.7})$$

where x is the deviation of the mass from its equilibrium position, k is the elastic constant that characterizes the spring and the minus sign indicates that the force the string exerts is opposite to the displacement. The force tends to

restore the equilibrium state. Because the force increases linearly with the distance x, and according to the equation (I.1.6) it has to equal minus the derivative of the potential energy, we may conclude that the corresponding potential V satisfying that condition has to grow quadratically with x (up to an irrelevant constant term):

$$V(x) = \frac{1}{2}kx^2.\qquad (\text{I.1.8})$$

We have depicted the energies V, U and H corresponding to the resulting oscillatory motion in Figure I.1.13. The spring keeps oscillating with a fixed frequency, which is equal to $\sqrt{k/m}$, a fixed amplitude and a fixed total energy H. These motions correspond to the configuration space picture of Figure I.1.12, and phase space picture of Figure I.1.14. This *harmonic oscillator* is quite ubiquitous, because systems are most of the time in equilibrium. And if we perturb such a system, it typically starts oscillating around its equilibrium configuration and in real cases it usually relaxes back to equilibrium because of frictional forces. So the harmonic potential is the simplest approximation that corresponds to the 'linear' response of

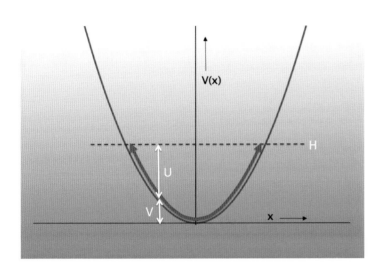

Figure I.1.13: *The harmonic oscillator.* The harmonic potential $V(x) = -\frac{1}{2}kx^2$ in red. The equilibrium point is at the origin, the resulting force is $F = -kx$ and is always directed towards the equilibrium point. If there is no friction, the position x will oscillate around the origin with a fixed amplitude and a fixed total energy H.

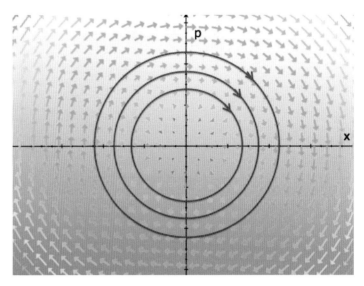

Figure I.1.14: *Periodic orbits.* The phase space vector field corresponding to the harmonic oscillator with $m = k = 1$ becomes $(dx/dt, dp/dt) = (p, -x)$. The orbits correspond to limit cycles. The origin is a fixed point that coincides with the particle at rest.

the system, which should hold as long as the perturbations are small. This quadratic potential is crucial and will also show up in many different guises at all levels of (quantum) mechanics.

Newton's gravitational potential. The most well-known potential is the gravitational potential due to a mass M located at the origin in Newton's theory, defined as:

$$\mathcal{V}(r) = -\frac{G_N M}{r}, \qquad (I.1.9)$$

where we are now in three dimensions and r denotes the length of the position vector $r = |\mathbf{x}|$ Note that the potential energy is taken to be zero at infinity. The potential energy of a mass m at a position at a distance r equals $V = m\mathcal{V}(r)$. And it does indeed lead to Newton's celebrated 'inverse square' law (I.1.1). If we let the particle go at some position r, it will move radially inward thereby lowering the potential energy, but at the same rate increasing its ki-

netic energy so that the total energy remains the same. The conclusion of this part of the story is that if the conditions (I.1.6) are met, the total energy will be conserved if the system evolves according to Newton's laws.

Angular momentum. Another important conserved quantity (in a problem with spherical symmetry) is the angular momentum $\mathbf{L}$, which is a vector quantity just like position or momentum (velocity) and has three components, each of which is conserved. You experience that conservation law if you are cycling. If the wheels spin fast, the angular momentum vector will be directed perpendicular through the axes of the wheels, and the conservation law is reflected in the stability of the bike at high speed. Kids apparently know about this law because they like to take both hands off the handlebars. However, if they slow down, they have to be careful to not tripple over sideways, as small external disturbances may cause a torque that changes the angular momentum, breaking the conservation law.

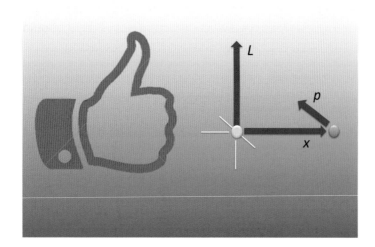

Figure I.1.15: *The Like-rule.* The defining relation of 'angular momentum,' or the 'amount of rotation' of a particle in some orbit. It is given by the vector $\mathbf{L} = \mathbf{x} \times \mathbf{p}$ where the 'times' symbol $\times$ is called the vector product, which is a well-defined multiplication rule for three-dimensional vectors. Whether you like it or not, the Facebook inspired 'Like' symbol on the left symbolizes the 'Like-rule' that tells you in which direction the resulting $\mathbf{L}$ vector is pointing. The instruction is also called the right-hand or corkscrew rule and their importance derives from the fact that they unambiguously link a direction to a rotation.

We have illustrated the defining relation $\mathbf{L} = \mathbf{x} \times \mathbf{p}$ in Figure I.1.15. So $\mathbf{L}$ is a vector perpendicular to the surface spanned by the vectors $\mathbf{x}$ and $\mathbf{p}$. Whether it is pointing up or down is determined by the right-hand rule, which in modern parlance could be better termed the right 'Like' or 'L' rule: point your right-index in the direction of the first vector $\mathbf{x}$, bend your fingers in the direction of the second vector $\mathbf{p}$, then the resulting vector $\mathbf{L}$ will point in the direction of your thumb. This rule explains the meaning of the *vector* or *cross product* or $\times$ sign for vectors. The length of $\mathbf{L}$ is given by the product of lengths of $\mathbf{x}$ and $\mathbf{p}$ times the sine of the angle between them, implying that

$$|\mathbf{x} \times \mathbf{p}| = |\mathbf{x}||\mathbf{p}|\sin\theta = \begin{cases} 0 & \text{if } \mathbf{x} \text{ and } \mathbf{p} \text{ parallel} \\ |\mathbf{x}||\mathbf{p}| & \text{if } \mathbf{x} \text{ and } \mathbf{p} \text{ perpendicular}. \end{cases}$$

$$(\text{I.1.10})$$

The vector product of two vectors is a vector that is pointing perpendicular to the plane defined by the two vectors, and indeed the product better be zero if the vectors are pointing in the same direction, because then they do not even define a plane.

In three dimensions we have two types of products for vectors. The *dot, inner,* or *scalar product,* which maps a pair of vectors into a number, $\mathbf{a} \cdot \mathbf{b} = |\mathbf{a}||\mathbf{b}|\cos\theta$, and the *cross, exterior,* or *vector* product which maps a pair of vectors into another vector. These definitions may at first sight seem contrived, but the opposite is true: all this symbol-mumbo-jumbo is mostly there because it offers notational convenience, efficiency and transparency.

This crash course of high school and first-year classical mechanics underscores once more that Newton laid the foundations of a general approach to dynamical systems irrespective of what they precisely describe. The variables could refer to either mechanics or to fluid- or electrodynamics, but for that matter they could equally well refer to ecology or economics. By creating the language and syntax of dynamical systems, Newton opened a monumental gateway into scientific thinking and modelling. Indeed, we are standing on the shoulders of giants. ■

Classical mechanics for *aficionados*

In this addendum we present two alternative ways in which classical mechanics can be cast. The reason to do so is that these formulations, though more abstract, are relevant if we move into the quantum domain.

Canonical (Hamiltonian) structure. Let us first recast the setting of classical mechanics in a – what is called – *Hamiltonian form.* It is just a matter of reformulating the same physics in a slightly different but convenient mathematical form. First we note that from the alternative form of the equations (I.1.5-I.1.6), we learn that $d\mathcal{U}/dp = \partial H/\partial p$

and $dV/dx = \partial H/\partial x$.[4] Now we can write the equations of motion (I.1.3) in their Hamiltonian form as

$$\frac{dx}{dt} = \frac{\partial H}{\partial p}, \qquad (I.1.11a)$$

$$\frac{dp}{dt} = -\frac{\partial H}{\partial x}. \qquad (I.1.11b)$$

This form of the equations is also called *canonical* and the x and p variables are called *canonically conjugate*.

Poisson structure. Having pushed the juggling with derivatives this far, it pays to go yet one step further and add one more element, which will present classical Hamiltonian mechanics in yet another elegant form. This formulation in terms of *Poisson brackets* was much preferred by Paul Dirac as it brings the classical theory tantalizingly close to its quantum descendants. We should first note that for an arbitrary function on phase space $f(x, p)$ we can derive its time evolution as a first-order dynamical system like:

$$\frac{df}{dt} = \frac{\partial f}{\partial x}\frac{dx}{dt} + \frac{\partial f}{\partial p}\frac{dp}{dt} = \frac{\partial f}{\partial x}\frac{\partial H}{\partial p} - \frac{\partial f}{\partial p}\frac{\partial H}{\partial x}, \qquad (I.1.12)$$

where we used the equations (I.1.11). Next we may define the Poisson bracket of two *arbitrary* functions $f(x, p)$ and $g(x, p)$ by

$$\{f, g\}_{pb} \equiv \frac{\partial f}{\partial x}\frac{\partial g}{\partial p} - \frac{\partial g}{\partial x}\frac{\partial f}{\partial p}. \qquad (I.1.13)$$

It is an expression which is antisymmetric in f and g, as $\{f, g\}_{pb} = -\{g, f\}_{pb}$. With this definition we can write the time derivative of any function on phase space (i.e. any dynamical variable) as the Poisson bracket with the Hamiltonian:

$$\frac{df}{dt} = \{f, H\}_{pb}. \qquad (I.1.14)$$

We say that the Hamiltonian 'generates' the time evolution of the dynamical variables. For a conserved quantity Q we

have by definition that $dQ/dt = 0$, which by the equation above implies that $\{Q, H\}_{pb} = 0$. A trivial instance is the case $Q = H$, where $dH/dt = \{H, H\}_{pb} = 0$ as it should. In this way, we may also observe that the equations

$$\frac{\partial f}{\partial x} = \{f, p\}_{pb} \text{ and } \frac{\partial f}{\partial p} = -\{f, x\}_{pb}, \qquad (I.1.15)$$

hold as well. The first one states that the x derivative, i.e. the effect of an infinitesimal translation in x-space on f, is 'generated' by the momentum p. Finally I should also point out the remarkable relation

$$\{x, p\}_{pb} = 1. \qquad (I.1.16)$$

Variables which satisfy this relation are called *canonically conjugate*. These classical equations involving Poisson brackets have striking quantum lookalikes in the form of *commutators* as we will explain in the second Volume of the book.

Lagrangian formulation of mechanics. There is another formulation of classical physics that is of great importance, particularly if one turns to relativistic systems. When we think of simple particle mechanics, the formulation uses the coordinate $x(t)$ and the velocity $v(t) = dx/dt$ as dynamical variables. The central quantity now is not the energy but rather the *Lagrangian* $L(x, v)$ defined as:

$$L(x, v) = \frac{1}{2}mv^2 - V(x), \qquad (I.1.17)$$

where we have assumed that the time dependence is fully contained in the position and velocity variables. Of particular interest is the so-called *Action* functional $S[x(t)]$ correponsing to the time integral of the Lagrangian:

$$S[x(t)] \equiv \int_{t_0}^{t_1} L(x, v). \qquad (I.1.18)$$

The action is not just a function of x but a so-called functional of the function $x(t)$. You may think of the variable as being the path taken by a particle that from a position

---

[4]We introduce the curly or *partial derivatives* which mean that for a function of several independent variables you only take the derivative with respect to one of them (keeping the others fixed).

$x_0 = x(t_0)$ to some other position $x_1 = x(t_1)$. So if you give me $x(t)$ for all t then I can calculate $v = dx/dt$ and therefore also S, and that is why S is functional of $x(t)$. The Newtonian force law of mechanics can now be derived from a variational argument with respect to the possible paths. The variational principle says that the action is stationary under a small variation of the path. It is like saying that the extremum of a function corresponds to points where the derivative of that function is zero, indeed at a maximum or minimum of a function the slope of that function is zero. For the functional the equivalent statement is to say that an extremum for the action of a particle to go from A to B along a path corresponds to paths for which the variation in the action vanishes. So, if we make a local change of the path $x'(t) = x(t) + \delta x(t)$, then that will lead to a change in the action $S'(x(t) \equiv S(x'(t)) = S + \delta S$. The requirement that the variation $\delta S = 0$ gives rise to the so-called *Euler-Lagrange equation(s)* which reads:

$$\partial_t \left(\frac{\partial L}{\partial v} \right) - \frac{\partial L}{\partial x} = 0 . \qquad (I.1.19)$$

One easily verifies that for the particle Lagrangian (I.2.27) one obtains Newton' second law, $m dv/dt + dV/dx = 0$. To go from the Lagrangian to the Hamiltonian formalism involves the definition of the generalized or canonical momentum p and the Hamiltonian $H(p, x)$ as follows,

$$p \equiv \frac{\partial L}{\partial v}$$
$$H(p, x) \equiv pv - L . \qquad (I.1.20)$$

There are two reasons to introduce the action one is that for relativistic systems the action is a Lorentz or relativistic invariant quantity while the energy or Hamiltonian is not, and the second has to do with quantum mechanics. There is a formulation of quantum theory, the so-called *path integral formalism* in which the quantum probability amplitude to go from x_0 to x_1 is given by a weighted sum (or integral) over all possible paths between the two points, and

 Finding the shortest path. If light or a photon goes from point A to point B, it presumably follows the shortest path and that path is a straight line between the two points. However if you use a navigator in your car, it may ask you to specify whether you mean the shortest route in a spatial sense (the cheapest) or the shortest route in time (the fastest). Knowing that 'time is money' this can be a tough decision to take.

A kindergarten model for calculating the fastest path is to show kids a chopstick and stick it into a bowl filled with water. Hey! What's happening? It looks like the stick is broken! So you pull it out again and 'no' it is not broken. You hear their brains rattling. 'If there is no water it's not broken,' says one. 'It breaks at the surface,' says another. 'I think that the light ray is broken instead,' says a girl in the back. Bravo! That must be it!

The answer is given in the figure below. We have a landscape with two countries; point A is situated in the one with a maximum speed of $c_1 = 120 \text{ km/hr}$ and point B is in the other where the maximum speed is $c_2 = 140 \text{ km/hr}$. Clearly the straight line segment AB is the spatially shortest connection. However if we want the path that takes the shortest time, we have to make a little calculation. We have indicated that the car after a distance s_1 crosses the border at a point F, which is at position x after which it goes a distance s_2 in the other country. So we choose as our action the time T it takes to get from A to B. From the figure that

$$s_1 = \sqrt{h_1^2 + x^2} \quad \text{and} \quad s_2 = \sqrt{h_2^2 + (d-x)^2}$$

Then the calculation of T proceeds as follows:

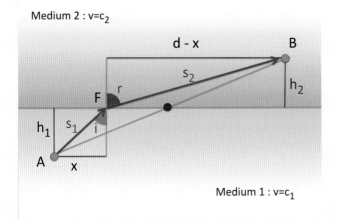

Medium 2 : $v = c_2$

Medium 1 : $v = c_1$

brings us back to the deep connection between a broken chopstick and Google maps. After the only adult in the room had explained all this, the girl in the back still had a question: 'How does the photon know which path to choose, as I presume it doesn't know how to take a derivative?'

☐

where the statistical weight depends on the action. Somehow in quantum theory there are corrections to the classical picture, those are contributions that correspond to paths that are classically forbidden. ■ ■

Maxwell's electromagnetism

$$T(x) = \int_A^B dt = \int_A^B (dt/ds)\, ds \qquad (I.1.21)$$

$$= \int_A^F (1/c_1) ds + \int_F^B 1/(c2)\, ds \qquad (I.1.22)$$

$$= s_1(x)/c_1 + s_2(x)/c_2, \qquad (I.1.23)$$

To find the minimum of $T(x)$ we have to solve for the x-value where the derivative of T vanishes:

$$\frac{dT(x)}{dx} = \frac{1}{c_1}\frac{x}{s_1} - \frac{1}{c_2}\frac{d-x}{s_2} = 0. \qquad (I.1.24)$$

We observe that the two quotients correspond to the sines of the angles i and r respectively, so that the condition implies the simple identity:

$$\frac{\sin i}{c_1} = \frac{\sin r}{c_2}, \qquad (I.1.25)$$

which is known as Snell's law for the refraction of a light ray at the interface of two media. And that

It appears to me therefore, that the study of electromagnetism in all its extent has now become of the first importance as a means of promoting the progress of science.

James Clerk Maxwell, 1873

The Maxwell equations give a unified description of electricity, magnetism and electromagnetic waves such as light or radio waves. Electromagnetism introduced the powerful concepts of a field and of field dynamics. After we discuss some of the familiar electromagnetic phenomena in relation to the Maxwell equations, we will introduce the gauge potentials which reveal two fundamental symmetries that turned out to underlie all of modern physics. The first is the so-called Lorentz invariance which lies at the root of special relativity, and the second refers to the notion of gauge invariance, a principle that underlies the description of all fundamental interactions.

Besides gravity there are basic natural phenomena of an

Figure I.1.16: *Rainbows over Holland.* Light and all its optical effects like rainbows are fully described by Maxwell's equations. Note on the right that in the barely visible secondary rainbow the sequence of colors is inverted. This is due to a third reflection of the light ray in the vapor droplets (Photo: V. de Vries).

essentially different nature to be accounted for, those related to electricity and magnetism. For these the universal laws in their splendid generality were written down in a treatise by James Clark Maxwell almost two centuries after Newton's seminal contributions in about 1865. His four laws were universal as well, as they accounted for all electric and magnetic phenomena observed to that date and as a bonus turned out to also describe the propagation of electromagnetic waves in its many guises such as light, radio waves or X-rays. Maxwell created for us the grand synthesis of many of the laws that were proposed earlier on by Coulomb, Ampère, Faraday, Lenz and many others. And a unified picture emerged of what once were considered entirely disconnected phenomena: electricity, magnetism and optics.

Electromagnetic Fields. Maxwell's theory is formulated in terms of a magnetic field $\mathbf{B}$ and electric field $\mathbf{E}$, which depend on space and time. So at any instant in time at any point in space, the fields have a particular strength $(\mathbf{E}(x, t), \mathbf{B}(x, t))$. You may think of them as two little arrows (vectors) pointing in some directions in space. The Maxwell laws describe in detail how electric currents cause magnetic fields, and how changes in magnetic flux result in currents which counteract that change. The laws also describe how accelerated charges emit electromagnetic radiation. From a more formal point of view they brought the fundamental but rather abstract concept of a *field* to life, in the sense that this concept was promoted from a mere mathematical abstraction and calculational tool to a physical reality. Electromagnetic fields by themselves propagate through space and time as waves and radiation, and turned into physical entities carrying energy and momentum. When you spend a day on the beach and forgot your sunscreen, you learn the hard way how much energy the electromagnetic waves emitted from the sun can carry. But also the beauty of a rainbow on a both sunny and foggy day is a manifestation of the electromagnetic interaction of light rays with the tiny vapor droplets in the fog.

The Maxwell equations

I am going to write down the Maxwell equations in their full glory: in other words, in their gory detail. Not to scare or impress you but because they are truly iconic. I think you need to have seen them, otherwise it is like going to Paris for the first time and missing out on the Eiffel tower, that would presumably make you mad at your tour operator. The comments I will make are rather general and descriptive which hopefully makes showing them less daunting. These are the four equations that could equally well be called 'the four Maxwell laws of electromagnetism and light.' These equations are usually presented in the following form:[5]

$$\nabla \cdot \mathbf{E} = \rho \,, \tag{I.1.26a}$$

$$\nabla \cdot \mathbf{B} = 0 \,, \tag{I.1.26b}$$

$$\nabla \times \mathbf{B} = \frac{\mathbf{j}}{c} + \frac{1}{c}\frac{\partial \mathbf{E}}{\partial t} \,, \tag{I.1.26c}$$

$$\nabla \times \mathbf{E} = -\frac{1}{c}\frac{\partial \mathbf{B}}{\partial t} \,. \tag{I.1.26d}$$

We see that the equations, besides the $\mathbf{E}$ and $\mathbf{B}$ fields, depend on the charge and current densities $\rho(x, t)$ and $\mathbf{j}(x, t)$, and on the velocity of light c. That the charges and currents appear in these equations is no surprise as they

---

[5]The way they look depends on the precise choice of units, here I work in Heaviside-Lorentz units because that choice makes them look simpler. The physical parameter is the velocity of light c, and as we will see it will pop up in most relations.

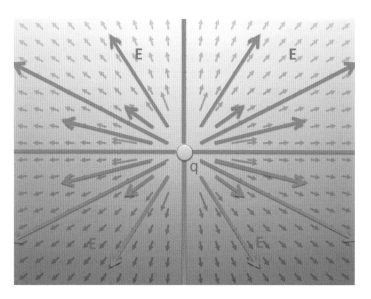

Figure I.1.17: *Coulomb's law.* If we put a positive charge at rest at the origin, then the first Maxwell equation corresponding to *Coulomb's law* will yield an electric field pointing radially outward. The strength of the field (given by the length of the vector) falls off as $1/r^2$ in three dimensions. This equation by itself describes what is called *electro-statics.* The second Maxwell equation tells you that the magnetic equivalent of such a radial field does not exist.

are the *sources* of the fields.

The *first equation* is often called *Coulomb's* or *Gauss' law*, and it determines the electric field that is caused by a given charge distribution. It says in particular that a single charge causes a radial electric field around it, as illustrated in Figure I.1.17.

The *second equation* is the magnetic analogue of the first equation for isolated magnetic 'North' or 'South' charges. The right-hand side is put to zero, for the excellent reason that magnetic monopoles have never been observed, at least up until now. This is the *'no monopole' equation*, but one sees that the system could be adapted to a situation where monopoles would show up, a situation that cannot be excluded *a priori.*

The *third equation*, also called *Ampère's law*, states that a current (or moving charge) causes magnetic fields and

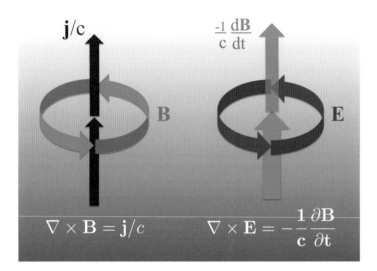

Figure I.1.18: *Ampère's and Faraday's laws.* This figure illustrates the two Maxwell equations involving the curl of the fields. The left picture refers to *Ampère's law* for the case of magnetostatics, where a straight current yields an axially symmetric B field. The picture on the right depicts *Faraday's* or *Lenz's law* describing how a changing magnetic field or flux gives rise to an electric field. If we think of the **E** loop as a closed conducting loop, a current would start flowing so as to counteract the change in the magnetic field.

a changing electric field. In other words, given the distribution of charges and currents in space and time, the Maxwell equations tell you exactly what the electromagnetic fields will look like. The third and fourth equation involve the so-called curl of a magnetic and electric field. In Figure I.1.18 we have indicated how the fields indeed 'curl' around the source which is a vector like the current. It is another instance of the 'Like-rule.'

The *fourth equation*, also called *Faraday's* or *Lenz's law*, describes how a changing magnetic field causes (induces) an electric field, which in turn can give rise a current. If you take a conducting loop and you change the magnetic flux through that loop, then that change induces a current through the loop. If the loop is made of a superconducting material, the current will keep running forever. Also

in this equation we note that a potential 'magnetic current term' is manifestly absent for the same reason as before. It is this absence of magnetic monopoles and currents that breaks the would-be symmetry between electric and magnetic phenomena.

All the magnetic phenomena we have observed up to now are understood as caused by currents, meaning moving electric charges. Indeed, the second equation tells you that there are no magnetic purely radial monopole fields, while the third equation tells you that if you make a tiny closed current loop, it will act like a tiny magnetic dipole, and the overall configuration is a magnetic 'dipolar' field. You guessed it: all real magnets correspond to zillions of microscopic current loops, all neatly lined up. With the well-known consequence that if you break a bar magnet in half, you do not get a separated North and South pole, you just get two smaller dipolar bar magnets.

Linearity. It is important to observe that the system of Maxwell equations is linear in the fields. This means that one can simply add different solutions. In other words if I have any set of solutions, then any linear combination of these would again be a solution. This is illustrated in Figure I.1.19 This linearity of the dynamical system basically means that the electromagnetic field does not interact with itself.

Electric-magnetic duality. We have emphasized that the asymmetry of the Maxwell equations reflects the asymmetry of nature with respect to the existence of electric charges and magnetic monopoles. Indeed if we restrict the equations to a source-free situation, meaning that ρ and **j** are zero, then the equations exhibit a manifest symmetry which is referred to as *electric-magnetic duality*. The system of equations is in that case invariant under the dual transformation or mapping, where we simultaneously make the replacements $\mathbf{E} \rightarrow \mathbf{B}$ and $\mathbf{B} \rightarrow -\mathbf{E}$. This mapping transforms the first pair of equations into each other, and similarly likewise the second pair.

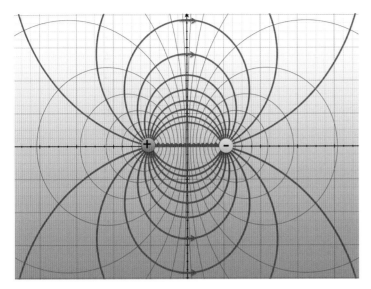

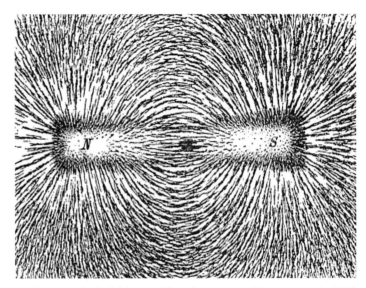

(a) Electric dipole field resulting from two opposite charges. The electric field lines are red, and the equipotential lines are blue.

(b) Magnetic dipole field caused by a bar magnet. They are made visible byputting the magnet on a table and spread some iron filings around it.

Figure I.1.19: *Dipolar fields.* If we put two opposite point charges at some distance of each other, the resulting field becomes dipolar, meaning that the field lines start at the positive charge (magnetic north) and end on the negative charges. In (a) we have the electric dipole field and in (b) we have the magnetic example. The second is approximated by an ordinary dipolar bar magnet. The field configuration is because of the linearity obtainedby just adding at every point the two coulomb fields of the single charges as depicted in Figure I.1.17

Light as an electromagnetic wave. The most impressive and surprising achievement of Maxwell was the great discovery that even in the absence of sources, the equations allowed for solutions describing electromagnetic waves that propagate through empty space at the velocity of light. This explains why the only parameter that appears in these equations is the velocity of light. We will return to these electromagnetic waves shortly.

It is gratifying to see how much 'truth' about physical reality can be described with so few symbols. You could say that the ultimate elegance of nature is most manifest once it is expressed in the powerful language of mathematics. Awesome indeed!

Partial differential equations. The equations form a system of partial differential equations, partial because the fields depend on space and time variables, and the derivatives that appear are with respect to the spatial coordinates as well as time. This explains also the appearance of the *'del'* or *'nabla'* operator ∇, which is just the 'vector of spatial derivatives,'

$$\nabla = \{\frac{\partial}{\partial x_1}, \frac{\partial}{\partial x_2}, \frac{\partial}{\partial x_3}\}. \qquad (I.1.27)$$

To systematically solve equations involving the vector operator ∇, mathematicians have developed a special subject called *vector calculus*. That is what physics students have to study and are supposed to master, and as such, it is far beyond the scope of this book. You will believe me if I say that many shelves in our university libraries are full of books and journals that are stuffed with explicit solutions of the Maxwell equations for virtually any imaginable situation. With all due respect, we will stay far from those im-

pressive halls of wisdom, though we discuss some fundamental theorems involving the nabla operator ∇ in a *Math
Excursion* at the end of Part III on page 621. My narrative only tries the convey the overall structural aspects of
the theory, which by the way does not force my story to
become superficial, in fact quite the contrary.

A dynamical systems perspective. We may elevate the
dynamical systems' pespective of the previous section on
mechanics to the Maxwell equations and say that the dy-
namical 'variables' are now the components of the $\mathbf{E}$ and $\mathbf{B}$
fields which satisfy certain dynamical equations or equa-
tions of motion,

$$\frac{d\mathbf{B}}{dt} = f_B(\mathbf{E}, \mathbf{B}), \qquad (\text{I.1.28a})$$

$$\frac{d\mathbf{E}}{dt} = f_E(\mathbf{E}, \mathbf{B}). \qquad (\text{I.1.28b})$$

Locality. These are indeed only two of the four Maxwell
equations, those with time derivatives in them. Note that
on the right-hand side I have for convenience suppressed
the dependence on the spatial derivatives of the fields, because at a given time t these can be calculated from the
field themselves at time t.The main point here is that the
equations are local: loosely speaking one could consider
the fields as an infinite collection of independent variables
which are only locally coupled.

Constraints. The other pair of equations without time derivatives are constraint equations; in order for the system to
be consistent, these have to be obeyed at all times. So if
these equations are satisfied at some initial time $t = 0$,
then consistency of the system requires that they remain
valid for all t, and this requires that the time derivatives of
those equations should vanish.

This, in turn, can be proven from the Maxwell equations.
For the second equation the argument is quite straightforward: one finds that by taking the time derivative of that
equation one obtains the same expression as by taking

the divergence of the right-hand side of the fourth equa-
tion. The latter, in turn, equals $\nabla \cdot (\nabla \times \mathbf{E})$, which vanishes identically, meaning that it is zero for any field $\mathbf{E}$.
This is discussed in the *Math Excursion* on vector calculus on page 621 of Part III. For the first and third Maxwell
equations a similar argument can be applied, comparing
the time derivative of the first and the divergence of the
third equation we see that consistency requires the following relation to hold:

$$\frac{\partial \rho}{\partial t} = \nabla \cdot \mathbf{j}. \qquad (\text{I.1.29})$$

This equation is the continuity equation for electric charge,
it relates the time derivative of the charge in a given volume with the current through the surface bounding that
volume. In other words, it is the local conservation law
for electric charge. The conclusion is that the consistency
of the Maxwell equations requires local charge conservation.

Constraint equations can be used to reduce the number of
independent degrees of freedom, fields in this case. What
that means is that electromagnetism does not really have
two times three equals six independent field components
as the two equations above suggest. Maxwell's second
and fourth equations express two local $-(x, t)$ dependent
'constraints,' which reduce the number of independent field
variables from six to four. And these correspond to the four
gauge potentials we will get to shortly. Nevertheless, from
this dynamical systems point of view there is a remarkable
structural similarity between the mechanical and electromagnetic systems.

The electromagnetic force exerted on a charge. The
Maxwell equations feature external sources in terms of
charges and currents. Clearly these refer to charged particles or collectives thereof. So to complete the dynamical system approach we should also include the dynamics
of the charges and currents. This in turn means that we
specify the forces that these are subject to in given electric and magnetic fields. The expression for this so-called

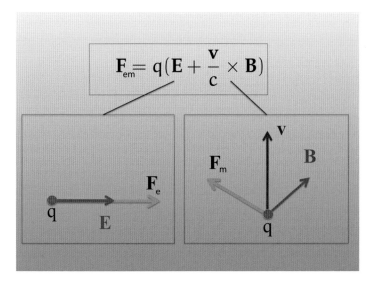

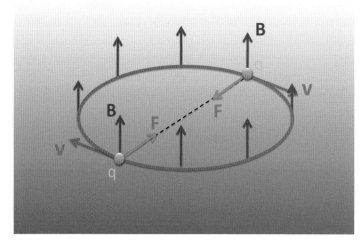

Figure I.1.20: *Motion of charge in an electromagnetic field.* This figure illustrates how the Lorentz force works on a charged particle. We show that the force has two contributions: one proportional to and in the direction of the electric field and one proportional to the magnetic field and the velocity in a direction perpendicular to the field and the velocity.

Figure I.1.21: *Motion of charge in a constant magnetic field.* This figure shows the orbit of a charged particle with a velocity perpendicular to the field. The force is constant and perpendicular to the velocity and will cause the particle to have a circular orbit. As the force is always perpendicular to the orbit the magnetic field does not do any work, and the magnitude of the velocity remains constant.

Lorentz force exerted on a charge at a point $(\mathbf{x}, t)$ by the fields $\mathbf{E}(\mathbf{x}, t)$ and $\mathbf{B}(\mathbf{x}, t)$ is the following:

$$\mathbf{F} = q(\mathbf{E} + \frac{\mathbf{v}}{c} \times \mathbf{B}) . \qquad (I.1.30)$$

The first term is a force in the direction of the electric field that any charge will feel, and the second term is the magnetic, so-called *Lorentz force*, which is orthogonal to the velocity of the charged particle. It is proportional to the magnitude of the current $\mathbf{j} = q\mathbf{v}$ and clearly vanishes when a particle is at rest. The fact that the magnetic component of the force is perpendicular to the velocity means that that component is always perpendicular to the trajectory, and consequently implies that the magnetic field cannot do any work on the charge. A charge in a constant magnetic field perpendicular to its velocity would therefore move in a circular orbit as we depicted in Figure I.1.21.

Clearly, the dynamical system to be solved is the coupled system of Newton's and Maxwell's equations where

Newton's equations have to include the Lorentz force and the charge(s) and their currents have to be included as sources in the Maxwell equations. This system is of course non-linear because of the feedback caused by the interaction terms.

We will later show how the electromagnetic interaction affects the energy function or the Hamiltonian of a charged particle, but that is more conveniently expressed in terms of the gauge potentials that we will introduce shortly.

Field energy and momentum. If we put a charged particle in a constant electric field, the field will exert a constant force on the particle which will therefore start to accelerate uniformly. This in turn means that its energy will increase. Now if we want to maintain the sacred principle of overall energy conservation, then one is forced to assume that the electromagnetic field also carries energy.

Indeed, the mere fact that the Maxwell equations without any charges and currents describe propagating waves means that the fields should carry both energy and momentum. Furthermore, once properly defined, it turns out that both the total energy and momentum for the whole system including charges and currents and fields is conserved again, assuming of course that the fields evolve according to Maxwell's equations.

Because the electric and magnetic fields as fundamental variables are space-time dependent – we say that they describe *local* degrees of freedom, it is then natural to define field energy and field momentum *densities*. This means that in order to get the total energy/momentum within a given volume one has to integrate the densities over that volume.

The expression for the energy of the electromagnetic field is basically the sum of (or better the integral over) the contributions in all points in space of a field energy density

$$\varepsilon(x, t) \ = \ \frac{1}{2}(|\mathbf{E}|^2 \ + \ |\mathbf{B}|^2),$$

which is quadratic in $\mathbf{E}$ and in $\mathbf{B}$, where you may think of the first term as corresponding to the 'kinetic energy' and the second to the 'potential energy.' This total energy is conserved. The fields also carry a momentum density, which is called the *Poynting vector* $\mathbf{S}(x, t) \ = \ c\,(\mathbf{E} \ \times \ \mathbf{B})$ and an angular momentum density $\mathbf{L}(x) \ = \ (x \ \times \ \mathbf{S})/c^2$ in complete analogy with particle angular momentum $\mathbf{L} = x \ \times \ \mathbf{p}$. This comes out most clearly in the electromagnetic wave solutions to the Maxwell equations illustrated in Figure I.1.23, which shows that the fields form propagating waves that are transversal, meaning that at any point in space the vectors $\mathbf{E}$ and $\mathbf{B}$ are mutually perpendicular, and also perpendicular to the direction of propagation. From the figure one verifies that the field momentum density $\mathbf{S}$ is, as expected, directed along the propagation direction of the wave.

Three fundamental principles. The remainder of this

section is devoted to two fundamental symmetry principles underlying the Maxwell equations of electromagnetism.

The *first principle* refers to the notion of *Lorentz invariance* which forms a key link with the theory of relativity.

The *second principle* refers to the notion of *gauge invariance* which amounts to a hidden redundancy that is present if we describe electromagnetism in terms of $\mathbf{E}$ and $\mathbf{B}$ fields as we usually do.

The *third principle* concerns the quantum nature of electromagnetism, of which the most basic manifestation is that we have to think of electromagnetic fields in terms of particle-like excitations or quanta, called photons. The latter principle is the main subject of the book and will be fully explored in the forthcoming chapters; we will not discuss it any further here.

The Maxwell equations refer to the fields $\mathbf{E}$ and $\mathbf{B}$, because these fields are the physical fields we can measure quite directly. The equations are beautiful, but that beauty has its price in the sense that the description is highly redundant and therefore basically inefficient! The reason we already touch on these rather sophisticated symmetry principles here is that in hindsight it turns out that these two invariances, combined with the principles of *quantum theory*, really form the conceptual backbone of all of modern fundamental physics. The tremendously successful Standard Model of fundamental forces and particles is a particular expression of these three underlying principles. Moreover, understanding these principles played an essential guiding role in discovering the Standard Model.

Electromagnetic waves

The source-free Maxwell equations can be recast in the form of wave equations. The wave equations manifestly display the underlying Lorentz or relativistic invariance of the Maxwell theory. In that sense Maxwell theory was the cradle of relativity.

Relativistic wave equations.

By mathematically manipulating them we can cast the Maxwell equations (I.1.28) in an alternative form. In the case of vanishing sources – with zero charges and currents in other words – they take the form of two wave equations: one for the electric and and one for the magnetic field.[6]

These wave equations are Lorentz and therefore relativistically invariant, which means, as we will discuss later in the corresponding section on page 60, that they will take the same form for different observers that move at a constant speed with respect to one another. Such observers have coordinate frames that are different, but the statement is that the frames of two such observers are related by a so-called Lorentz transformation, which depends on their relative velocity. An alternative way to express the fact that the equations 'look the same' for the different observers is to say that the equations are invariant under Lorentz transformations.

Four-vectors. Let us look at this a little closer. In ordinary space we can define a coordinate vector $\mathbf{x}$, and then we know that a rotation will change the direction it is pointing. What does not change is the dot product or the length of the vector, $\mathbf{x} \cdot \mathbf{x} = x^2$. The length of any vector is invariant under rotations, and this also holds therefore for the square of the vector operator ∇. To explain the notions of Lorentz invariance and of space-time we do something similar. First we define a space-time coordinate *four-vector* $x^\mu = \{x^0, \mathbf{x}\}$ with $x^0 \equiv ct$, the factor c is there to also give x_0 the dimension of a length. Next we define the relativistic 'length' or *space-time interval* s of that coordinate vector by the relation $s^2 \equiv x^\mu x_\mu \equiv x_0^2 - \mathbf{x} \cdot \mathbf{x}$, where indeed the repeated upper and lower μ index by definition means that we have to sum over its range $0, ..., 3$, with the minus sign for the spatial components included. The notion of Lorentz invariance refers now to the fact that the

Figure I.1.22: *Aurora Borealis.* The *Northern Lights* are caused by collisions of charged particles coming from the sun and gas particles from the earth's atmosphere. The most common auroral color, a pale yellowish-green, is produced by oxygen molecules located about 60 miles above the earth. Rare, all-red auroras are produced by high-altitude oxygen, at heights of up to 200 miles. (Source: Wikimedia)

space-time interval is invariant under Lorentz transformations, just like the length of an ordinary vector is invariant under rotations. So Lorentz transformations are the generalization of ordinary rotations in three-dimensional Euclidean space to four-dimensional space-time (also called Minkowski space).

The box-operator. The wave equations feature second order spatial and time derivatives in a unique relativistically invariant combination denoted by

$$\Box \equiv \partial^\mu \partial_\mu \equiv \frac{1}{c^2}\frac{\partial^2}{\partial t^2} - \nabla^2 . \qquad (I.1.31)$$

The electromagnetic wave equations can then simply be written as

$$\Box \mathbf{E} = 0, \qquad (I.1.32a)$$
$$\Box \mathbf{B} = 0. \qquad (I.1.32b)$$

---

[6]A typical 'wave equation' is discussed in the *Math Excursion* at the end of Volume III on page 613.

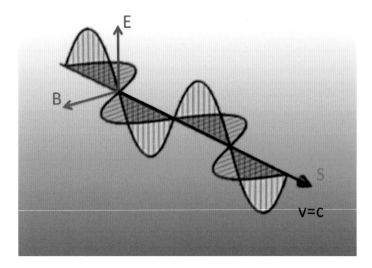

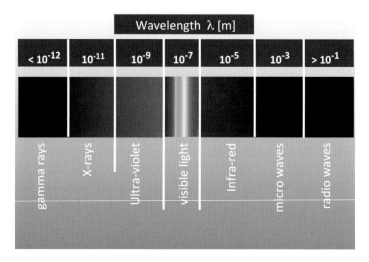

Figure I.1.23: *Electromagnetic wave.* This is a propagating wave of periodic electric and magnetic fields. The polarizations of the electric and magnetic field are orthogonal, and both are orthogonal to the direction of propagation which is along the direction of the field momentum **S**.

Figure I.1.24: *Electromagnetic radiation spectrum.* Classical electromagnetic waves can have any wavelength, from very long wavelength radio waves to the ultra short wavelength hard gamma rays. Visible light represents a narrow range in the center.

In the 'box operator' □ we see that time and space appear on an equal footing, which amounts to saying that this operator is relativistically invariant. The 'box' operator is the relativistic wave operator, and the equations above are the equations for electromagnetic waves. And indeed, it was this property of invariance of the Maxwell equations under the Lorentz transformations, named after its discoverer, the Dutch physicist and early Nobel laureate Hendrik Antoon Lorentz, which was a crucial key used by Einstein to unlock the gateway to the world of relativity.

Basic properties of waves. Like all waves, the electromagnetic waves are characterized by a wavelength λ, a frequency ν, and a velocity **v** which in this case of course equals the speed of light, $|\mathbf{v}| = c$. These three quantities are not independent, since they satisfy the relation $\nu = c/\lambda$. So electromagnetic waves are special in that they always travel with the speed of light, you can't speed them up or slow them down. If you put more energy into the

waves, two things may happen: (i) the amplitudes of components may go up (the signal becomes more intense), and/or (ii) the frequency may increase, meaning that the colour (in the case of light) will be shifted towards the blue. In the quantum world where we think of photons or particles of light, the corresponding mechanisms are, (i) that we can create more particles of light, or (ii) we can give the particles themselves more energy by increasing the frequency.

We have depicted the characteristic spatial structure of a classical electromagnetic wave in Figure I.1.23, and one sees that for such waves the directions (or polarizations) of the electric and magnetic field amplitudes are orthogonal and orthogonal to the propagation direction as well. The discovery of these wavelike solutions was a seminal contribution to electromagnetic theory, because it unified electromagnetism with the field of optics. The waves can in principle have any frequency or wavelength. We have sketched the spectrum of electromagnetic radiation in Figure I.1.24 , from which we see that spectrum of visible light only covers a narrow range in the center. At the long wavelength side the spectrum continues via the infrared into the micro and radio waves. On the short wavelength side it continues in the ultraviolet via X-rays into hard gamma rays. This side of the spectrum corresponds to ionizing radiation, where ionizing means that the electrons in the outer shells of atoms and molecules will be kicked out so that positively charged ions stay behind. This among other things means that this radiation is very damaging to biological tissue and one should avoid being exposed to it. In other words, avoid spending the weekend on a tropical beach without sunscreen.■

Lorentz invariance: the key to relativity

We introduce the electromagnetic potentials, and rewriting the electromagnetic fields in terms of these reduces the number of independent equations to four. In this form the invariance of the system under Lorentz transformations becomes manifest, establishing that the system is fully relativistic. This and the following section basically show a form in which the Maxwell equations can be cast that maximally exhibits their fundamental structure and beauty.

Gauge potentials. It is interesting that in the context of quantum theory it is far more profitable to use a different parametrization of the electromagnetic field in terms of so-called *gauge potentials* denoted by $A_\mu(x, t)$. As before, the index μ runs from $0, ..., 3$, with 0 the time component and $1, 2, 3$ the space components.

The four-vector $A_\mu = (V, -\mathbf{A})$ are the electromagnetic potentials where V is often referred to as the electrostatic or *scalar potential* and $\mathbf{A}$ as the *vector potential*. From these potentials the electric and magnetic field can be calculated

directly through the defining relationships:

$$\mathbf{B} = \mathbf{\nabla} \times \mathbf{A}, \qquad (\text{I.1.33a})$$

$$\mathbf{E} = -\mathbf{\nabla}V - \frac{1}{c}\frac{\partial}{\partial t}\mathbf{A}. \qquad (\text{I.1.33b})$$

Let us indicate how these expressions come about. One may show that for any magnetic field configuration $\mathbf{B}$ with zero divergence, meaning that it satisfies equation (I.1.26b), there is a vector field $\mathbf{A}$ that satisfies equation (I.1.33a). In fact that $\mathbf{A}$ is not unique as we'll see later. Indeed one finds that the equality $\mathbf{\nabla} \cdot (\mathbf{\nabla} \times \mathbf{A}) \equiv 0$ holds for *any* $\mathbf{A}$; it is a mathematical identity which basically follows from the definition of the vector derivative $\mathbf{\nabla}$. If we proceed by substituting this expression of $\mathbf{B}$ into the equation (I.1.26d), we get an equation of the type $\mathbf{\nabla} \times \mathbf{C} = 0$, with $\mathbf{C} = \mathbf{E} + \frac{1}{c}\frac{\partial}{\partial t}\mathbf{A}$. Now there is another identity that says that any field $\mathbf{C}$, whose rotation vanishes, can be written as a gradient of some scalar field V. This means that we may write $\mathbf{C} = \mathbf{\nabla}V$, from which the equation (I.1.33b) then follows. So by changing from the $\mathbf{E}$ and $\mathbf{B}$ fields to the potential $A_\mu = (V, -\mathbf{A})$ we have identically satisfied two of the four Maxwell equations. From the other two follow equations that the gauge potentials have to satisfy.

The electromagnetic field strength. You might wonder why I – clearly being in love with relativity – don't come up with four vectors E_μ and B_μ. Alas, 'It ain't necessarily so....' Better even, 'it just ain't gonna work!' The appropriate relativistic place for the electric and magnetic fields is that they correspond to the components of an antisymmetric two index object (a tensor) called the *field strength* $F_{\mu\nu}$:

$$F_{\mu\nu} = \partial_\mu A_\nu - \partial_\nu A_\mu. \qquad (\text{I.1.34})$$

The three spatial components F_{ij} correspond with the components of $\mathbf{B}$, and the space-time components F_{0i} correspond with the components of $\mathbf{E}$. The $\mu - \nu$ antisymmetry can be visualized more conveniently by writing F as an antisymmetric 4×4 matrix:

$$F = \begin{vmatrix} 0 & E_1 & E_2 & E_3 \\ -E_1 & 0 & -B_3 & B_2 \\ -E_2 & B_3 & 0 & -B_1 \\ -E_3 & -B_2 & B_1 & 0 \end{vmatrix}. \qquad (\text{I.1.35})$$

It clearly shows how the components of the **E** and **B** fields are not part of four vectors, which means that the **E** and **B** components may mix if we make a Lorentz transformation from one reference frame to another, just like the space and time components of the position four-vector do. This mixing is not entirely unexpected, since if we can transform a particle at rest in one frame to a moving particle in another frame, then the static particle has a pure radial electric field. The moving charge, however, is like a current and generates a magnetic field as well. So one expects that under a Lorentz transformation the **E** and **B** fields should mix. And if each of them was a four-vector, transformations would *not* mix the two sets of components.

From the manifestly relativistic definitions above, we see that the symmetry between electric and magnetic fields is particularly special to four-dimensional space-time. If we consider what the matrix $F_{\mu\nu}$ would look like in different dimensions, this becomes very clear: (i) in two-dimensional space-time there is only a single electric field component along the space direction and there is no magnetic field; (ii) in three dimensions we have an electric vector field with two components and a single component magnetic field which is therefore like a (pseudo) scalar.

We can now also write the Maxwell equations in manifestly relativistic form. The equations with sources (I.1.26a) and (I.1.26c) will then read:

$$\partial^\nu F_{\mu\nu} = \frac{1}{c} j_\mu, \qquad (\text{I.1.36})$$

where a repeated upper and lower index implies a summation over that index from $0, ..., 3$. On the right-hand side we have the current j_μ, which is now also a four-vector. Its

time component j_0 is equal to the charge density ρ times the velocity of light c, and the spatial components j_i are the components of the usual electric current-density vector **j** :

$$j_\mu = (c\rho, \mathbf{j}). \qquad (\text{I.1.37})$$

The other two – sourceless – Maxwell equations can also be written in a manifestly Lorentz invariant way as,

$$\partial^\nu \widetilde{F}_{\mu\nu} = 0. \qquad (\text{I.1.38})$$

Where we have constructed the *dual field strength* $\widetilde{F}_{\mu\nu}$ marked with a 'tilde,' by applying the electric-magnetic duality transformation discussed on page 22, to $F_{\mu\nu}$, yielding,

$$\widetilde{F} = \begin{vmatrix} 0 & B_1 & B_2 & B_3 \\ -B_1 & 0 & E_3 & -E_2 \\ -B_2 & -E_3 & 0 & E_1 \\ -B_3 & E_2 & -E_1 & 0 \end{vmatrix}. \qquad (\text{I.1.39})$$

Again these sourceless equations are solved identically by substituting the field strength in terms of the gauge potentials. In other words, by substituting the expressions (I.1.33) of **E** and **B** in terms of the gauge potentials into the equation (I.1.38).

The action for the Maxwell field. We have, in the closing subsection about classical mechanics, highlighted the importance of the concept of an action (and Lagrangian) for relativistic systems. As the Maxwell system is a relativistic system with the fields and their derivatives as fundamental degrees of freedom, we should ask whether there is a suitable form of the Lagrange formalism in this case. The answer is affirmative, so let us show what it looks like. First of all let us introduce the Lagrangian density which corresponds to the Lorentz invariant expression that is quadratic in the derivatives of the field:

$$\mathcal{L}(A_\mu, \partial_\nu A_\mu) = -\frac{1}{4} F_{\mu\nu} F^{\mu\nu} - j_\mu A^\mu. \qquad (\text{I.1.40})$$

The Lagrangian L would be given by the integration over space of the density $\mathcal{L}$, and the action S is obtained by an additional integration over time. This yields the fully covariant expression,

$$S[A_\mu] = \int \mathcal{L}(A_\mu, \partial_\nu A_\mu)\, d^4 x.\qquad (I.1.41)$$

One may show that the Maxwell equations (I.1.36) correspond to the Euler-Lagrange equations for this action.

Current conservation. The previous equations require that the current j_μ is conserved, which means to say that

$$\partial^\mu j_\mu = 0.\qquad (I.1.42)$$

The substitution of the definitions yields the continuity equation which expresses the local conservation law for electric charge,

$$\frac{\partial \rho}{\partial t} = \nabla \cdot \mathbf{j}.\qquad (I.1.43)$$

Integrating this equation over some volume $\mathcal{V}$, it states that the increase of the charge in $\mathcal{V}$ per unit time (and divided by c) equals the net electric current flowing inward through the closed surface that bounds that volume.

A way to think about this is to consider an office building where people go in and out. Then if we state that the number of people in the building is locally conserved, it means that the total number of people in the building is equal to the number that are already in there, plus or minus the people who enter or leave the building. It is local because you can apply it to any volume, for example the law also applies to any floor of the building, or any individual room for that matter.

The energy of a charged particle. A good reason to introduce the gauge potentials is that the coupling of the electromagnetic field to charged particles and fields takes a particularly simple form. The correct expression for the interaction with a charged particle is directly obtained by replacing, in the non-interacting particle theory, the momentum vector $\mathbf{p}$ of the particle by $\mathbf{p} + q\mathbf{A}/c$, and the

energy E by $E - qV$, where q is the charge of the particle. The energy function or Hamiltonian H for the charged particle simply becomes:

$$H - qV = \frac{1}{2m}(\mathbf{p} + \frac{q}{c}\mathbf{A})^2.\qquad (I.1.44)$$

From this expression for the Hamiltonian, one obtains the equation of motion for a charged particle, which yields as one might expect the Newton force law featuring the Lorentz force:

$$\frac{d\mathbf{p}}{dt} = q(\mathbf{E} + \frac{1}{c}\mathbf{v} \times \mathbf{B}).\qquad (I.1.45)$$

What has become clear from my exposition so far is that the electromagnetic 'field' as we know it in classical physics basically corresponds to a system with an 'infinite' number of degrees of freedom, namely the $\mathbf{A}$, or $\mathbf{B}$ and $\mathbf{E}$ fields that can vary at any point in space, so that a field represents a degree of freedom in any point of space. We have emphasized the dynamical systems perspective because it is significant if we consider the quantum theories of fields and want to compare them to the quantum theory of particles. ∎

The charge degree of freedom. If we speak of 'a charge,' we commonly imagine a point-like particle carrying a certain charge, and as far as we know that charge q is quantized in units of the fundamental electron-charge $-e$. If the charge q has a velocity, it corresponds to a current $\mathbf{j} = q\mathbf{v}$, localized at the position of the particle. Often, though, we think of a *charge density* which is taken to be a continuous distribution.

The charge and current density $(c\rho, \mathbf{j})$ become the charge and current of a point charge q and $\mathbf{j}$, multiplied by a distribution function f^2, which specifies how the charge and currents are spread around $x_\mu(t)$.

A preliminary leap into quantum mechanics. At this point it may be illuminating to jump ahead into the quantum domain where things are so very different. For one thing, in quantum theory a charged particle is represented by a the complex function, the so-called wavefunction $\Psi(\mathbf{x}, t)$, which describes the quantum states of the particle. 'Complex' here means that the wavefunction has a 'real' and 'imaginary' part, and we may write the wavefunction therefore as $\Psi(\mathbf{x}, t) = e^{-i\alpha} f(\mathbf{x}, t)$, the product of a local factor with a phase $\alpha(\mathbf{x}, t)$ and a real function $f(\mathbf{x}, t)$. Whereas the state at some time t of a classical particle is determined by specifying its position, velocity (and parameters like mass and charge), in quantum physics the state is specified by the wavefunction which is defined over all of space. This means that the Lorentz equation of motion for a charged particle (I.1.45) will turn into the famous Schrödinger equation for the wavefunction Ψ. Quite a difference indeed, and in the second Volume of the book we will fully explore what it all implies.

In quantum theory for a single particle the momentum $\mathbf{p}$ is represented by the differential operator $\mathbf{p} = -i\hbar\boldsymbol{\nabla}$ which is supposed to act on the wavefunction. And it is basically here that the famous Planck constant 'h-bar' $\hbar \equiv h/2\pi$ enters the mathematical formalism. The coupling with the vector potential is, as mentioned before, implemented following the minimal replacement $\mathbf{p} \Rightarrow \mathbf{p} + q\mathbf{A}/c$, meaning the in the quantum world we have to replace the ordinary vector derivative $\boldsymbol{\nabla}$ with the *covariant derivative* $\mathbf{D} \equiv \boldsymbol{\nabla} + iq\mathbf{A}/\hbar c$.

The distribution $|\Psi|^2 = \Psi^*\Psi = f(\mathbf{x}, t)^2$ represents the *probability density* of finding the particle at the position $\mathbf{x}$ upon a position measurement at time t. This distribution is independent of the phase α. So it is not the charge which is distributed over space, it is the probability of finding all of that charge at a certain location in a position measurement of the particle. That is what 'charge density' means in the quantum theory of a charged particle. Similarly, the electric *current density* takes the form:

$$\mathbf{j} = -ih(\Psi\boldsymbol{\nabla}\Psi^* - \Psi^*\boldsymbol{\nabla}\Psi) = (\hbar\boldsymbol{\nabla}\alpha)f^2, \quad (I.1.46)$$

proportional to the same distribution, and in some indirect sense 'proportional' to the momentum which brings in the

factor of $\hbar$ and the phase α. We will return to this wavefunction towards the end of this section where we discuss the 'quantization' of charge which can be linked to this particular quantum representation of a particle.

The wave equation for the potentials. Having defined the field strength in terms of the potentials in the equation (II.6.8), one finds that (in a suitable gauge) the Maxwell equations (I.1.36) reduce to the relativistic *wave equation* for the potentials:

$$\Box A_\mu = \frac{1}{c}j_\mu. \quad (I.1.47)$$

Also this form of the equations manifestly displays the relativistic invariance of the system: the potentials, and the charge density and current, are neatly organized in four-component relativistic vectors. The wave depicted in Figure I.1.23 corresponds to one of the solutions of the equation (I.1.47) in empty space (without charges or currents).

The solutions of the wave equation are not surprisingly the transversal electromagnetic waves. The wave solution for the gauge potential will look like $A_\mu \simeq \varepsilon_\mu \exp(i\mathbf{k}\cdot\mathbf{x} - \omega t)$ with the polarization four-vector ε_μ, the so-called *wave-vector* $\mathbf{k}$ and *angular frequency* ω. Substitution in the wave equation shows that we have to impose the condition that $|\mathbf{k}|^2 - \omega^2/c^2 = 0$. The solution corresponds with a wave that propagates in the direction of the vector $\mathbf{k}$, where it has a wavelength equal $\lambda = 2\pi/|\mathbf{k}|$, and a frequency $\nu = \omega/2\pi$. And as expected, the wave condition $\nu = c/\lambda$ is satisfied.

To see the link with the wave depicted in Figure I.1.23, we have to do some more work. First we have to realize that the derivative vector nabla acting on the gauge potential just brings down a factor $\sim \mathbf{k}$ while the time derivative brings down a factor $\sim \omega$. Then we can look at the definitions (I.1.33) to conclude that $\mathbf{B} \simeq \mathbf{k} \times \mathbf{A}$, while we can choose $\mathbf{k}\cdot\mathbf{A} = 0$ which gives $\mathbf{E} \simeq \omega\mathbf{A}$. With these choices we have ascertained that the three vectors $\mathbf{E}$, $\mathbf{B}$ and $\mathbf{k}$ are mutually orthogonal and that indeed the field momentum is in the direction of $\mathbf{k}$ as $\mathbf{S} \simeq (\mathbf{E} \times \mathbf{B}) \sim \mathbf{k}$. By finally noting that the waves for $\mathbf{A}$, $\mathbf{E}$ and $\mathbf{B}$ are in phase, we have verified all the features of the figure.

This wave equation for the potentials creates the best starting point for the 'quantization' of the electromagnetic field. As we will see later, the A fields are preferred for two reasons. Firstly, if one wants to quantize the electromagnetic field, it is convenient to think of the A_i fields as generalized 'coordinates,' while the electric fields $E_i \simeq \partial A_i / \partial t$ are like the 'momenta' of the field.

It is actually a quite remarkable fact about the Maxwell equations that as equations they survived both the relativity and the quantum revolution. As we will see it is in the interpretation of going from classical fields to those of quantum that the great revolution took place.

Figure I.1.25: *Gauge transformations of the author as Mr Vector Potential.* The pictures illustrate the idea of smooth local transformations. The information content (the person) is the same but the representations or copies are different.

Gauge invariance: beauty and redundance

The introduction of gauge potentials naturally leads to the notion of gauge invariance. *In one sense it signals a residual redundancy in the formulation of the theory. This principle is worth exploring as it plays a crucial role in the formulations of all theories that describe fundamental interactions.*

Once you write the equations in terms of the gauge potentials, another fundamental but somewhat elusive property becomes apparent. We have successfully reduced the electromagnetic field from six to four components, by introducing the potentials A_μ, but what we will argue next is that there is still a redundancy in the definition of the system. Whereas giving the gauge potentials yields a unique answer for the physical $\mathbf{E}$ and $\mathbf{B}$ fields, the converse is not true: a given set of $\mathbf{E}$ and $\mathbf{B}$ fields does not uniquely fix the gauge potentials, and this redundancy is called *gauge invariance.*

Let us change the gauge potential by – yes indeed – a *gauge transformation* involving an *arbitrary* function $\Lambda = \Lambda(x, t)$ as follows:

$$A_\mu \to A'_\mu = A_\mu - \partial_\mu \Lambda, \qquad (\text{I.1.48})$$

where Λ is an arbitrary function. If we calculate the transformed fields $\mathbf{E}'$ and $\mathbf{B}'$, we learn that the field components are invariant: $\mathbf{E}' = \mathbf{E}$ and $\mathbf{B}' = \mathbf{B}$, because for any pair of indices μ and ν we have that $\partial_\mu \partial_\nu \Lambda - \partial_\nu \partial_\mu \Lambda = 0$. In other words the contributions of the gauge function cancel.

Let me note that the gauge transformations form a group: they satisfy the group property that two successive transformations, form again a gauge transformation (where $\Lambda = \Lambda_1 + \Lambda_2$).[7] The observable physics, which resides in the $\mathbf{E}$ and $\mathbf{B}$ fields, is independent of Λ, and therefore the theory is said to be *gauge invariant.* In other words, we have

---

[7]The curious reader may like to jump ahead and look at the *Math Excursion* on groups on page 635 of Part III.

the freedom to choose any convenient function Λ to describe the physics, which is referred to as the freedom to choose a 'suitable gauge.' This choice is useful for example if one needs to construct explicit solutions, but if one has to quantize the electromagnetic field, then this blessing becomes a burden. You could say that the description of the physics in terms of the gauge potentials is elegant but at the same time redundant. It obscures to a certain extent what exactly the real physical degrees of freedom of the (quantized) electromagnetic field are. The wave equation for each of the four components of the vector potential suggests that there are four independent components to the field, yet looking at the electromagnetic wave of Figure I.1.23 we see that in fact it has only two physical components. This further reduction of degrees of freedom from four to two is due to the gauge invariance of the equations.

Gauge symmetry and charge conservation. The Maxwell equation (I.1.36) and the fact just mentioned that the field strength is gauge invariant means that this system is only consistent if the current itself is also gauge invariant. This property can be used to show that the continuity equation $\partial^\mu j_\mu = 0$ follows from gauge invariance. In other words the conservation of charge is a consequence of the gauge symmetry.

A nice way to show this more directly is by noting that the interaction term between the current and the gauge potentials has to be (i) local, (ii) Lorentz-invariant, and (iii) has to give rise to the correct Maxwell equations, which means that it has to be of the form $\int A_\mu j^\mu \, \mathrm{d}^4 x$. If we now make the gauge transformation (I.1.48), the coupling term acquires an extra term $\int (\partial_\mu \Lambda) j^\mu \, \mathrm{d}^4 x$, which has to vanish if the theory is gauge invariant. This term can be recast in a convenient form using the following mathematical identity:

$$\int \partial_\mu (\Lambda \, j^\mu) \, \mathrm{d}^4 x = \int (\partial_\mu \Lambda) j^\mu \, \mathrm{d}^4 x + \int \Lambda (\partial_\mu j^\mu) \, \mathrm{d}^4 x,$$

which is just writing the derivative of a product of two functions as a sum of derivatives on the individual factors and then integrating over space-time. The first term can be integrated to yield the integrand integrated over the three-dimensional boundary of the space-time volume, but on the boundary of space-time we assume the current j_μ will vanish and therefore so does the integrand. And as the integral of zero is zero, the left-hand side of the equation above is zero. This in turn means that the effect of the gauge transformation on the interaction term equals:

$$\int (\partial_\mu \Lambda) j^\mu \, \mathrm{d}^4 x = -\int \Lambda (\partial_\mu j^\mu) \, \mathrm{d}^4 x. \qquad (I.1.49)$$

Now the elegant argument continues by saying that because the gauge function $\Lambda(\mathbf{x}, t)$ can be chosen arbitrarily, and this means that the integral condition has to be satisfied locally, thus we have to require $\partial_\mu j^\mu = 0$ everywhere.

Stated in words, what we have shown is that imposing local gauge invariance requires the current to which the electromagnetic field couples to be conserved locally. This means that net charge can move around obeying the continuity equation, but it cannot just disappear into nothing. This is a not so surprising but vital result that resonates with our earlier observations that the conservation laws of momentum and angular momentum were a consequence of the space-time symmetries being translational and rotational invariance. In that sense one can say that the gauge transformation is like a rotation in a kind of 'internal space' of allowed gauge transformations. This discussion will be taken up in more detail and generality in Chapters I.2 and II.6 where we will have more to say about the geometry of gauge invariance.

A non-local observable: the loop integral of $\mathbf{A}$. Clearly the gauge potentials, as they are gauge-choice dependent, cannot be real observables, the physics resides in the gauge invariant observables being the electric and magnetic fields. These quantities are *local* in that they can be

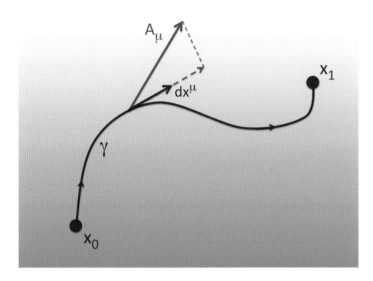

Figure I.1.26: *The line integral of the vector potential* A_μ . *The line integral of the four-vector potential* A_μ *from point* x_0 *to* x_1 *along a curve* γ . *It 'adds' the projections of* A_μ *along the tangent direction* $dx^\mu(\gamma)$ *of the curve for all points along* γ .

measured locally at a given point x^μ . We may, however, also consider other fundamental gauge invariant quantities, which are intrinsically *non-local* and involve the line integral of the gauge potential A_μ along a closed curve in space-time.

Let us just start by considering a line integral of the vector potential along some curve γ starting at a space-time point x_0 and terminating at point x_1 as depicted in Figure I.1.26 . We write this as follows:

$$I(\gamma;x_0,x_1) \equiv \int_{x_0}^{x_1} A_\mu\, dx^\mu(\gamma)\,. \qquad (1.1.50)$$

Now let us look what a gauge transformation does to this line integral:

$$I(\gamma;x_0,x_1) \to I'(\gamma;x_0,x_1) =$$
$$= I(\gamma;x_0,x_1) - \int_{x_0}^{x_1} \partial_\mu\Lambda(x^\nu)\, dx^\mu =$$
$$= I(\gamma;x_0,x_1) - \Lambda(x_1) + \Lambda(x_0)\,. \qquad (1.1.51)$$

Clearly the path dependent expression is only affected by the transformation at the start and end point. This implies that if we choose the start and end point to be the same, the resulting 'loop integral' will be gauge invariant as the gauge function Λ drops out. Let us take the example of a closed curve for a fixed time

$$\oint_{\partial D} \mathbf{A}\cdot d\mathbf{x} = \int_D (\boldsymbol{\nabla}\times\mathbf{A})\cdot\hat{\mathbf{n}}\, d^2S = \int_D \mathbf{B}\cdot\hat{\mathbf{n}}\, d^2S \equiv \Phi\,,$$
$$(1.1.52)$$

where $\hat{\mathbf{n}}$ is the unit vector perpendicular to the surface element $d^2S = dx\, dy$ of the surface D bounded by the curve ∂D . The first equality is an application of the 'Stokes theorem,' which is a mathematical identity explained in the *Math Excursion* on vector calculus at the end of Part III. The second equal sign follows from using the defining relation (I.1.33b) between the vector potential $\mathbf{A}$ and the magnetic field $\mathbf{B}$. Because the contribution of the gauge transformation drops out, this loop integral is gauge invariant and corresponds therefore to a physical and observable quantity, which is not so surprising once you realize that it 'measures' the total magnetic flux Φ through any surface D bounded by the curve, which *is* a gauge invariant quantity.

Gauge versus topological invariance. Yet, there is something quite remarkable about this result. Let us for simplicity consider a two-dimensional plane and have some non-vanishing magnetic flux piercing through the surface area bounded by – say – the unit circle, depicted as the dark region in Figure I.1.27. Outside the unit circle the physical $\mathbf{E}$ and $\mathbf{B}$ fields are zero but that does not imply that the gauge potentials have to be zero there as well. It only requires that the gauge potentials are pure gauge: $A_\mu = \partial_\mu\Lambda$, in other words, that they are a gauge transformation of field $A_\mu = 0$.

Then the result above tells us that you can measure the total magnetic flux Φ through any finite domain, by taking the line integral of the gauge potential around a closed loop which is arbitrarily far removed from that domain. You can

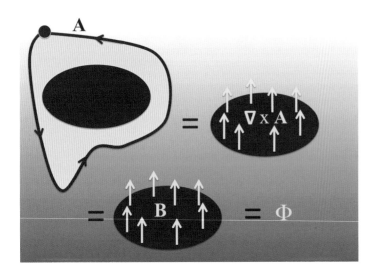

Figure I.1.27: *The loop integral of the vector potential.* A line integral of the vector potential **A** along a closed spatial loop is a gauge invariant but non-local quantity. The dark region inside the loop is the region where the magnetic field is non-zero, so, everywhere along the loop there is zero magnetic field, yet the line integral will yield a non-zero magnetic flux Φ .

measure the total flux without ever entering a region where the magnetic field **B** is non-zero. Indeed there is a non-local, gauge invariant quantity, corresponding to a measurement outcome that may assume any non-zero value, and that involves probing only a region of space where all physical fields are zero! Quite remarkable indeed!

Imagine we choose the closed loop around a big circle at infinity (the boundary of space) parametrized by ($r = \infty, \varphi$), then we find for the loop integral simply:

$$I(\gamma = S^1_\infty) = \Lambda(\varphi = 2\pi) - \Lambda(\varphi = 0). \qquad (I.1.53)$$

Here we run into an apparent contradiction, because on the one hand we argue that the gauge function has to be single-valued meaning that the right-hand side of the above equation should vanish, but on the other hand the left-hand side of the equation is nothing but the loop integral (I.1.52) which equals the total flux Φ !

The resolution of this paradox lies in the appreciation of what we precisely mean by a gauge transformation. We keep the definition simple: a gauge transformation $\Lambda(\mathbf{x}, t)$ is a smooth, single-valued function. Indeed, under such a transformation the value of the loop integral (I.1.52) cannot change. The converse also holds true, if we make a transformation that is *not* single valued, we by definition *do* change the outcome of the loop integral and thereby somehow have changed the magnetic field through the loop.

Let us illustrate this by a simple example: imagine somebody tells me that they have chosen $\Lambda(\mathbf{x}, t) = b\,\varphi$, a constant times the polar angle φ. than the loop integral would give a flux $\Phi = \Lambda(2\pi) - \Lambda(0) = 2\pi\,b$, this does *not* correspond to a proper gauge transformation because it is not single valued. Now it is a matter of semantics what you want to call this transformation; some physicists call it a 'singular' gauge transformation, and others call it a 'topologically non-trivial' gauge transformation. Presumably this is intended to emphasize that it looks like a gauge transformation while strictly speaking it is not, since it is singular at the origin of the plane ($r = 0$) where φ is not well defined. And indeed such a 'transformation' would 'create' a magnetic flux-line through the point (or the line) where $r = 0$.

In Chapter I.2, in the section on the geometry of gauge invariance on page 96 in, we will see that there is a rigorous topological characterization of the values that the loop integral traversing a vacuum region (or ground state region of some medium) can acquire. The physical situation is determined by a mapping of the closed loop (which is topologically equivalent to a circle S^1_φ) in space into the gauge group G. The outcomes are now determined by the number of topologically distinct ways we can do this and that depends on the global structure of the group-space of G.

For the case of electrodynamics where we have quantized charges the gauge group is the phase group which is also topologically a circle S_α^1. The elements can be represented as $g(\alpha) = e^{i\alpha}$. The constraint that follows is that $\alpha(\varphi) = n\varphi$, meaning that if we go around once in real space then we have to go around an integer n times in the gauge group (so that $g(2\pi) = g(0)$. So the distinct classes are labeled by this integer n with $-\infty < n < +\infty$. So in this theory both the electric charges and the magnetic fluxes would be quantized in suitable units. And because this number is fixed topologically, it is extremely robust. It will not change under *any* smooth deformation of the gauge potentials – not just gauge transformations. The winding number n is therefore a conserved quantity under any smooth deformation, but because it is conserved and quantized for a topological reason, it is called a *topological quantum number*.

We will see later that both gauge invariance and topological invariance play a fundamental role in quantum theory. The loop integral we just discussed is an observable quantity that can be measured as a shift in the interference pattern in a double-slit experiment with electrons, and is known as the *Aharonov-Bohm effect* effect, which is examined in Chapter II.3, after the theorists who proposed this experiment. This effect is a special case of a generalization known as the *Berry phase* which we cover in the same chapter. In an entirely different context the topological invariance of the loop integral can also be linked to the all-important feature of the *quantum statistics* properties of different particle types, like bosons, or fermions as we will discuss in Chapter II.5. ■ ▮

Monopoles: Nature's missed opportunity?

Charge quantization and magnetic monopoles. There is a brilliant, rather early use of the gauge invariance and parallel transport arguments we just presented, by Paul Dirac. In a famous 1931 article he boldly proposed the existence of magnetic monopoles, and proved that the mere

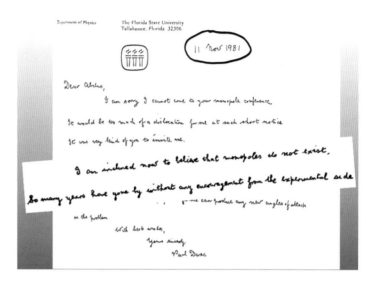

Figure I.1.28: *Dirac in doubt.* This is a fragment from a letter of Dirac to Abdus Salam from 1981, declining an invitation to attend a monopole meeting at the ICTP in Trieste. (Source: Proceedings of Monopoles in QFT, ICTP, Trieste, 1981.)

existence of just a single magnetic monopole in the whole universe would suffice to explain the observed quantization of electric charge! We have already mentioned that a magnetic monopole has never been observed, but that fact by itself does not really exclude the possibility that they somehow exist. May be they once existed and subsequently disappeared through some annihilation process, given that to our knowledge that was what happened to anti-matter, for example. 'To be or not to be,' that is the question, because just being there would suffice!

Dirac's proof goes in fact one way: he shows that if a monopole would exist, then electric charge would have to be quantized in integer multiples of some minimal charge e. In the concluding section of his 1931 article, after noting that the charges we have observed in nature *are* quantized, he modestly states: 'One would be surprised if nature wouldn't have made use of it.'

In practice we can of course do without monopoles because all magnetic phenomena that have been observed can be explained as being caused by electric currents, moving charges in other words. In all observed magnetic phenomena, there are always a combination of north *and* south poles involved. If you break a bar magnet into two pieces, you get two bar magnets, not a separated north and south pole. And that rule so far holds on all scales, even the smallest accessible. As we mentioned before, this is also the reason that the the sourceless Maxwell equation for the magnetic field reads $\nabla \cdot \mathbf{B} = 0$, where the zero on the right-hand side expresses the merciless verdict: 'No monopoles!' In theory there could have been a 'magnetic' source term there, but there is none. However, the price for it not being there is that the observed quantization of electric charge for the moment remains a mystery. A mystery that has not even been resolved by today's Standard Model of elementary particles and fundamental forces.

The charge quantization puzzle would actually be resolved if the so-called Grand Unified Theories or GUTS turned out to be correct. These theories unify all non-gravitational interactions in one overarching model, as we will discuss in Chapter I.4. This means that different particle types like quarks and electrons belong to a single representation which links their relative charges. Believe it or not, this is precisely the case because those models *necessarily* contain magnetic monopoles in their spectrum as was brilliantly shown by Gerard 't Hooft and Alexander Polyakov independently in 1974. And indeed in these models electric charge *is* quantized. However, these Grand Unified monopoles would be so heavy, of the order of 10^{15} proton masses, that there is no hope making them, even in a fancy lab like CERN. Yet, never say never, may be Dirac will turn out to be right after all. This in spite of the doubt that Dirac himself cast over his prediction towards the end of his life, as expressed in the short note to Abdus Salam depicted in Figure I.1.28.

Dirac's argument. Dirac's argument for charge quanti-

zation is sketched in Figure I.1.29. Imagine if we put a monopole with magnetic charge g in the origin, then the magnetic field would point radially outward. The total flux going out through any surface enclosing the monopole is then equal to g. Now imagine the situation sketched in Figure I.1.29, where I draw a sphere around the monopole and I take a charge q and make a closed loop on the surface. Clearly the product of the charge and the gauge invariant loop integral equals the charge times the flux going through the loop. Let me first look at the flux going through the 'northern' surface segment, giving me a flux going upward, say $\Phi_N = \alpha$. However, I could also have taken the flux through the 'southern sector' going down, then that flux would be $\Phi_S = -(g/c - \alpha)$. The phase factors have to be the same (because the flux through any two surfaces bounded by the loop has to be) so we get the following condition on the phases themselves:

$$\frac{q}{\hbar c}\alpha = -\frac{q}{\hbar c}(g - \alpha) + 2\pi n \quad \Rightarrow \quad qg = 2\pi n\hbar c. \quad (\text{I.1.54})$$

Indeed the flux α drops out as it should, because the argument holds for any arbitrary closed loop on the surface. Dirac used the argument exactly the other way around: if there somewhere exists a minimal magnetic charge g, then $qg = 2\pi n\hbar c$. This in turn implies: $q = ne$, so that $e\,g = 2\pi\hbar c$, where e is the minimal electric charge. Therefore he showed that the existence of a magnetic monopole implies the charge quantization that we observe in nature.

Conversely, it is also true that if there existed two particles with incommensurate charges, meaning to say that their ratio would be some non-fractional real number like π or $\sqrt{2}$, then that fact by itself would exclude the existence of magnetic monopoles. So we are left with a stunningly simple and profound explanation of the observed quantization of electric charge, except for the slightly inconvenient fact that we haven't seen any monopole (yet)!

The monopole or Hopf bundle. We have been somewhat cavalier about the precise argument. You could even

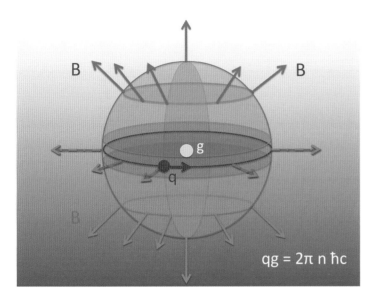

Figure I.1.29: *Electric charge quantization*. This figure illustrates Dirac's 1931 argument for the quantization of electric charge based on the hypothetical existence of a magnetic monopole. To describe the monopole field with potentials requires at least two overlapping patches with potentials $\mathbf{A}_{\pm}$.

What I am going to to describe you is the mathematical concept of a *fibre bundle*, and we will describe these in more general terms in the section on the 'Physics of geometry' in the next chapter. You could say that we have to enlarge the mathematical framework to that of fibre bundles to allow for situations we couldn't properly cope with before, like having magnetic monopoles.

We start by introducing two coordinate patches S_+ and S_- that cover the sphere, each having the topology of a disc, that have an overlap region with the topology of a cylinder. This is depicted in Figure I.2.30 on page 86 for the sphere S^2, with the blue and green patches S_+ and S_-, and their overlap region containing the equator. Then we define two gauge potentials, say $\mathbf{A}_+$ and $\mathbf{A}_-$ on these two patches that exactly give the magnetic fields present on the patches. So we don't care what $\mathbf{A}_{\pm}$ do *outside* their patch, they well may develop a singularity *there* but as we don't use them there it doesn't matter. In the overlap region these potentials define strictly identical magnetic fields and therefore have to be related by a gauge trasformation. This is shown in Figure I.1.29, where in the overlap region the two gauge potentials have to be gauge transformations of each other. In terms of equations the statement just made read:

$$\text{for } x \in S_{\pm} \qquad \nabla \times \mathbf{A}_{\pm} = \mathbf{B}_{\pm} \ , \qquad \text{(I.1.55a)}$$
$$x \in (S_+ \cap S_-) \qquad \mathbf{B}_+ = \mathbf{B}_- = \mathbf{B}, \qquad \text{(I.1.55b)}$$
$$\mathbf{A}_- = \mathbf{A}_+ - \nabla \Lambda. \qquad \text{(I.1.55c)}$$

Note that although locally the potentials produce the same magnetic field, what is also clear from the figure is that when we take the loop integral in the overlap region – around the equator for example – then for $e\mathbf{A}_+$, we get the monopole flux through the northern hemisphere $eg/2\hbar c$, but for $\mathbf{A}_-$ we get the flux through the southern hemisphere which has to yield the opposite $-eg/2\hbar c$. This means that the loop-integral over the gauge transformation has to be equal to their difference:

claim that I arrived at the correct answer by incorrect reasoning. You see, the moment I put a magnetic source on the right-hand side of the magnetic Maxwell equation, then it is no longer sourceless. In that case the mathematical identity that $\nabla.(\nabla \times \mathbf{A}) \equiv 0$ of equation (A.11a) can no longer hold, which appears to imply that you cannot write the magnetic field in terms of potentials if monopoles are present. Fortunately the situation is not that bad, because the proper use of the potentials turns out to be more subtle. In fact you can still use them, but only locally, as there is a topological obstruction to write a single potential to give the magnetic field everywhere on a surface fully enclosing the monopole. Somewhere on that surface that potential would become singular and the description in terms of a gauge potential would break down. There is a mathematical resolution however, but it is somewhat complicated, and it reveals a fundamental aspect of gauge theories in general. And that is the reason to explore this.

$$\frac{e}{\hbar c} \oint \frac{\partial \Lambda}{\partial \varphi} \, \mathrm{d}\varphi = \frac{e}{\hbar c}(\Lambda(2\pi) - \Lambda(0)) = \frac{eg}{\hbar c}. \qquad \text{(I.1.56)}$$

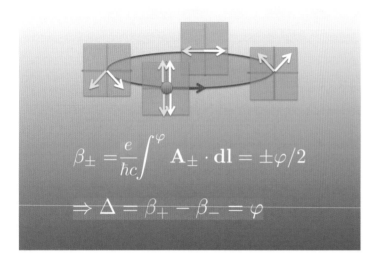

$$\beta_\pm = \frac{e}{\hbar c}\int^\varphi \mathbf{A}_\pm \cdot \mathbf{dl} = \pm\varphi/2$$

$$\Rightarrow \Delta = \beta_+ - \beta_- = \varphi$$

Figure I.1.30: *Parallel transport of charge vector or phase.* around the equator in the monopole field. The phase shifts $\beta^\pm$ calculated from $A_\pm$ in the northern/southern hemisphere respectively have opposite signs. The requirement for a U(1) bundle is that the transition function $f(\varphi) = e^{i\Delta}$ has to be single valued and has in this minimal case a winding number $m = 1$ because $\Delta(2\pi) = 2\pi$.

If we have a field carrying a charge e it will have an electromagnetic phase factor $e^{i\alpha}$, with a local defined phase $\alpha = \alpha(x)$. This phase will change under a gauge transformation Λ according to $\alpha \to \alpha' = \alpha - e\Lambda/\hbar c$. We may now impose that this charged field is single valued in which case it follows from he equation (I.1.56) that we to impose $eg/\hbar c = 2\pi n$, the Dirac quantization condition.

In Figure I.1.30 we show an explicit configuration of the phase factors for a charged field. For the elementary $n = 1$ monopole the angles $\beta_\pm(\varphi)$ are defined as

$$\beta_\pm = \frac{e}{\hbar c}\int^\varphi \mathbf{A}_\pm \cdot \mathbf{dl} = \pm\frac{\varphi}{2}. \qquad (\text{I.1.57})$$

We learn that the difference between the two line integrals is given by $\Delta = \beta_+ - \beta_- = \varphi$. The loop integrals are gauge invariant and $\Delta(2\pi) = 2\pi$, which means that the transition function $f(\varphi) \equiv e^{i\Delta}$ is single valued.

Topological sectors. The existence of this non-trivial U(1) fibre bundle corresponding to the fundamental monopole with $f(\varphi) = e^{i\Delta(\varphi)} = e^{i\varphi}$ was discovered independently by the German mathematician Heinz Hopf, amusingly in 1931, the same year that Dirac wrote his monopole paper. It took about forty years before the Chinese American physicists Tai Tsun Wu and Chen Ning Yang discovered the mathematical equivalence of these remarkable works of the mind. The bundle space describing the fundamental monopole is basically the three-sphere S^3, and Hopf showed that you can consider S^3 as an S^1 (which equals the group U(1)) bundle over a base manifold S^2. We will return to this topological classification of bundles in the next chapter.

So the fibre bundle perspective adds an essential insight into our understanding of electromagnetism as a gauge theory. It is the discovery and classification of topologically non-trivial sectors in the theory. These sectors are defined by mapping of boundaries (or overlap regions) of real space (which themselves are always spaces without boundary) into the gauge group or more generally some 'internal space.' These maps can be non-trivial, and if they are, they label certain topological sectors which define some discrete 'topological charge.' These charges are therefore quantized and conserved for a topological reason which is not directly related to the standard symmetry type argument. Indeed in electrodynamics with monopoles the conservation of electric charge is a consequence of gauge invariance, and the conservation of magnetic charge is topological in nature.

If you look at the monopole as a two-dimensional version of electrodynamics on a closed surface, then the total integral of the magnetic field strength over that closed surface would always have to be an integer in the appropriate units. The total flux is a topological invariant of the gauge field A, because you can make *any* smooth deformation of the gauge field over the surface – not just gauge transformations – and that integer would stay the same. This total flux which equals the magnetic charge is a topological invariant characterising the gauge field on the surface and is called the *Chern number*. So, indeed, on the two-sphere the discrete values of the magnetic total magnetic flux label different topological sectors of allowed electromagnetic fields. These topological features of gauge theories play an important role in many subfields of physics, for example in understanding the (integer) Quantum Hall effect.

To appreciate the subtlety of the argument let us once more step back and see how it is (quantum) physics that dictates the result. This has to be the case because how else could Planck's constant show up in the charge quantization fomula. That can't be accidental! We see that we map the circle in real space S_φ^1 into the gauge group which we was also a circle S_Δ^1. The topological sectors are labeled by the winding number of this map, telling you that $\Delta(\varphi = 2\pi) = 2\pi n$. The compactness of this group tells you therefore two things: (i) that the permitted charges are labeled by integers corresponding to the unitary representations of the group, and (ii) that there are topological sectors corresponding to quantized magnetic charges. If nature had given us particles with arbitrary electric charges like πe or $e\sqrt{2}$ besides e itself, then that would have implied that the gauge group could not have been the compact $U(1)$ but would have been the non-compact group $\mathbb{R}^1$. It's unitary representations are not labeled by integers, so there would be no charge quantization. But at the same time the argument for the existence of non-trivial topological sectors would also collapse. Any mapping of the circle S_φ^1 into a line are all contractable to a point, meaning that they are all topologically equivalent, and consequently that there is only one sector in the theory. The world would be without a discrete conserved magnetic charge: no monopoles!

As we will see later the state space of a qubit is also a three-sphere and we will also use the representation of the three-sphere as a bundle space in that context. We will

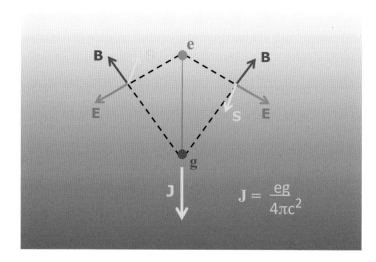

Figure I.1.31: *The charge-pole system.* The charge-pole system is static but has a angular momentum nevertheless. The total angular momentum can be calculated to be equal to $J = \dfrac{eg}{4\pi c^2}$, which with the Dirac's quantization condition yields values $J = (\frac{1}{2}, \frac{3}{2}, \frac{5}{2} \cdots)\hbar$.

return to and expand on these more extended geometrical and topological concepts in Chapter I.2 in the section on *The physics of geometry*. We emphasize these topological features of our mathematical representations of physical systems, because after all topological data refer typically to class labels which are in many cases discrete. In a sense this is a form of quantization that is may be less familiar but certainly no less quantessential. ■ ■

A remarkable case of 'static' angular momentum.

The system of a spatially separated electric charge – magnetic monopole pair has a curious property first pointed out by J.J. Thomson and presented it as a problem in the Cambridge University Tripod exam in the late 1890s. In Figure I.1.31 we have depicted the situation with the charge and pole located on the z-axis. At two points symmetric with respect to the z-axis we have the electric and magnetic fields $\mathbf{E}$ and $\mathbf{B}$, and the resulting Pointing or field-momentum vector **S**. The contribution to the angular momentum around the z-axis is clearly pointing along the charge-pole direction. When we integrate all the contributions, we find that the total angular momentum is non-zero and in fact exactly equal to the quantized product of e and g values in the appropriate units. A static system with a non-zero total angular momentum, a value that is quantized in half integral units and does not depend on the distance between the two sources is remarkable indeed. We will return to these properties in Volumes II en III where we discuss the spin and statistics properties of particles in two dimensions. ■

Statistical Physics:
from micro to macro physics

This section is about macroscopic systems consisting of very large numbers of atoms or molecules and focusses on the link between microscopic and macroscopic behavior, between individual and collective (equilibrium) degrees of freedom. The physics of macroscopic phenomena evidently started as a phenomenologically driven discipline, and it followed the Newtonian approach, by applying analytical methods using differential equations to describe continuous media like gases, liquids and to some extent solids. It lead to a rich variety of equations for thermo- , hydro- and aerodynamics. A crucial turning point came with the acceptance of the molecular hypothesis, *the realization that all forms of matter are made up of tiny molecules. This posed a new challenge, namely to derive and explain all the known macroscopic physics starting from applying basic Newtonian mechanics on the molecular level. As one is not interested in the detailed behavior of the individual atoms, statistics serve as a powerful bridge between the incoherent individual dynamics and the often perfectly coherent dynamics of the collective. This led to a fundamental branch of theoretical physics called*

statistical mechanics, which is considered the third great achievement of classical physics. This approach allowed us to understand numerous so-called emergent *phenomena - the properties of the collective that are not present on the level of the individual atoms. In this section we focus on thermodynamics: we will first give its macroscopic definition and its three basic laws, and then we will show how a statistical physics approach enables a deeper and unified understanding of the subject. The reason why we are focusing on thermodynamics is that it was within that field that the all-important concept of* entropy *as a measure of disorder and information originated.*

Thermodynamics: the three laws

Thermodynamics is a general theory that started with the noble aim to systematically improve the performance of steam engines and the like, but has now also found notable applications for less down-to-earth systems like black holes. A thermodynamical system – think of a fridge or a steam engine, or just an amount of gas in a container – can work and exchange heat or energy with other systems or its environment. Thermodynamics studies the relations between heat, energy and the ability of the system to do work.

Thermodynamics is a macroscopic theory; nowhere does it refer to the specific microscopic structure of the system. However, when we introduce the subject, it is easiest to envisage a simple gas in equilibrium in a container with particular values for the macroscopic state variables, pressure P, volume V, temperature T as depicted in Figure I.1.32. The fourth state variable, the entropy S, is more hidden as it provides a link between temperature and heat as we will see. This system has an internal energy $U(T)$ which is the total energy of its internal degrees of freedom.

The essentials of thermodynamics are expressed in three

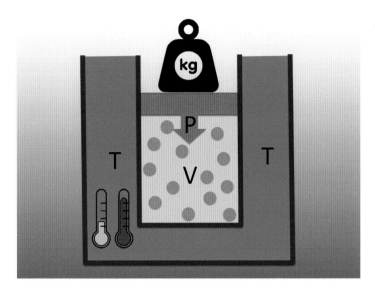

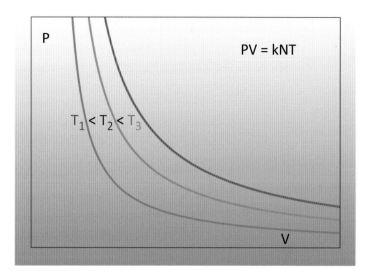

Figure I.1.32: *Gas in thermal equilibrium.* Gas in a container with a movable piston kept at a given temperature T and pressure P, yielding a certain volume V. The three state variables are not independent but satisfy an *equation of state.* For an ideal gas that relation is given in the next figure.

Figure I.1.33: *Ideal gas law.* This graph shows the ideal gas law $PV = kNT$, expressing the dependence between the thermodynamical variables P, V and T, with k the Boltzmann constant and N, Avogadro's number.

famous laws. In fact there is a fourth law, which is usually referred to as the zeroth law of thermodynamics, presumably because it is considered to be self-evident.

The *zeroth law* introduces the notion of thermodynamical equilibrium, and stipulates that it is a transitive property, that is to say that if system A is in equilibrium with B, and A is also in equilibrium with C, then B and C are also in equilibrium. This allows you to define the thermodynamical (absolute) temperature of a system.

The *first law* is basically the statement that energy is conserved. This is expressed in a relation stating that adding some heat dQ to the system will result in an increase of the internal energy dU and the ability for the system to do mechanical work, which for the gas in the container equals the pressure times the change in volume $dW = PdV$:

$$dU = dQ - PdV. \tag{I.1.58}$$

The *second law* is the most famous: it features the notion of *entropy*, denoted by S, which is defined by the following relation between heat and temperature:

$$dQ \equiv TdS. \tag{I.1.59}$$

This fundamental state variable of any thermodynamical system was introduced by Rudolf Clausius around 1850, as was the second law. The law states that for a closed system (say a fixed quantity of gas in a thermally isolated vessel) entropy can never decrease in time:

$$\frac{dS}{dt} \geq 0. \tag{I.1.60}$$

$$\lim_{T \to 0} S = 0. \tag{I.1.61}$$

More precisely it goes to a constant which measures the ground-state degeneracy of the system.

Entropy is a sort of measure for disorder: the law boiled down to the familiar phenomenon that (closed) systems

Figure I.1.34: *Ludwig Boltzmann's epitaph.* The expression for the entropy S of a macroscopic state in terms of the number W of microscopic states corresponding to it appears as epitaph on Boltzmann's tomb stone in Vienna's Zentralfriedhof, where he was buried in 1906. (Source: Wikimedia.)

have a natural tendency to become maximally messy or mixed. This applies to teener rooms as well as to tea particles in a pot filled with hot water. As the entropy reaches its maximum value the system reaches an equilibrium state. So, if we put a droplet of ink in a bowl of water, and neither change the amount of water, nor the temperature, nor the volume, then we still see the distribution of the ink molecules through the water changing. In this process the entropy increases until the ink is completely mixed and distributed uniformly and equilibrium is reached. So increasing entropy, you could say, is linked to this process of increasing 'disorder.' To get a deeper understanding of the entropy concept it is necessary to include the microscopic structure of the system whatever that may be. This is our next topic.

Understanding entropy.

The fundamental expression for the entropy S of a given macroscopic state was derived by the great Austrian physicist Ludwig Boltzmann, who stated that it is proportional to the logarithm of the number of microscopic states W corresponding to the macroscopic state under consideration. So

$$S = k \log W, \tag{I.1.62}$$

where k is not surprisingly called the Boltzmann constant. Now $\log W$ is a pure number and therefore k has units $\mathrm{Joule/Kelvin}$. This famous expression was the precursor of the general notion of the *information capacity* of a system as the logarithm of the number of available states, as it was defined by Claude Shannon in his 1948 foundational paper on information theory. Shortly we will generalize the formula as to establish an explicit connection between statistics and entropy. This relation between entropy and information theory will also be taken up again in the section *The physics of information* in Chapter I.2.

Context dependence of the entropy. To illustrate some features of the entropy concept, we start with some examples of pure *configurational entropy*. Take a system of N boys and N girls that can be located in any of $2N$ positions. If we furthermore assume that the macroscopic observer is pretty much blind and would have no possibility of distinguishing between boys and girls, nor how many people sit at a given position. So there is no constraint on the configurations and there is only a single macro state. In this case the question is to count the number of possible configurations of $2N$ people on $2N$ positions. Now we have to specify the conditions that the micro states have to satisfy. If the people were distinguishable (have names) then the number of possible (micro) states would be $W_1 = (2N)^{2N}$ as any person can be in any of $2N$ positions. If we assume they are *indistinguishable*, then we count a micro state where two people are interchanged as the same state, for $2N$ people we have $2N$ factorial different orderings that count as one, and the number of configurations is therefore reduced by this number: $W_2 = (2N)^{2N}/(2N)!$. If we are now on the microscopic level, we could add the distinction between boys and girls, we can exchange the same gender only, and we have to replace the $2N!$ with the much smaller number $N!\,N!$, yielding $W_3 = (2N)^{2N}/(N!)^2$. Next we may add the constraint of *exclusion* meaning that only one person per position is allowed (they behave like fermions), which for the system at hand means that all positions are taken. With name identification the number of configurations is equal to the number of permutations of $2N$ names given by $(2N)!$. With gender identification only we identify the $N!$ permutations of boys and girls separately, yielding $W_4 = (2N)!/(N!\,N!)$.

The effect of resolution and/or constraints. What this little exercise conveys is that the definition of entropy is very much context dependent. Firstly there is the microscopic context of what the degrees freedom are that one wants to take into account and what the microscopic restrictions are (like distinguishability, exclusion etc.), and secondly there is the macroscopic context determined by what the macroscopic observer is able to distinguish, resolve, or measure (names, gender, spatial compartments etc). So, in general the system has two levels and the entropy is a quantity that basically relates the resolutions (the set of observables and the precision with which these can be probed) and the constraints that determine which states are accessible at each level, and how these observables at the two levels are related. Again, in the examples given above, (i) there was only a single macroscopic state for any given N, and (ii) on the micro level we saw that more resolution leads to more states, while more constraints lead to fewer accessible states. In that sense within a given closed system, indeed, eliminating a constraint leads to 'more disorder' and also a larger number of accessible micro states and thus to an increase of the entropy. In the sequence above we have $W_1 > W_2$ (less resolution), $W_2 < W_3$ (more resolution), and $W_3 > W_4$ (adding a constraint).

The common statement that 'higher entropy means more disorder' is actually quite subtle, and to get a better understanding of this question we add one further structural element to the above example.

Maximal entropy. We consider the previous system with $2N$ positions, but take there to be two compartments, with N positions each separated by a gate, and in each position sits one person. The basic interaction is one where two people exchange position. We start with a special (historically determined) initial state or configuration with all the red-haired girls on the left and the blue-eyed boys on the right. The boys and girls have no names, so exchanging two boys and/or two girls does not change configuration. This means that the initial strict gender separated configuration is a unique one: there is only one such state and it has minimal entropy $S = k \ln 1 = 0$. Next we open the gate in the middle and boys and girls start mixing. I am vaguely suggesting that we are talking about a college dormitory complex in the 1950s, say with $N = 10^3$. The level of frustration among students about the gender separation is like a temperature, and when that becomes high enough, the youngsters start jumping the fences everywhere to go coed. Nice analogy, but now you ask me why this college only admits blue-eyed boys and red-haired girls. I haven't thought about a suitable interpretation for this but no doubt there is one. Physicists, I fear, prefer to think of an ideal gas consisting of equal number of red and blue atoms where $N = 10^{23}$. Let us now increase the resolution of the macro observer and assume that they can somehow measure the number n of boys/girls that are in the 'other' compartment, so the macro-states are labeled by n. Now we ask how many microscopic possibilities there are to realize that particular macro state. The question is to distribute $2N$ youngsters over two partitions. Let us start with one boy/girl jumping the fence: the boy and girl can each come from any of N positions, so for state with $n = 1$ we have $N \times N = N^2$ possible configurations (or micro-states). In the second cross-barrier move, the boy/-girl has only $N - 1$ positions to come from or go to, which

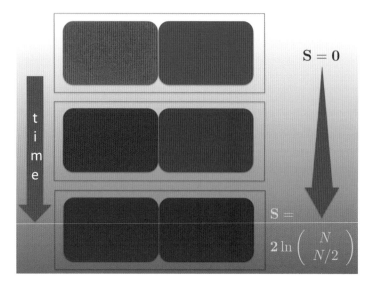

Figure I.1.35: *Gender mixing.* The initial state is the one with all red-haired girls in the left and all blue-eyed boys on the right. When we let them interact through some random girl/boy exchange mechanism, the entropy will increase; equilibrium is reached when the left and right colors have become equal.

means there are $[N(N-1)]^2$ possible $n = 2$ configurations, but now we over-count configurations: we should not have counted the gender neutral exchange of two boys or of two girls as different, so we still have to divide by a factor 4. What we see is that the number of configurations increases extremely rapidly as function of n. The general answer is not too hard to understand from the previous examples:

$$W_n = \left(\begin{array}{c} N \\ n \end{array} \right)^2 \equiv \left[\frac{N!}{n!\,(N-n)!} \right]^2, \qquad (I.1.63)$$

where the notation $\left(\begin{array}{c} N \\ n \end{array} \right)$ stands for the binomial coefficient N over n. Note that this function is symmetric under interchange of n and $(N-n)$. Furthermore we observed that the function increases for growing n, then these observations imply that the maximum for W_n is achieved for $n = N - n = N/2$. Thus, if all micro-configurations are equally probable, the macro-state with $n = N/2$ has the

largest number of possible micro-states and therefore the largest entropy:

$$S_{\max} = k \ln W_{N/2} = 2k \ln \left[\left(\begin{array}{c} N \\ N/2 \end{array} \right) \right].$$

This means that if we let the random dynamics run for a sufficiently long time from any initial macro-state, and we then probe the system, that we will almost certainly find a configuration with $n = N/2$. So the remarkable insight we gain is that a random process drives the system to a particular macroscopic state, namely the state that is the most probable because it has the most microscopically distinct realizations, which is the state with the highest entropy. And this is the second law of thermodynamics at work. A system has the natural tendency to move from a less to a more probable macro state. That state is the maximally mixed and therefore maximally disordered state that is admissible.

This process is schematically illustrated in Figure I.1.35. To give you a feeling for the numbers involved we have listed the binomial coefficients for various modest values of N and n in Table I.1.1. If N is large, we may approximate the logarithm of a factorial using the famous Stirling formula, which says that, $\ln N! \simeq N \ln N$. With this formula one can show that S in the above equation is well approximated by $S_{\max} \simeq 2N \ln 2$, and this in turn implies that in equilibrium the number of micro-states is a number with roughly $0,6\,N$ digits. This implies that the probability for finding the completely gender-separated initial macro-state when the system is in equilibrium is of the order of $p_0 = 10^{-0.6\,N}$. If you take into account that N is of the order of Avogadro's constant $\sim 10^{23}$, p_0 is extremely small indeed.

The arrow of time. There is something rather profound going on in this red-blue dynamics. If you look on the micro-scale all the interchanges are equally probable. In fact any move is its own inverse, and therefore the micro dynamics is invariant under time reversal. If you would re-

n	$\binom{50}{n}$	N	$\binom{N}{N/2}$
1	1	10	252
10	1.0×10^{10}	20	184756
20	2.2×10^{12}	50	0.12×10^{15}
25	1.2×10^{14}	100	0.10×10^{30}
30	2.2×10^{12}	1000	0.27×10^{300}
40	1.0×10^{10}	...	...
50	1	N	$\sim 10^{0.3N}$

Table I.1.1: *The binomial coefficients.* We have listed some values of the binomial coefficients $\binom{N}{n}$ to demonstrate the steep increase as a function of n on the left, and the maximum value of the distribution as a function of N on the right.

Figure I.1.36: *Coarse graining a portrait.* We average the color content over larger and larger (overlapping) squares. In the 'blurring' process the image looses resolution and is therefore hiding ever more information content. The entropy is increasing and the process is irreversible. The entropy is a measure for the amount of micro level information that is 'hidden' for the macroscopic observer.

verse the time direction you wouldn't see the difference in individual moves. On the microscopic level time has no direction! Interestingly, if you look at the macroscopic behavior it clearly has a time direction (namely defined by the increasing entropy) that is not an abstract something or other, this is directly observable. From a macroscopic point of view, when N is large, you see the red compartment slowly turning blueish and the blue compartment slowly turning reddish, but the process stops at a point where both halves have acquired the same purple color. So, somehow the system has created its own *arrow of time*, whatever macro-state you start with it will always move towards the uniform purple color distribution with maximal entropy.

This 'coarse graining' mechanism (see Figure I.1.36) lies at the basis of the time arrow in the real world as well, be-

cause, as we have shown in the previous sections, both Newton's and Maxwell's equations are time reversal invariant if the interactions are. What this means is that given a solution to the equations, turning the time around, meaning that we replace t by $-t$, also produces a solution (but may be a different one). On a microscopic level playing the film backward would show another, equally acceptable sequence of events, but on a macroscopic level this is not true. If I drop my bowl of yogurt, fruit and granola on the floor, showing that sequence of events in reverse order, it may be hilarious but it is certainly not of this world. Indeed, this elementary example teaches us that the direction of time is *emergent*, since it has everything to do with the relative number of micro-states belonging to a given macro-state. A randomly propagating system tends to move from a less to a more probable state, and reaches equilibrium in the most probable maximal entropy state.

Two cultures. The second law of thermodynamics paradoxically owes part of its fame to the fact that it is so little known. This was poignantly pointed out by the author (and physicist) C.P. Snow in his provocative essay entitled *Two cultures* published in the *New Statesman* in 1954, in which he bitterly complained about the scientific illiteracy of the cultural elite, and where he used the manifest ignorance about the *second law of thermodynamics* (which in his opinion had a cultural importance comparable to the works of Shakespeare) as a criterion to underpin his criticism. Let me say that Snow's intervention on behalf of thermodynamics did not turn Boltzmann into a Shakespeare. Some years later, however, it did at least provoke a strongly worded reaction from the literary critic F.A. Leavis making the mutual incomprehension even more acute. In a remarkable piece of word craft Leavis stated: 'Snow doesn't know what he means, and doesn't know he doesn't know.' 'The intellectual nullity' he added, 'is what constitutes any difficulty there may be in dealing with Snow's panoptic pseudo-cogencies, his parade of a thesis: a mind to be argued with – that is not there; what we have is something other.' 'But what else to expect from a crappy writer like Snow?' 'As a novelist,' wrote Leavis, 'he doesn't exist; he doesn't begin to exist. He can't be said to know what a novel is.'

The sad point about the situation described by Snow is that it has barely changed over the past half century. So don't ask friends to recite the second law in public, your popularity will most probably instantly plummet. □

This being said we should be cautious, in any given system there will be fluctuations where the entropy actually decreases. The micro-dynamics do not preclude such moves,

but on average it is not possible.

It is an awesome idea but certainly correct that in the system we just studied, there is a non-zero albeit inconceivably small probability for the system to pass through the same initial state again!

But that was a state with a lower entropy! The existence of such a recurrence time was proven by Henri Poincaré in 1890. A rough estimate for this recurrence time will be of the order $\tau \simeq 10^N = 10^{10^{23}} \, sec$, which is of the order of 10^{22} times the age of the universe. In whatever units you like to express this truly dazzling number, it is evident that this recursion is not an event to just sit-and-wait for!

This amusingly may remind you of the problems that people who have no understanding of statistics and probability encounter. Events, like the spontaneous gender separation under the given random dynamics in our example, is logically not excluded, but it would take for ever! Assigning outrageously large probabilities to events which are logically not excluded but highly improbable is a specialty of so-called *conspiracy theorists*. Indeed, it would take a conspiracy of extreme proportions to realize such super improbable events, like having all air molecules accumulate in one tiny corner of the room, and you dying because of a lack of oxygen.

Statistical mechanics

The molecular hypothesis. A major step forward was the acceptance of the *molecular hypothesis*, implying that all matter is ultimately build up from microscopic, molecular or atomic constituents. One of the strongest protagonists for this hypothesis was Ludwig Boltzmann. For the number of particles in such macroscopic systems the scale is set by the constant of Avogadro of the order of 6×10^{23} the number of atoms in a mole of some gas,[8] a number that makes even strong people quiver. *This molecular perspective raised the fundamental challenge for physicists to establish an explicit connection between microscopic physics (mechanics and electromagnetism) and the aforementioned macroscopic laws.* The molecules obey the classical laws, and one - pretty naive - way to think about addressing this challenge would be to face the problem head on and try to solve $\sim 10^{23}$ coupled Newtonian equations for the individual particles simultaneously. Hmm, apart from the computational power needed, this doesn't sound like a very smart idea, does it? Particularly since we are not at all interested in the precise behavior of every individual particle.

Statistical approach. A successful approach is the statistical one, where one links the macroscopic properties like pressure, temperature and entropy to certain average properties of the collective of molecules. Indeed, with such huge numbers statistical methods become extremely powerful and precise as any insurance company can tell you. What properties of the molecular collective could be meaningfully lifted to relevant variables at the macroscopic level? These would typically be the conserved quantities like energy, momentum and particle number. The energy is conserved and for a closed system would be just an additive quantity: the energy of the macroscopic system is just the sum of the individual particle energies and their interactions. The total energy is rigorously conserved: in other words, constant.

Open and closed systems. One is not limited to closed systems, and one might also consider an open system that is coupled to an energy reservoir kept at a fixed temperature (also called a 'heat bath'), which means that one allows for energy (heat) flows between the system and the reservoir as we depicted in Figure I.1.32. If we raise the

temperature of the reservoir, heat will flow to the system, raising the internal energy and allowing it to do a certain amount of work. And this gives you an idea of how the first law of thermodynamics can be derived from the microscopic laws. In other words, temperature is the external parameter that sets the average energy of the system, and in that sense imposes an external constraint on the system. For the particle number an analogous reasoning holds. Here one may couple the system to a particle reservoir which is kept at a fixed *chemical potential* μ. This potential corresponds to the energy it costs to add one more particle to the system. These considerations can be made very precise and are part of the field of statistical mechanics, developed by physicists like Boltzmann, Maxwell and Gibbs.

Equipartition of energy. One can show that for a system in equilibrium, on average, the energy is equally partitioned over the individual particles, which means that the notion of temperature is linked to the average energy per particle in the system. In fact the correct way to say this is that the energy is equally distributed over the degrees of freedom, where for a system in equilibrium at temperature T, each degree of freedom gets an energy $\langle \varepsilon_i \rangle = kT/2$. A particle in three dimensions has three independent velocity components and therefore three degrees of freedom. Consequently, for a system of N particles the average energy will be $\langle E \rangle = 3NkT/2$.

Phase space representations of a multi-particle system. Imagine we have a gas that consists of N identical particles in a volume V, then there are two distinct phase space representations of the system possible. One is relevant if one wants to study the average single particle properties or (auto)correlations and refers to the one-particle phase space, while the other concerns the distribution over different multi-particle micro-states that correspond to a single macro-state.

---

[8] As explained in Chapter I.3, a new definition as of May 20, 2019, of Avogadro's number or constant sets it exactly equal to $N_A = 6.02214076 \times 10^{23}$.

γ - *space.* Let us start with the one-particle phase space $\gamma = (\mathbf{x}, \mathbf{p})$, and represent the state of each particle in the system as a point. This yields a certain density of points, corresponding to a distribution $f(\gamma, t)$.[9] If the system is in equilibrium, then we expect: (i) the particles to be uniformly distributed in ordinary $\mathbf{x}$'-space, (ii) the distribution to be time independent, and (iii) the momentum dependence to be isotropic. This tells us that in equilibrium $f(\mathbf{x}, \mathbf{p}, t) \rightarrow f(|\mathbf{p}|)$, which gives rise to the famous Maxwell – Boltzmann distribution, which is a Gaussian distribution in $\mathbf{p}$ space with the exponent equal to minus the energy: $-\varepsilon/kT = -p^2/2mkT$. Why the exponential energy suppression factor? There are two elementary requirements which make this plausible. If for a simple system like an ideal gas where the particles do not interact and are independent, we look at two particles, then the joint probability to find one of them with p_1 and the other with p_2, we would just be the product of the one-particle probabilities: $f_2(p_1, p_2) = f(p_1)f(p_2)$. In other words the two-particle configuration should then be weighted by the total energy which is the sum of the two energies. This should hold for any partitioning of non-interacting components which means that the exponential factor is the unique answer, because by multiplying two exponentials the exponents add.

Γ-*space.* We can also define the phase space for the whole system, that total phase space is defined as the Cartesian product of the N individual spaces. This multi-particle phase space $\Gamma_N = \{(\mathbf{x})^N, (\mathbf{p})^N\}$, of N coordinates and momenta, is $6N$-dimensional, as each particle has three position and three momentum components. This is a very high-dimensional space, and at any given instant the system as a whole is represented by a *single* point in that space. The particles will bounce around which means that the point representing the system will move around in that space and to study the macroscopic properties of the system we would have to consider long-time averages of

those properties. Clearly variables defining macro-states, like for example the total energy, define a constraint on the micro-states, which means that these variables will define certain subspaces or strata in Γ. The micro-states in such a domain can be quite different but cannot be macroscopically distinguished.

Ergodicity. A basic assumption of statistical mechanics, called the *ergodic principle*, is that we can replace the time averages of the system with Γ-space averages using the appropriate distribution representing the equilibrium micro-states. The principle is supposed to hold in the *thermodynamic limit*, where time, volume and the particle number go to infinity (keeping $n = N/V$ fixed).

In this setting one may with a single equilibrium state of the macro-system associate a stationary distribution of points corresponding to the probability for the different micro-states representing that macro-state to occur. One introduces a weight function $\rho(\Gamma)$ which may depend on external parameters like temperature or particle number that represent the macroscopic conditions one imposes. Now $\rho(\Gamma)$ defines what is called an *statistical ensemble* of micro-states. If the system is closed (fixed total energy), we speak of the *micro-canonical ensemble.* if we couple it to a thermal bath, we have the *canonical ensemble* with weight function, $\rho(\Gamma) = e^{-H(\Gamma)/kT}$, where $H(\Gamma)$ is the energy function (Hamiltonian) for the multi-particle system. If we also let the number of particles N vary, we get the *grand canonical ensemble.* It was the American physicist Josiah Willard Gibbs who introduced the notion of an 'ensemble' of micro-systems, and the 'ensemble distributions,' to calculate the desired averages in all types of macro-states.

May be to illustrate these rather abstract notions it helps to extend our red-eyed/blue-haired, excuse me red-haired/-blue-eyed youngster model to include variables like 'money' and 'group size.' Clearly the group size is just the number N, we introduced before and we could make it a variable

---

[9]I refer readers who are not familiar with the basics of probability theory to the *Math Excursion* 'On probability and statistics' on page 626 of Part III.

by coupling to a reservoir of similar pairs who are allowed to join. The amount of money would be the social equivalent of energy, and in a closed system money would be conserved, people could exchange money as long as the total amount of money stays conserved.

If you don't like the analogy, you certainly have a point: whereas in the world of particles there is such a wonderful thing as the equipartition of energy, that is to say that on average every particle has an equal energy, the same does not to seem to hold in the world of money. It's quite the opposite: we witness a process of wealth accumulation. This is a non-equilibrium situation which tends to result in a macabre final state where presumably one person owns all the money. In this case one could speak of the capitalist singularity whereas for the particles one ends up with a socialist uniformity. In this analogy the thermal bath would be represented by the central banks who can raise the fiscal 'temperature' by printing money. I invite the ambitious reader to think about how to include taxation in the model. What these analogies try to convey is that for all these systems there is a notion of a phase space, of external parameters and a statistical ensemble that describes the probability distribution of micro-states depending on an external parameters.

The partition function. The *partition function* of a many-body system is now defined as a phase-space integral, $Z = \int_\Gamma \rho(\Gamma)\,d\Gamma$. You could say that the partition function gives the 'volume' of the domain in Γ–space, corresponding to the external (macro) parameter choices made in ρ. For example, with ρ describing the canonical ensemble, for a system in contact with a heat bath kept at a temperature T, the partition sum would depend on T as an external parameter.

Emergence. Let us also point out another interesting feature of this statistical approach to systems consisting of many degrees of freedom (particles). In many ways this perspective allows one to introduce 'mean fields' as an

approximation to the many body system that underlies it. One passes from a corpuscular perspective to a continuous one. From the macroscopic point of view, a water flow in a river would be described by a mass density field $\rho(x,t)$, a velocity field $\mathbf{v}(x,t)$, and an energy density or temperature field $\varepsilon(x,t)$. These continuous fields are defined by smearing out the local average properties of many particles. You may say that this assumes the existence of a local equilibrium in the system. One may show that these local fields have to obey certain specific dynamical field equations called the laws of hydro-, aero- or plasma-dynamics. These field equations follow from averaging the continuity equations for the locally conserved quantities of the interacting micro system. The resulting laws are '*emergent*' and describe approximately many novel so-called emergent collective properties, in the case of water, you should think of waves and vortices.[10] Water waves are a phenomenon of which the individual water molecules have no idea, the wave property is not present at the constituent level, and it is in that sense that people like to say that the 'whole is more than the sum of its parts.' And it is for that reason that water waves are called an 'emergent' phenomenon. In the simple red-haired-girls/blue-eyed-boys model, we saw the arrow of time emerging, and the emergent (phenomenological) law was telling us that the two colors would uniformly change to the same color purple.

Statistical thermodynamics.

Let us return to thermodynamics. In the statistical approach to a system in *thermal equilibrium*, say, a fixed quantity of gas in a container that we keep at a fixed temperature T, we think of the macro-states labeled by the thermodynamic state variables P, V, S, N and T. In this situation heat can flow from and to the heat reservoir, which

---

[10]It is striking to see that Maxwell himself believed that his own electrodynamics was an effective description of the collective behavior of an underlying molecular world. As we will see later on, the quantum theory of fields is in a certain way a vindication of that point of view.

means that in thermal equilibrium the energy of the microscopic system is not constant. It will typically fluctuate around the thermal average $U = \langle E \rangle = 3NkT/2$. The relevant energy variable is the (Helmholtz) *free energy* which is defined as:

$$F = U - TS, \qquad (\text{I.1.64})$$

and should be thought of as a function of T and V, because it follows from the first law that a change in the free energy is given by

$$dF = dU - SdT - TdS = -PdV - SdT. \qquad (\text{I.1.65})$$

Note that from its definition, minimizing the free energy combines the natural tendencies to minimize the internal energy U and maximize the entropy S.

Let us consider a simple discrete model where each macro-state corresponds to a well-defined set of different configurations on the microscopical level called *micro-states*. This example aims to illustrate how the link between micro- and macro-physics is established. These micro-states are labeled by an index 'i' and each have a certain energy E_i. The probability p_i that a micro-state occurs is again proportional to the Boltzmann weight $w_i = \exp(-E_i/kT)$, which says that the high-energy states are exponentially suppressed.

We may then write that the probability is:

$$p_i = \frac{e^{-E_i/kT}}{Z}, \qquad (\text{I.1.66})$$

where Z is the *partition sum* defined as

$$Z = \sum_i e^{-E_i/kT}. \qquad (\text{I.1.67})$$

Note that the sum of all probabilities indeed equals one. The link between the macroscopic and microscopic states is established by giving the expression for the free energy in terms of the partition sum:

$$F = -kT \ln Z. \qquad (\text{I.1.68})$$

From this relation the thermodynamical quantities can be derived. For example with this link it is possible to calculate the famous expression first derived by Gibbs, for the entropy in terms of the probability distribution. Subsequently using equations (I.1.68) and (I.1.66) we obtain

$$F = \sum_i p_i F = -kT \sum_i p_i \ln Z$$

$$= -kT \sum_i p_i (-\frac{E_i}{kT} - \ln p_i) = \sum_i p_i E_i + kT \sum_i p_i \ln p_i.$$

Given that by definition $U \equiv \langle E \rangle = \sum_i p_i E_i$, we find from (I.1.64) that the entropy can be expressed as

$$S = -k \sum_i p_i \ln p_i. \qquad (\text{I.1.69})$$

This is the famous expression for the entropy due to Gibbs which was (re)derived by Shannon, and being the formal definition of information (entropy), forms the basis for information theory. At this point it is important to emphasize the remarkable generality of this result, as it assigns an entropy or information capacity to any given probability distribution or statistical ensemble.

Note that in equation (I.1.69), for a isolated system with fixed energy (not in contact with a heat bath), the energies E_i become equal, and thus $p_i = p = 1/W$. This reproduces the Boltzmann result (I.1.62) for the entropy. Assigning equal probabilities is like saying that you have no a priori information about the states, so you are not imposing any constraint, and thus you get the maximum value for the entropy, the one given by Boltzmann. There is a formal, less physics restricted, method for constructing the maximal entropy distribution as defined in equation (I.1.69) which allows for the systematic inclusion of additional constraints or prior knowledge. This is called the *maximal entropy principle* and is further discussed in the *Math Excursion* 'On probability and statistics' at the end of Part III on page 626. ■

The energy distribution. To further elaborate on the statistical interpretation of thermodynamics, it is illuminating to look at the energy variable and to derive the energy weight function $s(E)$ from ρ. In the integral over the ensemble of all micro-states, we break the integral up into subsets of equal energy where state i and j belong to the same subset if $E_i = E_j = E$. We call $n(E)$ the volume of a thin shell at energy E. This allows us to write the partition function over all micro-states as

$$Z = \int s(E)\, dE = \int n(E) e^{-E/kT}\, dE$$

$$= \int e^{-E/kT + \ln n(E)}\, dE. \qquad (\text{I.1.70})$$

It is illuminating to go through this calculation for the simple case of an ideal gas, as we will do next.

The ideal gas.

Let us consider the ideal gas to show how explicit expressions for the thermodynamical functions in terms of microphysical variables can be obtained by using statistical mechanics. We have N particles in a container with volume V in thermal equilibrium at a temperature T. The total internal energy of a configuration, given by E, equals the sum over one particle kinetic energies: $E = \sum_n (p_n^2)/2m$. To get to the energy distribution we have to integrate (or sum) the general phase space distribution $\rho(\Gamma)$ over all $6N$ variables except the total energy. In an equilibrium state the spatial distribution is uniform and therefore integrating all the coordinates gives a factor V^N. The integral over the $3N$ momenta components has to satisfy the energy constraint that the total kinetic energy equals E. All $3N$–dimensional momentum vectors that satisfy this condition have a length $|p| = \sqrt{2mE}$. So the integral yields the area of a $(3N-1)$-dimensional spherical surface of a $3N$–dimensional ball of radius $R = \sqrt{2mE}$. This means that the density of states takes the form:

$$n(E) = C_N V^N E^{\frac{3}{2}N}, \qquad (\text{I.1.71})$$

where we have dropped a negligible term equal to $1/2$ in the exponent. The constant C_N is the area of the $(3N-1)$-

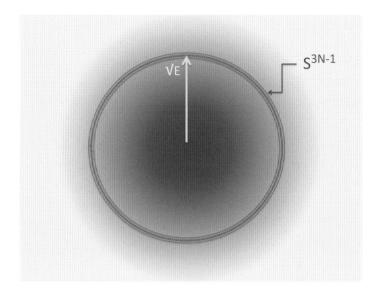

Figure I.1.37: *Phase space distribution.* The rapidly decaying density of points in phase space (in blue). A fixed energy surface (in red) is a very high-dimensional spherical surface. Adding up the points in a narrow shell yields an extremely steeply rising function $n(E)$.

dimensional unit hypersphere.[11]

At this point we can make the connection with thermodynamics, by noting that the entropy of the system is given by:

$$S(E, V) = k \ln n(E) = k \ln C_N + kN \ln\left(V E^{\frac{3}{2}}\right). \qquad (\text{I.1.72})$$

Solving this equation for the internal energy $U(S, V) = E$ yields:

$$U(S, V) = \frac{1}{V^{\frac{2}{3}}} e^{\frac{2}{3kN}(S - k \ln C_N)}. \qquad (\text{I.1.73})$$

If we now use the first law in the form $dU = TdS - PdV$,

---

[11] The actual expression, which does not enter our considerations, is: $C_N = 3N(\pi)^{\frac{3}{2}N}/(\frac{3}{2}N)!$.

we can determine T and P:

$$\left(\frac{\partial U}{\partial S}\right)_V = T = \frac{2U}{3kN} \qquad (I.1.74a)$$

$$-\left(\frac{\partial U}{\partial V}\right)_S = P = \frac{2U}{3V} = \frac{kNT}{V}. \qquad (I.1.74b)$$

The first equation gives the familiar expression relating the internal energy to the temperature and should be read here as a definition of the temperature in terms of the micro-state energy. From this we may also get the expression for the *specific heat* denoted as c_v, which is the energy needed to raise the temperature by one degree. It is defined as $(\partial U/\partial T)_V$, which in this case yields: $c_v = 3Nk/2$. The second equation gives the *equation of state* for the ideal gas, better known as the ideal gas law $PV = RT$, where the *universal gas constant* R is defined as $R = Nk$. It is an equation of state because it relates the three different thermodynamic state variables P, V, and T. It defines a constrained surface of allowed thermodynamic states, in the space of these three state variables. This basically concludes our first principles derivation of some high-school formulae that apply to the ideal gas.

It is instructive to reflect a bit more on the overall energy weight function s of equation I.1.70. On the one hand, we know that the density of points in the space drops exponentially because of the Boltzmann factor. However, the 'volume' $n(E)$ of the layers grows extremely fast like $E^{3N/2}$, because of the huge value of N. The overall weight, being the product of the two functions, becomes

$$s(E, N) \sim C_N V^N E^{\frac{3}{2}N} e^{-E/kT}. \qquad (I.1.75)$$

To determine the maximum of $s(E, N)$, we set its derivative equal zero:

$$\left(\frac{\partial s}{\partial E}\right)_N = \left(\frac{3N}{2E_m} - \frac{1}{kT}\right) s(E_m, N) = 0. \qquad (I.1.76)$$

This yields the value $E_m \simeq \frac{3}{2}NkT = \langle E \rangle$, confirming our expectation that for a very narrow and highly peaked function one expects the maximum and the average to coincide.

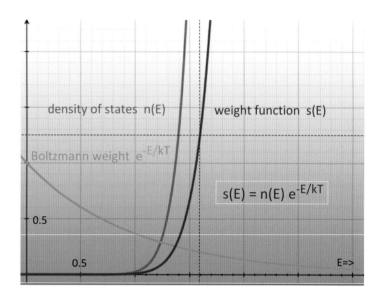

Figure I.1.38: *Energy weight function.* There are three curves, one represents the Boltzmann exponential suppression factor in blue, The density of states $n(E; N)$ in red, and their product, the energy weight function $s(E; N)$ in purple, are plotted near the origin for $N = 8$.

In the Figures I.1.38 and I.1.39 we have illustrated how the resulting weight function $s(E)$ (in purple) emerges as the product of the very steeply rising entropy driven density of states $n(E)$ (in red) and the exponential energy suppression (in blue). We have plotted the case where $N = 8$, which is not quite representative! Indeed it is striking that a narrow peak results: on the left the peak is driven high up by the degeneracy or entropy factor $n(E)$, and on the right it is forced down again by the energy dependent exponential suppression factor. For large N the position of maximum grows proportional to n: $E_m \sim N$, its maximum height increases exponentially: $s(E_m) \sim (\text{const.})^N$, while the width grows only with the square root: $\Delta E \sim \sqrt{N}$. So for large N the relative width decreases like $\Delta E/E_m \sim 1/\sqrt{N}$, and this implies that the weight function becomes proportional to a narrow Gaussian or rather a delta function. And this means that the essential behavior is very well represented by the narrow red band (the hyper-spherical shell) we have drawn in Fig-

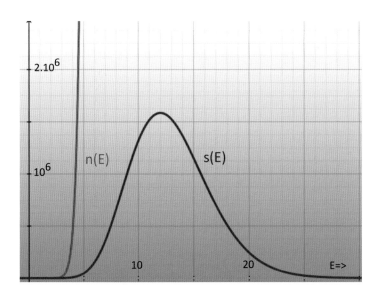

Figure I.1.39: *Ensemble energy weights.* The weight function $s(E; N)$ is the integrand of the partition function. Its maximum increases like $\sim (\mathrm{const.})^N$, the location of the maximum grows $\sim N$, while the width grows only as $\sqrt{N}$. In the limit of very large N, $s(\varepsilon)$ becomes proportional to a delta function. The micro states that matter sit all in an extremely narrow energy band as indicated in Figure I.1.37.

ure I.1.37. Effectively these estimates also show that the energy fluctuations in the canonical ensemble will be very small, which in turn means that effectively the canonical and micro-canonical ensembles are equivalent if we choose $E = E_m$. ■ ■

Classical versus quantum probabilities. We have chosen to highlight this statistical approach to classical many-body physics because we will see that also quantum theory is probabilistic and statistical at heart. And the comparison of the classical statistical physics perspective with the statistical aspects of quantum theory is illuminating. In quantum theory the probabilistic interpretation is forced upon us right from the start at the level of a single particle, and is encoded in the 'wavefunction' description of a quantum particle. The wavefunction is a 'probability amplitude,' and its absolute square represents a distribution.

That distribution gives the probability density $\rho(x, t)$ to find the particle at position x at time t, and in that sense it has some mathematical resemblance to the case of statistical mechanics, where the canonical distribution for example gives the probability $p(E_i)$ to find the many body system that has an energy E_i.

There is, however, a fundamental difference between classical and quantum probabilities; in classical physics a probability generally reflects a lack of knowledge about the system, which we in principle could eliminate by making more precise measurements. In quantum physics it reflects a fundamental indeterminism, meaning that even if we have complete knowledge of the quantum state, a property like the spin component along a certain axis for example need not be uniquely fixed. In spite of this difference in interpretation we will see that there are numerous mathematical concepts that can be carried over from statistical physics to quantum theory, and (information) entropy is one of them.

The path integral formulation of quantum theory. From a fundamental perspective a profound yet very direct relation between quantum and classical physics is established through the framework of the (Euclidean) *path integral* formulation of quantum theory proposed by Feynman following an idea of Dirac. The fundamental entity in quantum theory is the probability amplitude A_{if} for the system to go from an initial state labeled i to a final state labeled f. The probability p_{if} for the transition to take place is then given by the square: $P_{if} = |A_{if}|^2$. The amplitude for a quantum particle to go from A at time t_i to B at time t_f can in general be written as a weighted sum over all possible paths $L(t)$ in *classical* configuration space that satisfy the boundary conditions $L(t_i) = A$ and $L(t_f) = B$. As it involves the integration of all possible classical paths or field configurations, the mathematics is quite complicated and in many cases lacks a rigorous mathematical foundation. Yet it is a powerful method that in many ways shows striking mathematical parallels to statistical mechanics if one makes some substitutions like replacing the energy function with the action functional in the statistical weight, the temperature by the product $\hbar$ and *some coupling*. The notion that the 'free energy' is equal to the log of the partition function translates in the statement that the 'effective action' is the log of the unconstrained path integral over classical configuration space. We return to this topic towards the end of the book in Chapter III.4, after we have gained more familiarity with the quantum world.

Conclusion. Our guided tour along some of the highlights of classical physics has come to an end. To conclude this first chapter, we observe that towards the end of the nineteenth century, many physicists thought that the physical universe was basically fathomed, with only minor details remaining to be settled. The fundamental laws had been laid down by a bunch of geniuses and the program was reduced to merely applying them, skilfully applying them to be sure. That appeared to be a matter of diligent devotion, more something like stamp collecting than facing the challenge of building another Rome in one day...

Indeed, mission almost completed, but as we will see, not quite. Stated differently: Hell was about to break loose!

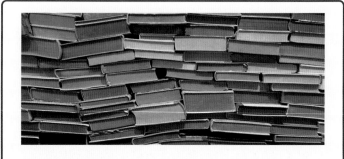

Further reading.

Some introductory textbooks on classical physics:

— *Classical Dynamics of Particles and Systems*
   S.T. Thornton, J.B. Marion
   Saunders College Publications; 4th edition (1995)

— *Classical Mechanics*
   J.E. Taylor
   Cambridge University Press (2008)

— *Electricity and Magnetism*
   E.M. Purcell
   Cambridge University Press; 3rd edition (2013)

— *Introduction to Electrodynamics*
   D.J. Griffiths
   Cambridge University Press; 4th edition (2017)

— *Fundamentals of Statistical and Thermal Physics*
   F. Reif
   Waveland Press Inc (2008)

— *An Introduction to Thermal Physics*
   D.V. Schroeder
   Oxford University Press (2020)

Complementary reading:

— *The Equations*
   S. Bais
   Harvard Univiversity Press (2005)

Chapter I.2

The age of geometry, information and quantum

And the continuity of our science has not been affected by all these turbulent happenings, as the older theories have always been included as limiting cases in the new ones.

Max Born

In spite of the prevailing scientific optimism towards the end of the nineteenth century, some of the most radical changes in our thinking about the workings of nature were about to surface. The monumental edifice of classical physics started to show cracks which would turn out to be fatal. The crisis in this would-be infallibility centered around some phenomena that were not just hard to explain but were in manifest contradiction with the cherished classical dogmas. The limited domains of validity of classical physics became apparent through the turning points of relativity and quantum theory.

This chapter aims to provide a broad perspective on the new opportunities that opened up for science and technology in the twentieth century, and were derived in some way or another from the turning points that occurred early on. The subsequent sections cover introductions to the physics of relativity, the physics of geometry, and the physics of information. We conclude this chapter with some general remarks on quantum theory.

Canaries in a coal mine

Challenges, contradictions and tuning points. It is interesting to note that already towards the end of the nineteenth century, there were some rather well-known experimental observations that seemed to challenge aspects of the central dogmas of classical physics. We may call these the canaries in the coal mine. Let us start with two results that were puzzling at the time and were only resolved by the radical shift in perspective caused by the theories of relativity, though Einstein himself never emphasized them as sources or motivations for his work. Then we move on to puzzles that pushed us toward quantum theory.

The Michelson–Morley experiment. This experiment succeeded in measuring the effect of the so-called ether (an all-pervading medium through which classical electromagnetic waves supposedly would propagate) on the propagation of light. A non-zero effect was anticipated because the earth would be in motion with respect to the ether and this would cause some dragging of the light in the direction of the relative motion of the ether. Light would therefore propagate at different velocities in different directions. The measurements of Michelson and Morley showed, however, that there was no such effect, leading to the conclusion that the ether was a delusion. It was Einstein who abolished the idea of an ether in his special theory of relativity of 1905.

The (anomalous) perihelion precession of Mercury. It had been observed as early as 1860 that the elliptical orbit of Mercury as a whole rotated very slowly in its orbital plane. This was a problem that even Newton's laws could not account for, even when perturbations like the other planets (even assuming the existence of a novel planet named Vulcanus), as well as the oblateness of the sun were taken into account. But it turned out that the observed anomalous part of the precession agreed to a high precision with the calculation using the *general theory of relativity*, the new theory of gravity formulated by Einstein in 1915. The anomalous perihelion precession thereby furnished one of the earliest experimental confirmations of general relativity.

Let us now turn to four early puzzles that could only be resolved with quantum theory.

The black body radiation law. If we heat a body, it starts to radiate. For a black body kept at a given temperature the classical formula describing the radiation intensity as a function of frequency due to Rayleigh and Jeans failed to describe the data, and in fact predicted an unphysical limit towards the high frequency end of the spectrum referred to as the *ultraviolet catastrophe* (see Figure I.2.1(a)). This all came about because one applied the classical equipartition of energy among the various modes of the electromagnetic field. The resolution of this problem by Max Planck in 1900 was based on the bold assumption that the minimal energy of a mode E is equal to the frequency ν times a fundamental constant denoted by h, according to his famous formula:

$$E = h\nu. \tag{I.2.1}$$

It is here that the proportionality constant h named after Planck entered physics as a new universal constant of nature. It is extremely small, in ordinary units the reduced Planck's constant – called h-bar – equals

$$\hbar = h/2\pi = 1.05 \times 10^{-34} \ \ \text{Joule seconds.} \tag{I.2.2}$$

This tiny constant had a huge impact, since this innocent looking quantization formula marked the very beginning of the tumultuous quantum era.

The classical radiation formula can be obtained from the quantum formula by taking the limit where $\hbar$ tends to zero, and in that sense quantum theory clearly marks the limited domain of validity of its classical predecessor.

The structure of the atom. It was known at the time that a gas of atoms of a particular type, like hydrogen or sodium, would absorb or emit light with a specific, discrete spectrum of frequencies. Only narrow lines of particular colors would appear in the spectrum (see Figure I.2.1(b)). Within the classical framework of Newton and Maxwell there was no way to account for this phenomenon, because even accepting the structure of the atom with a positive nucleus and orbiting electrons, there would be no discrete energy levels. Worse still: the electron would radiate and therefore lose more and more of its energy and finally fall into the nucleus. This fundamental instability was basically resolved by Niels Bohr in the quantum mechanical atomic model he proposed, and therefore the stability of all matter we observe is a direct consequence of its quantum nature. Bohr's model for an atom predicted an infinite but discrete set of bound states with a single unique ground state with the lowest energy. And this discreteness accounted for the discrete set of lines in the atomic spectra.

The Compton effect. This effect refers to the fact that when scattering a high frequency X-ray off a charged particle like the electron, the radiation itself behaves much like a particle with an energy E and momentum p given by the Planck formula, i.e.

$$E = cp = h\nu. \tag{I.2.3}$$

Furthermore, the conservation laws of energy and momentum were respected in such scattering processes (see Figure I.2.1(c)). This clearly suggested the later step made by Einstein who postulated the existence of the *photon* as

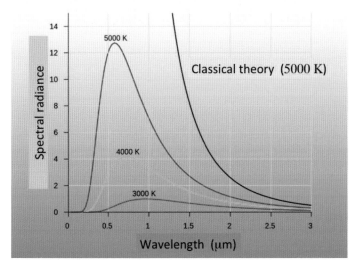

(a) Planck's spectrum of black body radiation solves the ultraviolet (short wavelength) divergence of classical theory.

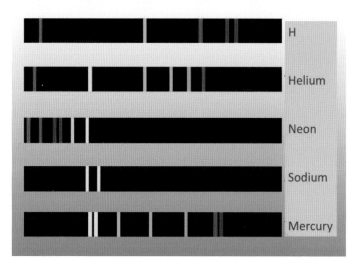

(b) Discrete lines in atomic spectra, indicating discrete energy levels of the atom.

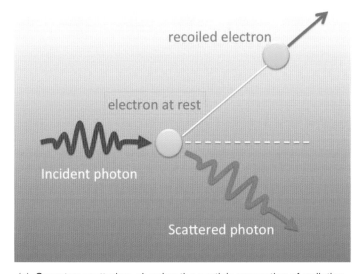

(c) Compton scattering, showing the particle properties of radiation.

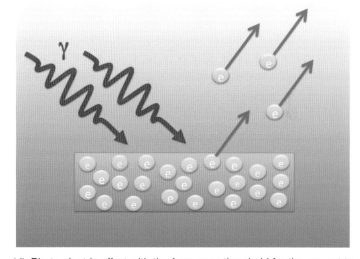

(d) Photo-electric effect with the frequency threshold for the current to flow.

Figure I.2.1: *Meeting the challenge.* Four crucial phenomena that early quantum theory successfully accounted for and where classical physics failed bitterly.

the 'particle of light' with precisely the energy and momentum properties just mentioned.

The photo-electric effect. This amounts to the effect that if we direct a light beam to a metal surface in a constant electric field parallel to the surface, a current might run because electrons get excited from the surface and flow through the circuit (see Figure I.2.1(d)). The surprise was that the magnitude of the current did not depend on the intensity of the radiation in the way predicted by the classical theory. It turned out that a current would only start running if the frequency of the light in the beam passed a certain critical value. If the frequency was below that threshold, there would be no current irrespective of the intensity of the beam.

This behavior was beautifully explained by Einstein in his 1905 paper, using the particle-like interpretation of the radiation. Only if the energy of a single photon (given by Planck's formula) became larger or equal to the binding energy of an electron in the metal, would the electron be liberated by absorbing the photon. The rest of the energy would be converted into the kinetic energy of that electron.

This concludes our brief summary of some of the deep crises that hit classical physics and that seeded the new paradigms of relativity and quantum theory. These constitute two turning points in our thinking that are unequalled in the history of science in the sense that they extended our understanding of the physical universe far beyond what we as humans could experience and perceive by direct sensing or observation. And to test these radical new ideas many new instruments and experimental techniques had to be developed as powerful extensions of the quite limited innate human ability to probe nature at very small or very large scales. Indeed, these radically new insights started a century of amazing progress, not only in physics and astronomy, but also in chemistry, material science and computer/information science.

The physics of space-time

The theories of special and general relativity, both largely connected with the person of Albert Einstein, showed that there is no objective way to separate time and space, thereby introducing the concept of space-time. *In the special theory of 1905, this implied the unique role of the velocity of light as a universal constant, and the equivalence of mass and energy. The general theory of 1915 furthermore showed that space-time could be curved and had to be thought of as something dynamical. The concept of space-time changed from an external mathematical abstraction to a physical entity, which itself carried energy and momentum. Einstein found the dynamical equations for the universe as a whole, as the inevitable consequence of this line of thinking. This means that we have to think of the universe we live in as a particular solution of the Einstein equations.*

Special relativity

The theory of special relativity is based on two assumptions: (i) the laws of nature should look the same for any set of observers that move with constant relative velocity with respect to each other, and (ii) the velocity of light in vacuum is exactly the same for all such observers. These assumptions, which have been confirmed by a wide variety of precise experiments, have far-reaching implications: for example that the relative velocity between two moving objects can never exceed the speed of light c, but also that moving clocks tick slower. Probably the most well-known consequence is the equivalence of mass and energy, so concisely expressed by the magnificent equation $E = mc^2$. This equation opened the possibility of predicting processes, where mass could turn into other forms of energy such as radiation, and the other way around, where for example a high-energy photon could create a particle

Figure I.2.2: *Einstein.* (Source: Wikimedia.)

anti-particle pair. These processes found ample applications in quantum physics, in particular nuclear and particle physics, as well as in the medical world – think of *positron-electron tomography*, or PET-scanning, as a diagnostic tool.

Space-time four-vectors. From a conceptual point of view Einstein's special theory of relativity introduced the notion of a flat four-dimensional space-time (also called Minkowski space-time) with four coordinates. These are usually denoted by $x^\mu = (ct, \mathbf{x})$ with the index $\mu = 0\ldots, 3$ where the zero index denotes the time component. A point in space-time labels an instantaneous *event* that takes place

at time t at a point $\mathbf{x}$ in space. Correspondingly, Einstein defined a *four-momentum* $p^\mu = (E/c, \mathbf{p})$ for a particle,[1] where the energy became the time component of the four-momentum, with the usual spatial component $\mathbf{p} = m\mathbf{v}$.

If two observers move with constant relative speed, their *four-vectors* that label a specific event, turn out to be observer dependent in a specific way. They would vary, but for the different observers the 'length' of the four-vectors has to be the same. This means that the *space-time interval* s for a given event, defined as $s^2 = c^2t^2 - |\mathbf{x}|^2$ has to be the same for different observers. And similarly, one may define the notion of *rest mass* m_0, for a particle as $m_0^2c^4 = E^2 - |\mathbf{p}|^2c^2$, which is invariant, that is to say that it takes the same value for all relativistically equivalent observers.

The special theory of relativity makes the statement that the physics may look different for different observers, but a complete description can always be given in the frame of any observer. Furthermore, the theory tells you how to calculate what one observer should see if you know the observations from another one. It tells you how to translate any four-vector from one frame of reference to another. And equally important, it also tells you which are the invariant quantities that will be the same in all frames. I emphasize this point about frames here because interestingly enough we will encounter similar challenges if we are to incorporate properties and frames of observers in quantum theory in a consistent way.

Relativistic versus rest mass. Let us dwell a little more on the equivalence of mass and energy. We have so far given two expressions for the energy: one is the canonical $E = mc^2$, and the other $E^2 = m_0^2c^4 + |\mathbf{p}|^2c^2$, involving its rest mass. The latter formula is depicted in Figure I.2.3.

---

[1]The appearance of the velocity of light c, with units $[m/s]$ in the above definitions, is natural as it ensures that the units of the four components of a relativistic vector are identical.

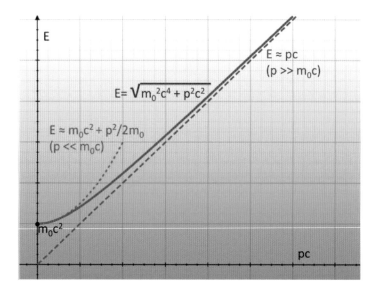

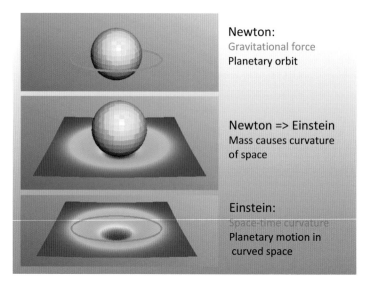

Figure I.2.3: *Relativistic particle energy.* The relation between energy E, rest mass m_0 and momentum p and its limiting behavior for $p \ll m_0 c$ and $p \gg m_0 c$.

Figure I.2.4: *Mass curves the surrounding space.* Comparing the Newtonian paradigm, where masses cause a gravitational attractive force between sun and planet, and the Einsteinian paradigm where mass curves the space, and the gravitational interaction is induced by way the curved space affects the motion of the planet.

The dashed red curve corresponds to the non-relativistic (Newtonian) limit with $E = m_0 c^2 + |\mathbf{p}|^2/2m_0$, whereas the dashed blue line corresponds to the ultra-relativistic limit where the energy is just proportional with the momentum, $E = pc$. Indeed, the latter formula is just the expression for a massless particle like the photon. The picture demonstrates nicely how the properties of a relativistic particle smoothly interpolate between Newtonian particle behavior and a photon. One can also say that the dispersion $E = E(|\mathbf{p}|)$ of the particle goes from quadratic to linear.

From the two energy expressions, there follows a relation between the relativistic mass m and the rest mass m_0 , reading: $m^2 = m_0^2 + m^2|\mathbf{v}|^2/c^2$. The conclusion is that in contrast with the rest mass m_0 , which is an invariant quantity characterizing the particle, the relativistic mass m is momentum, thus frame and observer dependent. The equation above tells us that $m^2 = m_0^2/(1 - v^2/c^2)$.[2] If

you want to accelerate a particle by applying a force, it is the relativistic mass m that comes in, and therefore particles become effectively extremely massive if their velocity tends to the velocity of light. This in turn implies that to accelerate them further will cost ever more energy. A fact that people who run big accelerators are painfully reminded of every time they receive their utility bills! To be fair I should mention that in an accelerator a large fraction of the energy is lost due to the particles radiating. The relation between masses tells us that the relativistic mass goes to infinity if the velocity approaches the speed of light. No wonder we cannot push particles beyond that universal value!

General relativity

The general theory of relativity – often called GR by physicists – is the fundamental theory of gravity proposed by

---

[2]From hereon we replace $|\mathbf{v}|^2$ simply by v^2 for convenience.

Albert Einstein in 1915, where the gravitational force is a direct manifestation of the curvature of space-time. In Figure I.2.4 we have indicated the paradigm shift between the Newtonian and Einsteinian perspective on planetary motion. In the Newtonian paradigm the sun and planet have a mass that causes a gravitational force between them, and that attractive force causes the planet to move in an elliptic orbit. In Einstein's picture the masses curve the space around them which is therefore no longer flat. The planet then just feels the curvature of the space it is moving in which causes it to move in an (almost) elliptical orbit. The gravitational interaction is then induced by the curvature of space, like the trajectory of a marble on a rubber sheet deformed by the mass of a heavy bowling ball placed on it. The gravitational interaction manifests itself though the curvature of space-time.

With GR, space-time became a dynamical part of our physical universe. It was lifted from a bunch of silly coordinates to a fully interacting participant. Space-time was promoted from merely a static mathematical arena in which physics unfolded, to a dynamical physical entity, representing physical degrees of freedom carrying energy and momentum itself. You could call it the 'emancipation' from passive mathematical framing to active physical reality.

This development is analogous to electrodynamics, where initially the electromagnetic fields were considered as mathematical constructs that could be used to calculate forces between charges and currents, and only with Maxwell's treatise did it become clear that the fields themselves in a very direct sense represent the physics of electromagnetic radiation. Mentioning this analogy prompts the question of whether a gravitational analog of electromagnetic radiation exists. The answer, as we will see shortly, is affirmative!

General relativity demanded the use of a mathematics that was quite remote from the practicing physicist's repertoire. The language in which gravitational physics was formu-

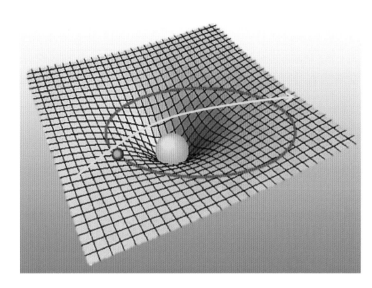

Figure I.2.5: *Bending of light by a mass.* In a curved space-time light moves along shortest distance curves. This means for example that a light-ray emitted by a distant star will be bended if it passes the sun. This effect provided one of the early experimental confirmations of GR.

lated changed from the Newtonian dynamical systems perspective to full fledged Riemannian differential geometry. Relativity marked the beginning of a new golden age of geometry in physics. That is a good reason to include a separate section, following this one, entitled *The physics of geometry*, which provides an introduction to the basic concepts in the mathematics of curved spaces. Concepts that have proven to be as elegant as useful in many domains of modern physics.

Seven predictions. The theory of General Relativity made seven almost independent predictions that in the past century have, one after the other, been confirmed experimentally. They are now part of the vast body of experimental evidence supporting the theory. We list them here with a brief explanation:

(i) Bending of light. Generally the geometry of space-time depends on the energy and momentum distribution of radi-

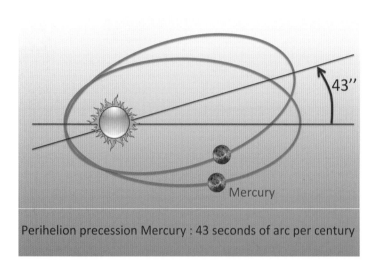

Figure I.2.6: *The perihelion precession of Mercury.*

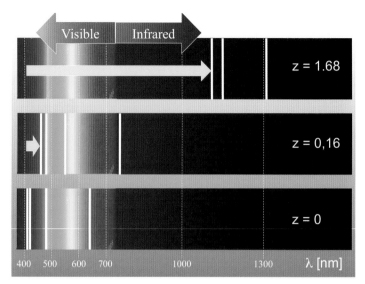

Figure I.2.7: *Gravitational redshift.* If a photon loses energy to the gravitational field moving away from a star its wavelength will increase and gets redshifted. Similarly, due to the expansion of the universe the wavelength of light emitted from far away objects is also shifted towards the red.

ation and matter in it, and in turn that geometry influences the motion of that matter and radiation as through the gravitational force acting on them. We have indicated this effect in Figure I.2.5. This was measured by the British astronomer Sir Arthur Eddington's expedition in 1918 during a solar eclipse, and provided one of the first solid confirmations of Einstein's theory.

(ii) The perihelion precession of planetary orbits. Another notable aspect of General Relativity is that it predicts a deviation from the strictly elliptic orbits for planets. In the Newtonian picture the axes of the ellipse are fixed in space, while in the Einsteinian picture the ellipse rotates slowly in the plane of the orbit as we have schematically illustrated in Figure I.2.6. One way to understand this is that in General Relativity the effective gravitational force that a static source like the sun exerts on an orbiting planet differs from the Newtonian one. If one expands the potential in powers of $(|\mathbf{L}|/mcr)^2$, one finds that:

$$F = \frac{GmM}{r^2}\left(1 + \frac{3|\mathbf{L}|^2}{m^2c^2r^2} + \dots\right), \qquad (\text{I.2.4})$$

where m and M are the earth's and solar masses, and $|\mathbf{L}|$

is the angular momentum of the earth. The thing to note is that the Newtonian inverse square law gets a $1/r^4$ correction. The effect is the largest for the inner planets (small r), for Mercurius the precession amounts to 43 seconds of arc per century. This very slow precession had in fact already been observed before the advent of GR at the end of the 19th century.

(iii) Gravitational redshift. In GR matter and radiation interact with space-time, which means that there will be an exchange of energy between the gravitational and non-gravitational degrees of freedom. So if a photon is emitted from a nearby heavy object like a star and moves radially out to some distant observer, it has to climb out a gravitational potential well and will thereby lose energy. For a single photon this means that the frequency will come down and therefore the wavelength has to increase. The light will therefore be shifted towards the long wavelength or the red end of the spectrum. This effect is called *grav-*

itational redshift denoted by z where the ratio between observed and emitted wavelength is defined by the redshift like $1 + z = \lambda_{\mathrm{obs}}/\lambda_{\mathrm{em}}$. This gravitational redshift is also predicted to exist for photons coming toward us in an expanding universe, and was the crucial ingredient in the demonstration by Edwin Hubble that our universe is actually expanding. This will be discussed in far more detail in the next subsection.

(iv) Gravitational waves. In a moment we will discuss how these waves were discovered in 2015, exactly one hundred years after their existence was predicted. Gravitational waves are waves in the fabric of space-time that travel with the speed of light. As we have seen the gravitational coupling constant, which is Newton's constant G_{N}, is extremely small compared to the electromagnetic coupling e. This implies that one needs violent motions of enormous masses to generate gravitational waves that are energetic enough to be detected. For example when black-holes form or collide, there will be huge amounts of energy converted to space-time degrees of freedom. The existence of the waves was one of the early predictions of Einstein's theory, by making a linear approximation to the empty space Einstein equations one does indeed find linear wave equations very much like the equations for electromagnetic waves. It took about a century before this type of radiation was first observed directly on 14 September 2015 by two gravitational wave detectors in the US.

The LIGO project proposed to detect gravitational waves with the use of two giant interferometers. An impressive international effort by the US, the UK, Germany and Austria, that altogether took some 30 years to complete, resulted in the LIGO observatory. Each interferometer takes a laser beam, splits it in two and sends it down two legs at right angles to each other see Figure I.2.9. At the end of each of the legs are mirrors, which bounce the beams back to the center. If there is any difference in the leg length, say caused by the passing of a gravitational wave, the two recombined laser beams create an interference

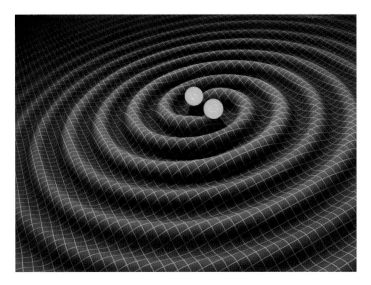

Figure I.2.8: *Two colliding massive objects.* The wavelike space-time profile caused by two extremely massive objects, like black holes, colliding. (Source: LIGO)

pattern. The LIGO setup was extremely sensitive: it could detect a change in the length of a leg ($\simeq 10^{3}\mathrm{m}$), on the order of the diameter of a proton ($\simeq 10^{-15}\mathrm{m}$).

The researchers managed to work out the source of the signal, because their model fitted the data so well. Supposedly it was two black holes, 29 and 36 times heavier than the sun merging into a single black hole of 62 solar masses (see Figure I.2.8) meaning that 3 solar masses were emitted in the form of gravitational radiation! As a result of the fundamental importance of the discovery meant that in 2017, the Nobel prize in Physics was awarded to Rainer Weiss, the other half jointly to Barry C. Barish and Kip S. Thorne, 'for decisive contributions to the LIGO detector and the observation of gravitational waves.'

We know that electromagnetic radiation when quantized is directly linked with a massless particle called the *photon*. Likewise, gravitational waves correspond to a massless quantum particle called the *graviton*. As I have said, it couples extremely weakly and therefore will not play any role

Figure I.2.9: *A LIGO gravitation wave detector.* An aerial photograph of one of the two gravitational wave interferometers. A laser beam gets split after which the beams travel forth and back through two orthogonal legs. If a gravitational wave passes through one of them, the two signals show a detectable phase difference after returning. (Source: Advanced LIGO)

in ordinary high-energy accelerator experiments. There is a second fundamental difference between the photon and the graviton: the former is a spin-one particle, and the latter has spin two. This comes about because electromagnetic waves are dipolar, while gravitational waves have a quadrupole moment. In modern views on gravity people tend to think of the gravitational interactions as an emergent phenomenon, which means that Einstein's equations correspond to an effective theory of space-time. It could be that there are more fundamental degrees of freedom (like so-called *superstrings* or *D-branes*) that space-time is really composed of. In that case the quantization of gravity would start from there, and the graviton would rather be a collective excitation, a so-called *quasi-particle*.

The remaining three predictions of GR are:
(v)   *The existence of black holes,*
(vi) *The expanding universe,*
(vii) *A cosmological constant.*

These are of fundamental interest in modern physics and therefore we will discuss them separately. The expanding universe and the role of the cosmological constant are the subject of the next subsection on cosmology, while we will discuss some aspects of black holes in the concluding section of next chapter on page 139 .

Big Bang cosmology

The Einstein equations are nothing less than a set of equations for space-time as a whole, which means that our universe should correspond to one of the solutions. These equations have played a glamorous role in 20th century physics and created the astoundingly successful field of observational cosmology. There are many good reasons to present the modern view on the cosmological evolution. It corresponds to the hot Big Bang model described by the Friedmann equation, generalized by Lemaître to include the effect of the cosmological constant. This model describes the dynamical arena in which the world became the way we know it. In the third part of the book we describe in more detail the physical processes that took place at the very early stages of the universe. We will come to appreciate that the combination of understanding basic quantum physics, and cosmology based on GR, leads to an impressive account of the evolutionary process towards an increasing complexity in inanimate matter that preceded the Darwinian biological evolution. Indeed it took the universe billions of years to produce the chemical building blocks of life.

The Friedmann–Lemaître equation. GR in its full generality is quite complicated. However, with a number of simplifying (yet entirely justifiable) assumptions about the structure of our universe, the general equations can be reduced to two strikingly simple equations. The assumptions are referred to as *homogeneity* and *isotropy*, where the meaning of the first is that the universe is the 'same' at any place at any given instant in time, and the second means that the universe looks the same in any direction at any given instant. And in fact one can show that the second assumption is implied by the first but not the other way around. The first of the resulting equations basically expresses the conservation of energy. The second is the so-called *Friedmann equation*, named after the versatile Russian mathematician and engineer Aleksandr Aleksandrovich Friedmann, who proposed the equation in 1922.[3] The equation reads:

$$\left(\frac{da}{dt}\right)^2 = \frac{8\pi G_N \rho}{3c^2}a^2 - kc^2, \qquad (I.2.5)$$

where $a = a(t)$ is the *scale factor*, a measure for the relative size of the spatial universe. You may think of a as the relative average distance between two galaxies, meaning that the distance $d(t)$ between the two galaxies at time t would be proportional to $a(t)$: $d(t) = a(t)d_0$. The distances between objects co-moving with respect to the expansion grow proportional to $a(t)$, where in addition we have made the choice that $a(o) = a_0 = 1$. On the right-hand side we have the total *energy density* $\rho = \rho(a)$. Clearly, this is the equation that governs the possible dynamics of homogeneous/isotropic universes. The *'curvature constant'* k, which can be scaled to take the values $1, 0$ or -1, determines whether the space is closed like a sphere, flat, or open like a hyperboloid as illustrated in Figure I.2.10. As we will see the k-value also decides whether the universe will ultimately end in a big crunch ($k = 1$), keeps expanding ($k = -1$), or sits in the critical state ($k = 0$) just in between.

Friedmann sent the equation to Einstein, showing that it had no static solution but did have a solution corresponding to an *expanding universe* originating from an initial singularity. Einstein didn't like the equation, while acknowledging that it was mathematically correct, he thought it was unphysical and 'suspicious' exactly because it predicted

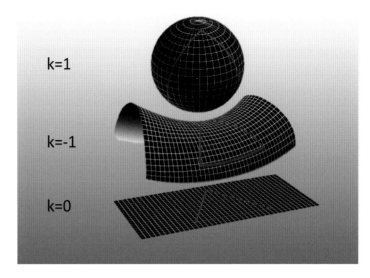

Figure I.2.10: *Curvatures.* The closed, open and flat curvatures corresponding to $k = 1, -1,$ and 0, respectively.

an expanding universe. He then put considerable effort in neutralizing the expansion by adding the so-called *cosmological constant* Λ, without much success. Important work generalizing Friedmann's work including the cosmological constant in 1927 by the Belgian priest and mathematical astronophysicist Georges Lemaître confirmed the expansion.

The real breakthrough came with the mind- and universe-blowing 1929 observations of Edwin Hubble in , which provided the experimental confirmation of the expansion. It was only then that Einstein realized the great importance of Friedmann's work and how he had missed a unique opportunity to make one of the greatest predictions in the history of science. Later in his life he called the introduction of the cosmological constant in his striving for a static universe the 'biggest blunder in my life.' After the expansion was established the new parameter alias cosmological constant silently faded away, until recently when it rather ironically made a glorious and dramatic comeback in a more subtle guise as a term representing the *vacuum* or *dark* energy.

---

[3]Many physicists also link the names of Lemaître and De Sitter to this law.

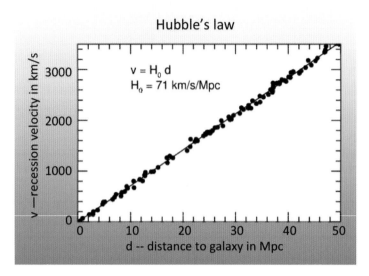

Figure I.2.11: *Hubble law.* Plotting recession velocity of distant galaxies versus their distance gives the linear relation $v = H_0 d$ which is Hubble's law. H_0 is thus the tangent of the angle which the line through the data points makes with the horizontal axis.

The Hubble parameter. An important observable quantity is the *Hubble parameter*, or *expansion rate*, or relative expansion velocity defined as:

$$H(t) \equiv \frac{1}{a} \frac{da}{dt}.$$ (I.2.6)

So, if we observe the present value H_0 for the Hubble parameter and we determine the total energy density ρ_0, and put those values back into the Friedmann equation, that would tell us whether k is positive or negative or zero. So in that sense the density determines our destiny. The in-between $k = 0$ case at present ($t = t_0$) defines a *critical density*:

$$\rho_{\text{crit}} \equiv \frac{3c^2 H_0^2}{8\pi G_N}.$$ (I.2.7)

Let me first go back to the definition of the Hubble parameter in equation (I.2.6). If we write it out explicitly for the present time it has a nice interpretation:

$$\left. \frac{da}{dt} \right|_0 = H_0 \, a_0 \quad \Rightarrow \quad v = H_0 \, d.$$ (I.2.8)

I read the correspondence as follows: looking from any fixed point in space, I see distant objects at distance $d = a_0$ receding from me with a velocity $v = (da/dt)_0$ then the relation just reads: $v = H_0 d$. This is the celebrated *Hubble law*, and depicted in Figure I.2.11. Clearly the slope in the observed $v - d$ plot gives you the observed value for H_0. The redshift observations by Hubble in 1929 was one of the great discoveries of 20th century (astro)physics because it implied that our universe was expanding. A fact that – as mentioned – Einstein himself up to that moment did not believe to be possible.

A mechanical analogue. To get a better understanding of the expanding universe we are going to massage the Friedmann equation into a more familiar form, so that we can apply some of our conventional intuitions. Let us first put the constant H_0 back into the Friedmann equation and write it as follows:

$$\left(\frac{da}{dt}\right)^2 = -H_0^2 \, \hat{V}(a) - kc^2,$$ (I.2.9)

where $\hat{V} = a^2 \rho(a)/\rho_{\text{crit}}$ is some effective 'cosmological' potential. In the modern approach the (relative) energy density has three parts, referring to radiation, matter and the vacuum respectively, thus we write:

$$\hat{V}(\rho, a) = -\left(\frac{\Omega_r}{a^2} + \frac{\Omega_m}{a} + \Omega_v a^2\right).$$ (I.2.10)

where the omega's are the present values fo the relative energy parameters to be obtained from observation. As I alluded to before, the vacuum term is a remake of Einstein's cosmological constant. It has to be added because other dramatic recent observations have shown that the term is actually there. To understand what all of this means we have plotted the potential for equal values of the Ω's in Figure I.2.12. The qualitative behavior is rather easy to understand: as indicated in the figure, for small a the radiation component dominates, because it comes with the $1/a^2$ factor. For large a it is the vacuum term which dominates as it comes with the a^2 factor. Note that the vacuum energy causes an expansive force, it remarkably corresponds to a gravitational repulsion or a negative pressure. The potential is certainly unusual because it has no stable minimum, it runs off to minus infinity, both for a going to zero and for a going to infinity. It is strikingly different from, say, the good old harmonic potential of Figure I.1.13. It is inverted, we have turned it upside-down!

To nevertheless make sense out of it let me remind you of equation (I.1.5) from Chapter I.1, where we derived the expression for the conserved total energy of a particle moving in a potential as:

$$E = \frac{1}{2}mv^2 + V(x), \qquad (I.2.11)$$

where the total energy E is a sum of the kinetic energy and potential energy $V(x)$. But, lo and behold, that is – up to some substitutions ($m = 2/H_0^2$, $x = a$, $v = da/dt$, and the conserved $E = -kc^2/H_0^2$) – exactly the same as the Friedmann equation (I.2.9).

How remarkable, we have ended up with a one-particle mechanical analogue in 1-dimension for the 4-dimensional universe! That is apparently what cosmic scenarios look like: just kicking a marble and looking at how it is running up and down hill! I don't know who ordered that pizza, but I'll certainly eat it!

The effective cosmological potential $\hat{V}(a)$ looks generically like the dark blue curve in Figure I.2.12. As we have mentioned, this potential has no stable minimum and in fact has two singularities, one at $a = 0$ and the other at $a = \infty$. Apparently there is no fixed scale for the marble-universe to come to rest. Now this is the joy of analogues, they force you to think about what these strange singular features could possibly mean. Cognitive laziness does not suffice, we have to think! Figure I.2.13 shows what the equations are trying to tell us. Well, the singularity at $a = 0$ represents the dramatic event which we called the Big Bang. You could think of it as a marble being shot uphill with considerable kinetic energy so that it can climb the mountain

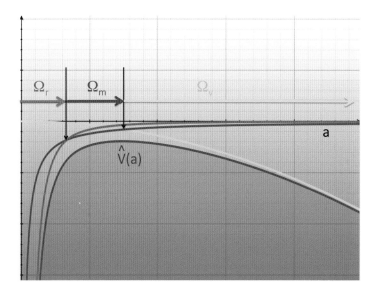

Figure I.2.12: *The effective cosmological potential.* The three terms in the generic cosmological potential $\hat{V}(a)$. The regions in a where the different contributions dominate are indicated (meaning that they are closest to the dark blue curve representing the total potential). For small a radiation dominates, for intermediate scales it is the matter term, while for large values of a the repulsive vacuum term takes over.

from the left. How high? Well, that depends on how hard it gets kicked. If it is kicked a little, it will roll back, and if we slam it hard it will move all the way up, go over the hill and start an infinite descent into another special state. In the latter case the marble-universe keeps accelerating if the vacuum energy density is non-vanishing, causing a race to the bottom on the other side of the potential, a bottom that isn't really there! It describes a state where the universe keeps expanding in an accelerating mode forever, and the matter and radiation will thin out forever with their densities approaching zero.

In Figures I.2.13 and I.2.14 the same three scenarios are depicted: the first shows the potential energy as function of scale factor, and the second the scale factor as function of time. They show three distinct possibilities (with non-vanishing vacuum energy):

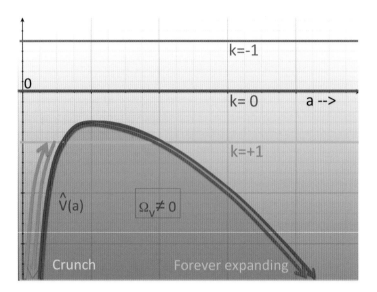

Figure I.2.13: *Evolution scenarios in the potential energy land-scape.* The universe with total energy equal to the lines labeled $k = \pm 1$. For negative energy ($\rho > \rho_{crit}$) the evolution follows the green arrows and the universe starts climbing up the potential barrier up to the green line and starts falling back towards a big crunch. If the energy is positive, ($\rho \leq \rho_{crit}$,) corresponding to the red ($k = -1$) and blue ($k = 0$) arrows, the universe easily climbs over the hill and starts accelerating indefinitely.

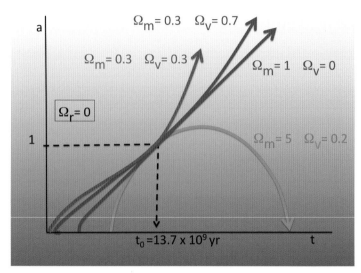

Figure I.2.14: *Cosmological evolution scenarios.* The solutions for the cosmic scale factor a as a function of the time for different choices of the (non-zero) relative mass and vacuum densities. The green scenario is a collapsing universe ending up in a *Big Crunch*. The blue graph on top represents our so-called *Big Chill* universe, it keeps expanding. Compare with the previous figure.

(i) The green scenario with $\rho > \rho_{crit}$ or $k = +1$ is ending in a Big Crunch, because the total energy corresponding to $-k/H_o^2 = -1/2H_0^2$ is not enough to get us over the top. At the point where the marble is turning around, its velocity is zero, which means that all the energy is just potential energy. Consequently the point where the total energy line, corresponding to $k = +1$, intersects with the blue potential energy curve is precisely the turning point of the green arrow that represents the trajectory of the universe.

(ii) In the red scenario with $\rho < \rho_{crit}$, or $k = -1$ the marble moves over the top after which the expansion will go on forever. In this case, there is not enough matter (and radiation) energy to pull the matter back in.

(iii) The $k = 0$ case is of particular interest. If there is a non-vanishing vacuum energy, the top of the potential is at an energy below zero, which means that in the k=0 case

the marble still has a non-vanishing velocity at the top and will therefore move over hill entering the domain of eternal expansion.

The Einstein universe. One could imagine cooking up a special case where the top of the potential would exactly touch the $k = +1$ line In this case the marble would end up exactly on the top, where in principle it could stay forever. Forever? But wait, this is like putting a marble on top of a bald head, there is indeed a fixed point, but it is clearly unstable, as any little perturbation will make the marble move one way or the other. In that special case the decision on the fate of our universe would be postponed! The future of the universe would boil down to tossing a coin! The very special solution where the universe just sits forever on top corresponds to the completely static universe that motivated Einstein to introduce the cosmological constant (or vacuum energy term) in the first place. He apparently didn't check the stability of the solution.

Figure I.2.15: *De Sitter and Einstein in 1932.* De Sitter and Einstein discussing some non-static solutions for the universe. (Source: https://repository.aip.org/islandora/object-/nbla:288847.)

Vacuum energy. From the last figures it is also clear that the vacuum energy term is peculiar in that it causes an outward directed force: it acts like a *negative* pressure term. It is apparently a form of energy that gravitationally *repels*! You might be tempted to think of anti-matter, but that can't be it because anti-matter has positive mass, so gravitationally it is attractive like ordinary matter, but this vacuum stuff is peculiar and is really repulsive! In the top-blue and red scenarios we see that for large times the behavior is completely determined by this vacuum contribution, so let

us see what happens to the scale parameter in that case. If we go back to the Friedmann equation (I.2.9) and only put in the dominant vacuum contribution ($\Omega_v = 1$, $k = 0$) and bring the a^2 factor to the other side, we get:

$$H(a)^2 = H_0^2, \quad \text{or} \quad \frac{1}{a}\frac{da}{dt} = H_0. \quad (I.2.12)$$

This equation is simple to solve[4] and yields an exponential expansion:

$$a(t) = a_0 e^{H_0 t}. \quad (I.2.13)$$

This exponentially expanding solution is called the De Sitter universe, after Willem de Sitter, the Dutch astronomer who came up with the solution already in 1917. So in the third picture we see the top-blue and red arrow indeed starting to go up exponentially. This solution played an important role in the debates that Einstein and De Sitter (see Figure I.2.15) had about the various non-static universes.

Cosmic event horizon. Expanding universes have the interesting but somewhat puzzling property that if things move away from me at a velocity proportional to their distance, then inevitably at some distance things recede with a faster then the speed of light. This clearly happens as soon as $r > R_H$, where

$$R_H = \frac{c}{H_0}. \quad (I.2.14)$$

Can it then be that 'things' move faster than the speed of light? Doesn't that make Einstein turn in his grave? Actually he will not, as his velocity veto concerns relative velocities at a given point in space-time. So indeed, expansion velocities of remote parts of space exceeding c are admissible, and are inevitable in expanding universes. They have a clear physical interpretation, in that they imply the existence of a *cosmological horizon*. In Figure I.2.16 we have sketched the situation. We imagine ourselves to be at the centre with concentric spheres around us. Points on

---

[4]We will solve it in the *Math Excursion* on functions in Part III.

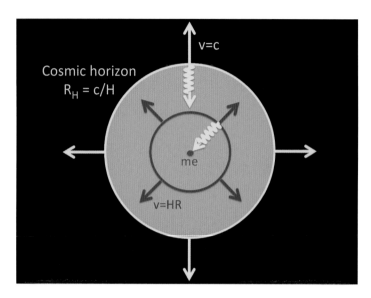

Figure I.2.16: *The cosmic event horizon*. This horizon is defined as the surface around us where the speed due to the expansion equals the speed of light c. Messages sent now from any point in the black region beyond the horizon would never reach us.

the sphere with radius r move away with the Hubble velocity $v = H_0 r$ and the horizon corresponds therefore to the sphere with $r = R_H = c/H_0$. What this means is that if somebody beyond that horizon decides to send us a light signal at this very moment, that signal will never be able to reach us, because it will not be able to cross the horizon. This horizon is at a distance of about 13.7 Giga light years, 'far out' so to speak. Very far away and nothing to worry about. That's what you would think, but after Stephen Hawking's great discovery that horizons have very physical properties: they are a source of thermal black body radiation. Therefore adventurous physicists have been speculating about the conceivable roles this horizon might play in the explanation of contemporary cosmological observations like dark matter and dark energy. We will comment on these ideas later on.

Cosmic inflation

Problems with the standard expansion model.

Particle horizons. We now turn to the phenomenon of a *particle horizon*. This type of horizon should not be confused with the *cosmic event horizon*, as it has a very different origin; the existence of a particle horizon derives from the fact that the universe had a beginning. That means that for any observer at any given instant in time, there is a specific 'particle horizon.' Light emitted from points beyond that horizon never had time enough to reach us. Basically the particle horizon defines the size of the observable universe at any given instant, and the definition naturally implies that the observable universe grows as time goes by. This is schematically illustrated in Figure I.2.17. The particle horizon is just the intersection of our past light cone, with the spatial surface where the time equals zero. This figure also illustrates the notion of a *causally connected domain*, since it has half the radius of the particle horizon. It is the domain in which any point would have had enough time to communicate with any other point in the domain. It is important to note that the younger the universe is the smaller the size of a causal domain. So our observable universe breaks up into ever more causal domains if we go back in time. And this leads to a problem with the standard big bang model and observations that we turn to next.

The (particle) horizon problem. The ever smaller size of particle horizons at earlier epochs of the universe create a notorious paradox known as the 'horizon problem.' This problem concerns a conflict between present-day observations and the original Friedmann-Lemaître expanding model of the universe. We at present observe the cosmic background radiation from all directions in the sky. This radiation was emitted at the moment that electrically neutral atoms formed, when the universe was about 300,000 years old. That radiation did not interact ever since, it de-

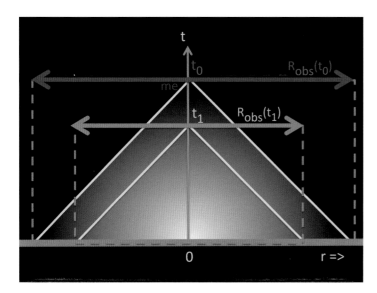

Figure I.2.17: *Particle horizons.* We have sketched the *particle horizon*, which defines the size of the observable universe, at present ($t = t_0$) and an earlier instant ($t = t_1$). It is defined as the present size of the domain that at $t = 0$ was contained in our past light cone, the dark blue arrow. For conceptual clarity the figure features a flat universe with a beginning. It illustrates the fact that our present causal domain breaks up in many independent domains at early times.

coupled from the matter. And that is the reason why we observe a perfect thermal spectrum now, which is redshifted because of the expansion of the universe after the decoupling took place. It constitutes the strongest direct observational evidence for the expansion of our universe. It appears exactly as predicted. However, there is something puzzling here: the radiation that comes to us from opposite sides of the universe shows exactly the same spectrum apparently originating from the same thermal plasma. How can that be? Because at the time the photons decoupled, the places where that radiation originated were not within one causal domain. To get an idea, let us ook at Figure I.2.17. If we imagine the radiation to be released at $t = t_1$, then it can have equilibrated over distances corresponding to the size of the causal domain with radius $R_{obs}(t_1)$ as indicated in the figure. My causal domain con-

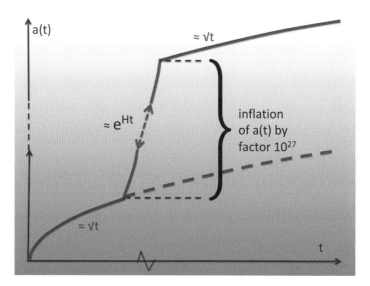

Figure I.2.18: *Causal domains.* The inflationary universe has a brief inflationary epoch of less then 10^{-30} s shortly after the big bang, in which it expanded exponentially with a factor of 10^{27}.

sists of all the points from which information could reach me within the age of the universe t_0. That would mean that at present we would be able to make observations all the way out to $R_{obs}(t_0)$, a much larger domain. Thus we would not expect the perfect black body spectrum we happen to observe. In other words at the time of decoupling the region corresponding to our presently observable universe contained many causal domains. At that age of the universe, there had not been time enough to reach thermal equilibrium over distances that comprise the total observable universe at present. This is an irrefutable fact if we assume that the standard expansion of the universe is correct. And this fact poses a serious problem for the standard Friedmann-Lemaître model. This problem has been resolved by making a major amendment to the course of events in the very early universe, This is a fundamental update: the expanding universe 2.0, also called the *inflationary universe*. But before we get into that we want to first mention another problem with the standard cosmological model.

The flatness problem. The flatness problem is posed by the observation that fitting the model to the data the conclusion is that we live in a universe where the curvature constant k is very close to zero. From a theoretical point of view there is no reason to expect it to be zero, it must have been zero all along. From the fact that our universe after 13.7 billion years has a k value so close to zero, one may show by calculating backward that this would impose a very unnatural initial condition on the universe. One finds that the value of the curvature constant would have to be fine-tuned to zero to some sixty decimal places! That is considered to be an exceptional choice, which begs for an explanation. It turns out that there is a satisfactory solution to this problem and again it involves the vacuum energy and the De Sitter solution.

If you go back to the Friedmann equation (I.2.9) and look at the right-hand side, you see that the vacuum energy is a constant positive part of the density ρ. However this constant is multiplied by a^2, and thus this term (if present) will under all circumstances grow faster with respect to the second term that corresponds to the curvature constant k. What this means is that a universe that goes through such an exponential phase will blow up and effectively become flat. The situation is somewhat analogous to the claim by some Dutch people that their country is flat; it is indeed effectively flat, but not really. It is better to say that the curvature radius of the earth is much larger than their visual horizon. Going back to the universe, what this means is quite interesting. If you could turn the vacuum energy on for a limited amount of time, the exponential expansion would basically flatten out the universe. This is a vital observation because it would furnish a dynamical mechanism by which the universe drives itself to that unique point in the solution space where k is effectively zero! The universe would end up being flat, becoming open *independent* of the initial situation.

What do the experiments tell us? The data unequivocally suggest that there must have been a brief period in the

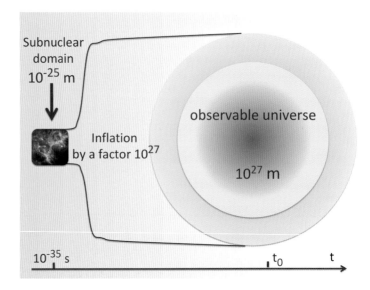

Figure I.2.19: *Cosmic inflation.* Inflation makes the present observable universe fit in the expanded image of a causal domain of subnuclear size.

very early universe, where it expanded exponentially. And that brief period of *cosmic inflation* as it is called is the reason we find ourselves in a flat ($k = 0$) universe now. We have pointed out two serious problems where the standard cosmological model clashes with the data, and both are resolved in the inflationary scenario to which we turn next.

The inflationary scenario.

The inflationary scenario involves a non-vanishing vacuum expectation value of a so-called *inflaton field*, presumably some scalar field that has not really been identified. In a very, very early stage of the universe, say, at $t \simeq 10^{-35}$ seconds, due to the cooling of the universe this inflaton field gets stuck in a metastable vacuum state. This means that it generates a constant vacuum energy in the universe, and this will last for about $t \simeq 10^{-32}$ seconds, after which it will decay to a new lower zero energy ground state. During this period with the non-vanishing vacuum energy present, the universe would inflate the linear dimension of the universe by a factor of 10^{27} (corresponding to 10^{81} for the volume). Inflating a causal domain by such a huge factor solves the horizon problem as is indicated in Figure I.2.19. The epoch ends with a phase transition of the early universe as a whole. The latent heat released in this transition will be converted into ordinary matter. Such a scenario implies a drastic revision of the very early stages of the standard cosmological model. Note that though the time periods appear to be extremely short, this is only relative, the inflationary epoch lasts a 1000 times the age of the universe at that time! You could therefore equally well say that it took 'ages.'

There is one other observational aspect of early universe cosmology that this scenario gives an answer to. The enormous inflation factor basically implies that our whole observable universe originates from an extremely small domain before inflation started. The domain would be so small that the physics within that domain would be governed by quantum theory. That particularly implies that within such a domain of size Δx there are substantial quantum fluctuations, and that these fluctuations have a flat, scale invariant spectrum, meaning that their amplitude is independent of their wavelength. These small wavelength fluctuations ($\lambda \leq \Delta x$) are blown up to large-scale inhomogeneities by the inflation. And it is believed that these inhomogeneities are the seeds of large-scale structures in the subsequent evolution of the universe. Knowing the initial spectrum at the end of the inflationary epoch allows one to predict what the inhomogeneities and anisotropies in today's cosmic background radiation would be. And indeed the scale invariant initial spectrum evolves in a highly nonuniform distribution with damped oscillations which agrees extremely well with what has been observed by space observatories like WMAP and PLANCK as is shown in Figure I.2.20.

This surprising scenario combines knowledge from the microscopic realms of quantum field theory, with knowledge from general relativity and cosmology and allows for a so-

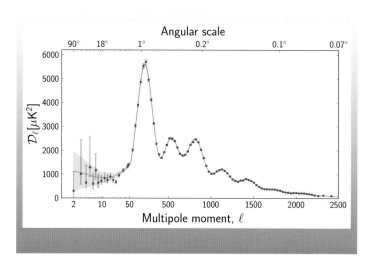

Figure I.2.20: *CMB anisotropy.* The inflation blows tiny quantum fluctuations in the initial causal domain, up to large-scale inhomogeneities that are believed to be the seeds of larg- scale structure in the present universe. These show up in the angular correlations in the spectrum of temperature anisotropies of the cosmic background radiation. From this data the three energy parameters and the cosmic curvature constant in the model can be determined. (Source: PLANCK mission)

lution of both the horizon and the flatness problem of standard cosmology. Scenarios of this type were proposed and developed in the early 1980s by Alan Guth from MIT, Andrei Linde presently at Stanford University, and Paul Steinhardt presently at Princeton University.

Splendid observations. Having presented these fascinating theoretical considerations, let us briefly review the stunning progress that has been made in observational astronomy and cosmology. The fundamental observational parameters in the cosmological models are the energy densities Ω_i, and the Hubble constant and these basically tell you what the curvature constant k is. Two completely different techniques have been used:

(i) The measurement of very distant Supernovae type I

events. These are basically very remote sources that allow us to extend the Hubble law plot of Figure I.2.11. A
great experimental effort by Saul Perlmutter and collaborators (1998) managed to expand the diagram by a factor of
ten, and the spectacular discovery they made was that the
plot does no longer stay linear but is curving upward. This
means that at large distances we see the expansion accelerate. They fitted the data and extracted the Ω values,
and clearly obtained a positive contribution for the vacuum
term. With Adam J. Riess and Brian P. Schmidt, Saul Perlmutter was a co-recipient of the Nobel prize for Physics in
2011, and the prize was awarded 'for the discovery of the
accelerating expansion of the Universe through observations of distant supernovae.'

(ii) The measurement of the curvature through measuring the anisotropy in the Mmcrowave background radiation also gives – among many other things – the Ω values.
There have been a number of space telescopes to do this
kind of work: first the COBE (1992), then WMAP (2003)
and most recently the PLANCK (2013) mission, with again
startling results. For this line of research the Nobel Prize
in Physics of 2006 was awarded jointly to John C. Mather
and George F. Smoot of the COBE collaboration 'for their
discovery of the blackbody form and anisotropy of the cosmic microwave background radiation.'

Concerning the relative energy densities, the upshot of
these experiments is summarized in the energy piechart
depicted in Figure I.2.21. After the PLANCK mission the
preferred fractions are: 68.3 % is in the form of vacuum
or dark energy, 26.8 % in the form of dark (not luminous)
matter and only 4.9 % is in the form of ordinary luminous
matter. The conclusion is crystal clear: we are living in
a vacuum dominated, flat universe! What that means ultimately is also not hard to understand. The remarkable
message is that 95 % of all the energy in the universe resides in the dark matter and energy components, and is
therefore in a form that is unknown to us! It reminds us of
the words of the Chinese philosopher Lao Tzu: 'The more

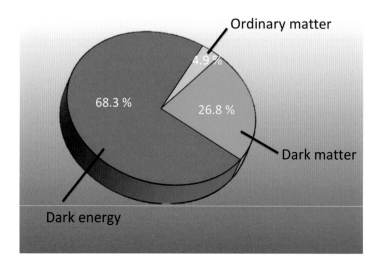

Figure I.2.21: *The energy piechart.* A piechart of the relative
contributions of dark (vacuum) energy, dark matter and ordinary
matter as determined by the WMAP and PLANCK space observatories. Conclusion: our universe is vacuum dominated.

we know, the less we understand!' More than anything
else, science is the story of work in progress, every time
reminding us of our ignorance, and forcing us to cope with
it. Or to find creative ways to beat it. Indeed, science will
always run into new walls, or to be more encouraging: new
profound challenges.

Today's challenges. We have to conclude that looking at
the presently available data, this consistent and convincing, evidence-based inflationary model of the evolution of
the universe still leaves us with some big puzzles.

Dark matter. The first is the question what actually is dark
matter. Clearly this is a question that has been taken up
by the particle physicists who built their Large Hadron Collider (LHC) at the European accelerator center CERN in
Geneva. They are presently hunting for a new particle
type that would fit the profile of dark matter. Such particles
should be 'sterile,' meaning that they interact very weakly
with ordinary matter and they should be massive in order

to cause the gravitational effects we observe. They are expected to form a species of so-called WIMPs: Weakly Interacting Massive Particles. Theoretical candidates are for example the species of lightest supersymmetric particles (a necessary ingredient of String Theory), or various types of massive particles that are called 'sterile' neutrinos (fitting in certain Grand Unified Theories).

Dark energy. The second even more profound puzzle is the observed non-zero value of the cosmological constant, or vacuum energy. It is 'small' but definitely non-zero, and the question is wheter we can find a theoretical explanation for its existence and its magnitude. The irony is that physicists have for quite some time been looking for arguments why it would have to be strictly zero exactly because there was an extremely strong bound on it from observation. They looked for a principle that would protect the zero value of the cosmological constant, like the gauge principle protects the zero mass property of the photon. Needless to say that they didn't succeed, fortunately in fact, because now we know that it is not zero to start off with. Answering this question requires a fundamental insight into the nature of the vacuum, and so far there is no way to calculate the quantum energy of the vacuum from first principles. Such an explanation should also allow us to make a first estimate of its magnitude, because in spite of the fact that it is the dominating energy content of the universe, its actual value is mesmerizingly small: $\Lambda = 1.1 \times 10^{-52}\,\mathrm{m}^{-2}$. This mass energy density is about four protons per cubic meter, which amounts to $\rho_{\mathrm{vacuum}} = 5.9 \times 10^{-27}\,\mathrm{kg/m}^3$.

From a theoretical point of view, the conclusion is that the De Sitter solution, which was discarded for a long time as physically irrelevant, has made a glamorous comeback, and presently plays a vital role in understanding the deep past, as well as the present and future of our universe. Remarkable!

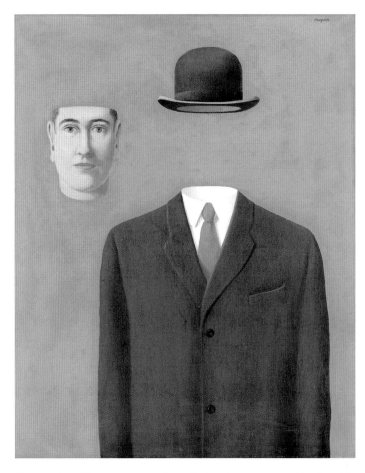

Figure I.2.22: *Magritte: the pilgrim (1966).* My title for this intriguing surrealistic painting would be: 'Let's face the void, and void the face.' If that isn't a deep thought, then neither is its negation! (Source: ©'Photothèque Magritte / Adagp Images, Paris)

 Much ado about nothing. The handicap of generalists is that they know virtually nothing about almost everything, and the handicap of nerds is that they know virtually everything about almost nothing. What? Knowing everything about nothing? I wish it were true. Closer inspection shows that the science in-crowd knows little to nothing about nothing. Scientists remain silent, but spend sleepless nights worrying about nothingness. Imagine some DOE Innovation Initiative inspection team performing a lab raid and asking what you are doing with all that taxpayers' money, and you would have to answer that you are working on 'nothing.' Oh yes, you are just mucking around, are you? That would undoubtedly result in you taking a deep dive in the cool lake of depression. Career-wise I would avoid talking about the void.

You would think that empty space – the vacuum, the void, nothingness – is a trivial no-brainer not worth pondering about. Note however, the following important remark that the legendary physicist John Archibald Wheeler made at some point: 'No point is more central than this, that empty space is not empty. It is the seat of the most violent physics.' Here, a deep truth appears to be lurking. A quantum truth.

The reason we don't need to talk about it in physics is because in real experiments we are always dealing with energy differences. We compare energies and the energy of the vacuum 'drops out.' We therefore can set it equal to zero if we would like to do so. This is fortunate, because we do not know how to calculate the vacuum energy from first principles, and all 'serious' efforts to do so typically give infinity as an answer. This means that the void is challenging our deepest scientific intuitions. General relativity is a comrade in arms, because as we saw, it *is* sensitive to something that other theories would not detect. Space-time itself allows for an *absolute* measurement of the energy including that of the vacuum. And moreover, space-time measurements have just told us that the vacuum energy is not just non-zero, it is in fact the dominant form of energy in our universe!

This much is certain, 'nothing' does not exist and the notion of nothingness is an apparent delusion. What does exist is our ignorance about it.

So, what's so tricky about nothing? An average fish would reply: 'Well, no fellow-fish, no water-plants, no play-rock and no gravel on the bottom.' But what the average fish would never say is: 'no water.' The fact that nothing is something in which he couldn't exist doesn't enter his fishy head. The average person by now understands damn well that without air he is going to choke, but apparently in nineteenth century educational institutions, that simple fact still had to be demonstrated by putting a little bird under a glass bell and pumping out the air. Just to prove that 'nothing' can also be quite harmful. Causing all sorts of panic because of the 'unbearable heaviness of not-being.' 'To be or not to be,' remains the question. Having answered that, 'to understand or not to understand' is the next question. □

The physics of geometry

With the advent of the theories of relativity and gauge theories for the description of the fundamental forces, a new golden age for geometry in the realm of physics emerged. This section on 'the physics of geometry' will give you an introduction to the basic notions of geometry that have played a crucial role in modern physics.

We will talk about the notion of curved spaces (smooth manifolds*) and which concepts are essential if one wants to do physics on and with them. Some aspects of topology are mentioned like* homotopy*, because it leads to an alternative way of understanding why certain physical quantities turn out to be quantized and conserved.*

Introducing regular coordinates on curved spaces often forces us to define overlapping patches or charts. One may introduce vectors that live in the tangent space *of some point, whereas the collection of the base manifold and all its tangent spaces form the so-called* tangent bundle *of the space. Now we may study the transport of vectors along paths. This leads to the notion of* holonomy *which is linked to the integrated curvature over a region of space. We complete this lightning review by summarizing the relations between the* metric, *which provides a local sense of distance and size, a* connection *which connects vectors in different points, and a* local *curvature which is very much like the field strength in a gauge theory.*

After this pure geometrical part we show the close relationship of gauge theories, describing the non-gravitational interactions, with fiber bundles. *This provides a geometrical understanding of the gauge potential or connection* A_μ *and a gauge invariant field strength or gauge curvature* $F_{\mu\nu}$. *This representation of gauge theories opens the door for understanding their topological features, like the existence of magnetic fluxes or monopoles, and more generally to the notion of topological charges and quantum numbers. This section aims to highlight the intimate relationship between physics, geometry and quantum theory.*

Living in flatland. When you talk about a space, most people have the natural inclination to think of a flat Euclidean space, like the plane denoted by $\mathbb{R}^2$. And on a plane life is simple not only for the Danes and the Dutch, but also for physicists. It is simple to choose a coordinate grid to label the points in the space. The shortest distance between points are straight lines, and to define vectors like momenta and the forces of electric fields is also simple. You just draw arrows based at a point in the space because a flat Euclidean space is also a vector space. There is no distinction; you may think of vectors as living in the 'same' space as you. On flat Euclidean space we can define functions and derivatives of functions (basically vectors), as well as their integrals. If we have a particle mov-

(a) Triangle in flat space, sum of angles is $180°$.

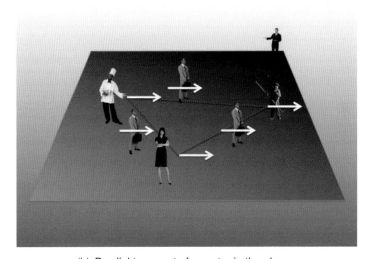

(b) Parallel transport of a vector in the plane.

Figure I.2.23: *Carrying vectors around.* Parallel transporting around a closed loop in a flat space has no net effect on the orientation of the vector.

ing on the plane in a potential $U(\mathbf{x})$ then it will experience a force $\mathbf{F}(\mathbf{x}) = -\nabla U(\mathbf{x})$ which corresponds to a field of vectors over the plane. In other words we can do calculus, and therefore flat space is the basic example of a space or manifold that is *differentiable*.

Parallel transport of vectors. In Figure I.2.23 we show a Master Chef and two of his branch managers running annexes in other parts of town. He wants to send a secret recipe around in the form of a vector, and it is in the orientation of the vector in which the subtle balance of spices that earned the Chef his Michelin star is encoded. So, it is crucially important to preserve the direction the direction in which the vector points, implying that the Chef cannot send the recipe by mail. He decides to hire a messenger, an apprentice so to say, in a grey suit and with a leather briefcase to carry around the vector. The messenger should take care to *parallel transport* the vector. This is not hard: while moving along the shortest route consisting of straight line segments, he has to ensure that the angle between the vector and the direction of his motion (the path) stays the same. The Chef has ordered him to pass by again at the end of the trip, so he can check whether he did the parallel transporting correctly. And as you see the apprentice succeeded in perfectly performing his task, as is confirmed by the independent juror standing in the corner.

In this subsection we have mentioned some features of flat space that are so natural that you wouldn't think of them as particularly interesting. However, what we will explore in the remainder of this section is that in a curved space, these simple concepts will become much more involved

Curved spaces (manifolds) and topology

Modern physics makes use of the mathematical knowledge about curved spaces or manifolds, both in the theory of relativity, but also in the theories that describe gauge interaction between elementary particles. What we want to introduce are what is known as differentiable manifolds,

curved spaces that look locally like flat Euclidean space and therefore globally allow for defining functions and their derivatives (and vectors). These are spaces on which one can consistently define calculus, a necessary tool to describe dynamical systems in such spaces. And that is what physicists like to do. We start by defining some elementary notions of *topology* , and then add the ingredients of differential geometry like coordinate systems, vectors, metric and curvature.

Positive and negative curvatures. It is easy to imagnine curvatures of a surface when we embed it in a higher dimensional Euclidean space. The surface can be defined by an algebraic equation.

Consider for example spheres S^n, these are defined by an equation $x^2 + y^2 + \ldots = 1$ in $(n+1)$-dimensional Euclidean space $\mathbb{E}^{n+1}$. In Figure I.2.24 we show the spheres S^0 (two points), S^1 and S^2. These spaces are finite or compact. They can be obtained from one another by suitable rotation in the Euclidean space two dimensions higher.

Spaces of negative curvature are for example hyperbolic spaces. In Figure I.2.25 we depicted two hyperbolic surfaces H^2 and the corresponding equations to contrast them with the two-sphere. One of the hyperboloids consists of two disconnected sheets while the other has only one sheet. These spaces are infinite. These two spaces can be generated by rotating a given hyperbola in the plane about an appropriate axis in that plane. The sphere is by definition the set of all points that have a fixed Euclidean distance to the origin. The double-sheeted hyperboloid can be thought of as the set of all events in three-dimensional Minkowski space, at a fixed space-time interval from the origin. The sheets also represent the three-dimensional energy momentum vectors $(E, \mathbf{p})$ of a particle with finite rest mass m satisfying $E^2 = m^2 + \mathbf{p}^2$.

Topological features. A topological feature or characteristic is one that doesn't change under a *continuous de-*

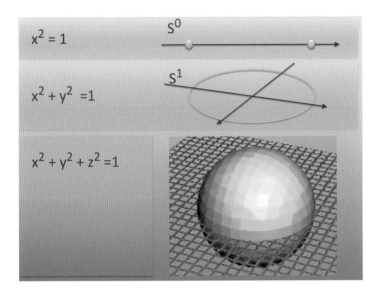

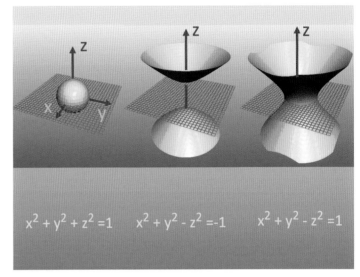

Figure I.2.24: *Three spheres.* This figure shows the spheres and their embedding equations. The 'zero'-sphere S^0, described by the equation $x^2 = 1$, consists of two points. The circle or one-sphere S^1 is defined by the equation $x^2 + y^2 = 1$, and S^2 by its natural higher-dimensional extension.

Figure I.2.25: *Hyperbolic planes.* This figure shows two different two-dimensional hyperbolic spaces and their embedding equations. They are closely related to the equation for the two-sphere, and differ by additional minus signs. The sphere has positive curvature, while the hyperboloids have negative curvatures.

formation of the space. Cutting and pasting the space is not allowed. Topology is like rubbersheet geometry where stretching and shrinking in any direction is allowed but tearing the sheet is not. Two spaces are topologically equivalent if they can be continuously transformed into each other.

Boundaries and holes. Let us start with one-dimensional spaces like smooth curves. For example a line segment is smooth and has two point-like boundaries. But we could also consider a closed curve. It may look like a circle or the number zero which has no boundary, but it has a hole. The figure 'eight' is also closed (has no boundary) and it has two holes but now it is not a one-dimensional space because it has a singular point where the lines split and where it therefore is locally *not* like $\mathbb{R}^1$.

Connectivity. The spaces just mentioned are all *path-wise connected*, meaning that for any two points one chooses

there is a path connecting them. The number 'I0' as a space is not connected it has two disconnected components: the 'I' and the '0'. One open component 'I' has two point-like boundaries, and the closed component has no boundary. If we consider any two points on the line segment then these can be connected by some path, and all paths can be continuously deformed into each other. Taking two points on the '0' or a circle, we find that there are many possible paths that connect the two points. These paths may wind an arbitrary number of times around the hole and such paths cannot all be continuously deformed into each other. We say that the 'I' is *simply connected* whereas the figure '0' is *multiply connected* because there are topologically distinct paths. So we are invited to further refine the notion of connectivity. Let us do that after we have moved the discussion one dimension up and consider smooth two-dimensional surfaces.

The simplest finite, two-dimensional spaces have the topology of a disc. It is simply connected and it has one boundary with the topology of a circle. Note that a boundary in two dimensions in general is a disconnected union of one-dimensional closed curves, which are topologically speaking circles. If the boundary has more than one component, the space becomes multiply connected.

To imagine a curved space one may for instance think of the two-dimensional surface of a sphere or torus as embedded in a three-dimensional flat Euclidean space $\mathbb{R}^3$. If you look at a small neighborhood of any point in these curved spaces S^2 or T^2, you see that locally, it is everywhere like the flat space $\mathbb{R}^2$.

It is only after you enlarge your horizon that it becomes clear that the sphere and the torus are quite different globally from flat space and from each other. Indeed the study of curved spaces descended on us with the insight that the earth turned out to be not flat. Both are globally *compact* meaning that they are finite: it takes a finite amount of paint to cover the two-sphere for example, whereas flat space is infinite and non-compact. Similarly a three-dimensional sphere would have a finite volume.

Spheres and tori are finite spaces, and they also have the property that they have no boundary. Indeed curved spaces can be finite and not have a boundary. Yet, they do have a different *topology*; for example the two-torus has a hole in it while the two-sphere has not. This means that the connectivity properties will differ and this in turn implies that the physics in the one space may exhibit features different from the other.

For two-dimensional manifolds without boundaries (also called closed Riemann surfaces) the number of holes is the only topological invariant characterizing the manifold. A *pretzel* is therefore distinct from a *donut*, not only qua substance and taste but also topologically, as it has two holes.

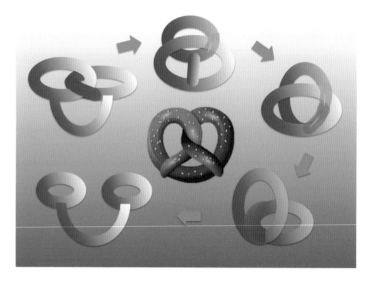

Figure I.2.26: *The pretzel-transformation.* This figure shows in clockwise steps how a self-linked pretzel (top left) can be smoothly unlinked (left bottom). It is a nice example of a topological deformation as prsented by Martin Gardner in his book (1987) on mathematical recreations.

In spite of the pretzel's simplicity its topology is surprisingly counter-intuitive as we have illustrated in Figure I.2.26. One can clearly imagine the left and right parts of the pretzel to be interlinked like the real pretzel in the center and schematically depicted at the top on the left. It appears like yet another two-dimensional closed surface which is topologically distinct with some two holes and a half! Is it really? The answer is: No! There is a well-known smooth topological deformation that corresponds to a smooth unlinking of the pretzel. In the figure we depicted the subsequent steps in the so-called pretzel-transformation which shows how a self-linked pretzel can smoothly be unlinked. I always imagined that this somehow must be of use if you end up in the unfortunate situation of being handcuffed for some reason, for example because of stealing pretzels!

Homotopy. An important topological characteristic is denoted as the *connectivity* of a space, which can be probed

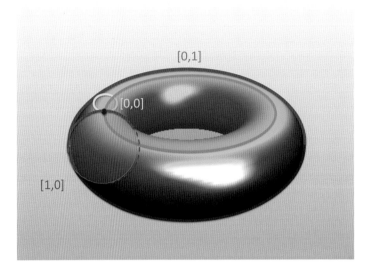

Figure I.2.27: *The two-sphere is simply connected.* If we take a point and consider closed loops starting and ending in that point, all possible loops can be smoothly deformed into each other, and all loops are contractable to the point. There is only one trivial homotopy class, denoted by $[0]$.

Figure I.2.28: *The two-torus is multiply connected.* We have depicted three loops through a point. The yellow one is contractable and belongs to the trivial class $[0,0]$. The green (red) one winds once around the large (small) hole and is non-contractable, and it belongs to the class $[0,1]$ ($[1,0]$).

by studying maps of closed paths or loops into that space. The loops that can be continuously deformed into each other are called *homotopic*. Homotopy is an equivalence relation. Two loops are either homotopic or not. Having such a relation allows you to divide the space of all maps of loops into distinct classes, *homotopy classes* in this case. For example if you draw a closed loop on a sphere, this loop can always be smoothly contracted to a point. The popular wording of this fact is that 'You cannot lasso a basketball.' From Figure I.2.27, we see that all loops on the sphere can indeed be deformed into each other and can smoothly be contracted to a point, so there is only one *homotopy class*, the trivial class denoted by $[0]$.

However, if you look at closed curves on a torus, then there are many possibilities. There are loops that can be simply contracted to a point, then there are loops that wind around the big hole, like the big circle on the outside, or closed curves that wind around that hole an arbitrary number of

times. There are also loops 'perpendicular' to the previous ones, going around the small hole a certain number of times. We have illustrated the situation for the torus in Figure I.2.28, where we have drawn three examples. The yellow loop is contractable and therefore belongs to the trivial class which we denote by $[0,0]$. The green loop encircles the large hole once: it is non-contractable and belongs to the class $[0,1]$. The red loop encircles the small hole once, and cannot be deformed to either of the other two, since it belongs to another class $[1,0]$. In general a loop that winds m times around the small hole, and n times around the big hole belongs to the class $[m,n]$. Think for example of a hiking boot as a closed two-dimensional surface: it may have ten holes for the shoe lace to go through. When I have tied the knot I should have created a closed loop belonging to a non-trivial class.

Having defined and labeled these classes in a systematic way we can go one step further and ask if additional properties can be assigned to them. The first thing that comes to mind is: can we assign an orientation or direction to them. This can be done by putting an arrow on them, and this allows you to assign negative winding numbers.

The first homotopy group. A nice property of closed paths is that we can compose them by connecting the end point of the first loop to the beginning of the second loop and so create a new closed path. This composition rule induces a map, or more precisely a multiplication rule for the homotopy classes: $[...]_1 \odot [...]_2 = [...]_3$. So here we have a set of objects (a set whose elements are classes) that we know how to multiply but there is not such a thing as addition defined. This means that this set forms a *discrete group* where the unit element corresponds to the trivial class of contractable loops, while the inverse element is the class corresponding to the opposite winding number. This group is called the *first homotopy group*, or *fundamental group* and can be determined for any manifold.

A question that may come to mind is: What does this have to do with physics? The answer is: quite a bit. In fact we have already seen examples of it. The notion comes up if you want to discuss line integrals of some field along a closed curves, as we did for example with the vector potential. The loop integral corresponded to the enclosed magnetic field, or the magnetic flux going through the loop. The group structure tells you how these magnetic fluxes 'add.' And as it turns out these fluxes can have highly unexpected composition rules once one studies phases, not of electrodynamics, but of non-abelian gauge theories. These considerations have also important applications in the study of quantum interference effects and the quantum statistics of particles. These are topics we will get to in later chapters of the book.

Higher homotopy groups. In higher dimensions there are more possibilities to consider. For one you may think of higher dimensional holes that correspond to non-contractable maps of higher dimensional spheres into the man-

ifold, and these in turn form higher dimensional homotopy classes. So the second homotopy group tells you how many topologically inequivalent ways there are to map a two-sphere (a closed two-dimensional surface) into the manifold and how those maps can be composed. Finally, the zero-dimensional homotopy classes label the disconnected components the space under consideration.

Coordinate systems. You may wonder why it took so long for mankind to figure out that the Earth's surface we are living on is a space that is not flat but curved. The reason is that on a local scale the world is basically flat and our naive expectations work well as long as you stay nearby. So, if we live in a curved space it has to be a space that is locally like Euclidean space. A space that is everywhere 'locally flat' is a space that we call smooth because we can systematically extend the whole mathematical apparatus of calculus concerning differentiation and integration of functions which we originally defined on flat space. So we may expect to be able to give adapted mathematical descriptions of the physical laws if we move from flat to curved spaces, as relativity tells us to do.

Euclidean space and coordinates. The first question that arises is to choose coordinates on the space. The choice of coordinates are often naturally suggested by the symmetries of the space. You could think that the symmetries generate the whole space from a single point, an 'origin.' For example, flat space has *translation symmetry*, we can move from any point to any other by performing a translation. $\mathbb{R}^n$ has n independent orthogonal directions in which a given point can be moved, and the natural choice for coordinates is therefore the Euclidean coordinate system $\{x_1, x_2, \ldots, x_n\}$.

Curvilinear coordinates. But nobody forces us to use that coordinate system. In fact as soon as we start considering a particular setting in that space, for example, we may single out a particular point as the center of our space. Think of how we used to put the Earth in the center, and

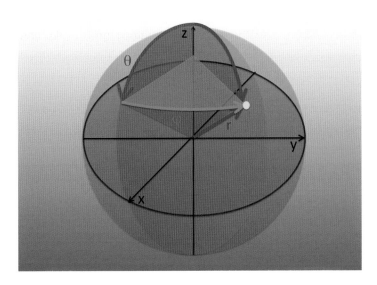

Figure I.2.29: *Spherical coordinates.* The definition of spherical coordinates in $\mathbb{R}^3$, denoted by r, θ, and φ.

after the Copernican revolution we put the Sun in the center and so on. Fixing one point as special, we break the translational symmetry, but still have the *rotational symmetry* which leaves that point fixed. And that symmetry naturally suggests another choice of coordinates, the system of spherical coordinates $\{r, \theta, \varphi\}$, as depicted in Figure I.2.29 . It is as if we think of $\mathbb{R}^3$, as built up of a point plus a continuous stack of concentric spheres around it. Similarly we may want to use cylindrical symmetry with coordinates $\{\rho, z, \varphi\}$, where we think of the space built up from a line with a continuous stack of concentric cylinders around it. And we have already seen that in many physical applications such orthogonal curvilinear coordinate systems are much more convenient; they lead to a convenient framing of the problem that makes it easier to obtain solutions. For example, if I have a current through a straight wire along the z−axis like in Figure I.1.18, the problem becomes cylindrically symmetric, and the magnetic field $\mathbf{B}(\mathbf{x})$ will have only a φ-component that will only depend on the radial coordinate: $\mathbf{B} = \mathrm{B}_\varphi(\rho)\,\hat{\mathbf{e}}^\varphi$.

Spherical coordinates. The observation that we think of

spaces generated by symmetries is useful if one wants to think of typical curved spaces which exhibit those symmetries. Indeed if we think of the three-dimensional rotations just mentioned, and we take an arbitrary point in $\mathbb{R}^3$, that point will indeed trace out a two-sphere, which is a highly symmetric two-dimensional space. So if we 'throw away' the radial coordinate, we are left with an orthogonal coordinate system on the sphere consisting of the two angles, the *polar angle* θ, running from 0 to π and the *azimuthal angle* φ running from 0 to 2π, as we have been using all along. Do these coordinates cover the sphere well? Not really, it turns out.

Coordinate singularities. The north and the south pole are clearly problematic. In these points the coordinate system breaks down, whereas the θ coordinate is well defined, the φ angle is not. There is no sensible way to assign a definite φ angle to the poles. Note that the real geometry of the sphere is completely smooth at those points. The poles are regular points just like any other point on the sphere. The problem is not the space, but the coordinate system we have chosen. To solve this coordinate problem in general one first has to accept that it is not possible to choose a single coordinate system that covers the whole sphere without singularity. There is a topological obstruction to doing that following on from the *hairy ball theorem*. This theorem states the easy to imagine fact that it is not possible to comb a hairy sphere. Just try doing it and you will quickly find out that there is always a point in which the hairs meet in opposite directions. This means that there is no globally defined, non-zero tangent vector field, or conversely, that any vector field on a sphere has to vanish at least in one point. And that fact implies that we cannot have a single globally defined coordinate frame of orthogonal unit vectors on the two-sphere.

Patches or charts. Knowing this fact, the best we can do is to cover the sphere by defining two coordinate *patches* or *charts*, that together cover the sphere and have an overlap so that we can identify points on the two maps that

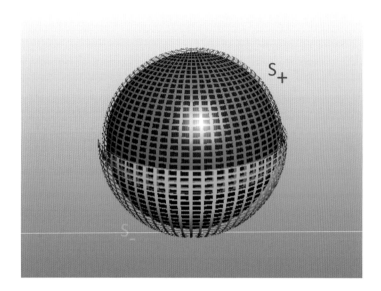

Figure I.2.30: *Two coordinate patches.* The two-sphere is covered by two overlapping coordinate patches $S_\pm$ to avoid coordinate singularities. There is a *transition map* which identifies points (and tangent vectors) in the overlap region. In this case we have $\varphi_+ = \varphi$ and $\varphi_- = -\varphi$. and $\theta_- = \theta_+ = \theta$.

correspond to the same points on the sphere. For example, one may define one patch covering a little more than northern hemisphere and call it S_+, and the other a little more than the southern hemisphere and call it S_-, as indicated in Figure I.2.30. The overlap between the patches is then a narrow band with the equator in the middle. Each patch has the topology of a disc and so we can put a regular coordinate grid on it. Now we can define a *transition map* on the overlap, which provides a map between the coordinate systems in both patches. And this map should be smooth as well. At this point we have succeeded in making an *atlas* of the sphere consisting of two *charts*, each of which can be smoothly mapped onto a flat page by a stereographic projection, which you may have encountered in high school geography classes. This is the way to deal with the complications that arise in defining coordinates on a sphere, and this allows us to globally define smooth functions and their derivatives, to define paths and vectors, all the things physicists and mathematicians

need and love. With this construction we have shown that the two-sphere also is a *differentiable manifold*, a curved space where we can do calculus. A differentiable manifold is a space that is locally like Euclidean space, and globally looks like a smooth patchwork of pieces that are much like flat space, sewn together in a consistent way by a network of smooth transition (sewing or gluing) functions.

Distance and path length. So far we have talked about topological characteristics of manifolds but that leaves the important aspect of form and scale undetermined. How long do I have to walk to get from A to B, that's the question! Mathematicians like to say that to settle it we have to add more structure to the space. In order to introduce the concept of size or distance we have to define a *metric* on the space. In flat space we know that the shortest distance between two points corresponds to the straight line between them. And the distance is calculated by applying the Pythagorean theorem. If we consider any smooth path in flat space, we can calculate its length by successively applying the theorem to infinitesimal segments of the path and adding the results. If the points are nearby, we have for the distance ds, that $ds^2 = dx^2 + dy^2$. If we start by defining a smooth *path* as a one-parameter curve $\gamma(t) = \{x_\mu(t)\}$, the *tangent vector* to the curve at the point $x(t_0) = \gamma(t_0)$ is just like the 'velocity' vector $\mathbf{v}(t) = dx/dt|_{t_0}$. The length L_{ab} of the curve between two points $\gamma(a)$ and $\gamma(b)$ is now quite naturally defined as the integral:

$$L_{ab} \equiv \int_a^b |\mathbf{v}(t)| dt \, . \qquad (I.2.15)$$

in a different, more familiar wording, the distance traveled is just the magnitude of the velocity integrated along the path over the appropriate time interval. It is this notion of path length that we like to generalize to curved spaces.

Metric and line element. To calculate the path length in a curved space we need a local definition for the infinitesimal distance ds which specifies the local (x-dependent) definition of an infinitesimal length. Once we have chosen

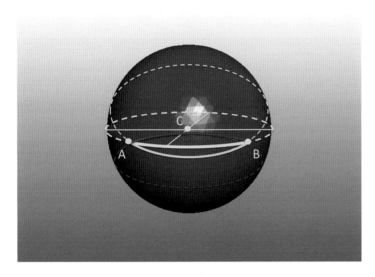

Figure I.2.31: *Shortest distance.* The shortest path between two points A and B on the sphere is given by the segment of the yellow 'great circle' which is defined as the intersection of the plane through A, B, and the center of the sphere C, and the surface of the sphere. The blue and red circles are smaller and yet yield longer paths between the points A and B.

coordinates $\{x_i\}$ on the space, where i runs from 1 to d, the dimension of space, then we formally define the so-called *line element* ds as:

$$ds^2 = g_{ij}(\mathbf{x})dx^i\,dx^j \qquad (I.2.16)$$

where the symmetric matrix $g_{ij}(\mathbf{x})$ is the so-called *metric tensor*. In flat space we saw that $ds^2 = dx^2 + dy^2$ and the metric thus corresponds to the unit matrix everywhere. If we choose polar coordinates r and φ, the line element would be $ds^2 = dr^2 + r^2 d\varphi^2$, and the metric a diagonal matrix $(1, r^2)$.

If we put a symmetric mass distribution around the origin, then the space would be curved as we illustrated in Figure I.2.4, where the two-dimensional surface embedded in $\mathbb{R}^3$ would be defined by fixing $z = f(r)$ with a function f interpolating between some constant $f(0) = -a$ and $f(r \to \infty) = 0$. The radial length measured along

the suface will now change, and indeed the metric would change in that $g_{rr} = 1 + (df/dr)^2$. The metric on the two-dimensional surface is *induced* from the trivial metric on $\mathbb{R}^3$ by substituting $dz = (df/dr)\,dr$.

It is important to realize that in principle there are many possible choices for the metric on a manifold, the only restriction being that it is smooth and compatible with the topology of the space. These choices lead to different geometries in the sense of distances, geodesics etc. In the case of the S^2 example we can make the 'natural' choice of metric as we did just before by inducing it from the standard everyday metric in the space $\mathbb{R}^3$ in which we have embedded the two-sphere. Squashing the sphere would naturally change the metric. What makes that choice natural is that our visual intuitions on vectors and path-length and angles still make complete sense.

Shortest distances: geodesics. We now are in a position to answer the question of what the shortest path between two points on a sphere is. That will again be the path along which photons and free particles living on S^2 would travel. Just like the route your child would presumably take on their way to the nearest two-dimensional ice-cream parlour. We will answer this question in more detail later, but let us first get a feeling and an intuitive idea of the solution. In Figure I.2.31 I have marked two points A and B on the surface, and drawn various paths between them, each of them corresponds to a segment of a circle on the surface. It is evident from the drawing that the bright yellow connection in the middle is the shortest, and it corresponds to a segment of the equator. The other paths are also segments of circles, but what sets the yellow one apart is that it is a segment of a 'great circle,' a circle of maximum size on the sphere whose radius equals the radius of the sphere itself. Great circles are defined as the intersection of a plane through the centre of the sphere (the point C in the figure) and the spherical surface. These great circles are so-called *geodesics* on the space S^2, and correspond to what straight lines are on the plane, they correspond to the trajectories of free particles like photons. Shortly we will discuss the equations that geodesics have to satisfy.

Vectors on curved spaces.

> And the curved space said: 'Vectors don't live here anymore.'

Tangent space. Assuming that physicists are also living on that sphere, they need vectors to describe what's going on: momentum vectors, forces, electric fields, and also quantum states. On a sphere, those vectors cannot live 'in the space' itself, because the sphere is not a vector space. In a curved space the notion of a 'position vector' makes no longer sense. To stay close to our flat space experience we do the following: to define a vector at some point on the sphere, we first construct the tangent plane to the surface at that point, and then put the vector there. Because the tangent space is a copy of R^2 we can add, subtract and take products of vectors there. So we attach a vector space to every point on the sphere. If we have a well-defined system orthogonal curvilinear coordinates, then locally, in any point x we can construct a set of orthonormal tangent vectors along the coordinate axes, and those define a smooth (othonormal) *frame* at any point in the patch. Having a set of smooth transition functions allows us to extend such frames over the whole manifold.

Parallel transport of vectors. Knowing how to deal with vectors at every point in space is not enough. We want to compare vectors at different points, and we want to move them around. We need to 'parallel transport' the vectors or frames from one tangent space to another. The question we are now equipped to answer is: what happens if we do the exercise with the Master Chef we did in 'flatland' before?

We put three people standing at the corners of a spherical triangle, then we draw the shortest paths between them

and ask the apprentice, the messenger, to bring copies of the Chef's vector around. What happens is depicted in the Figure I.2.32. The instruction is the same, in the point on the geodesic we first construct the vector tangent to the curve, which lies in the tangent space of the point. The Chef's vector to be transported makes a well-defined angle with the tangent vector. Parallel transport is now defined by keeping the angle between these two vectors constant while moving forward along the geodesics. The result of carefully parallel transporting a vector along the triangle is depicted in Figure I.2.32(d). On the first segment of the triangle the angle is 0, on the second segment it is $\pi/2$, and on the third it is π. It seems to work fine, except that when the apprentice returns to the Chef, the boss is furious. It is not hard to see why. Comparing the initial and final, parallel transported vector, we see that they are not parallel at all! The transported vector has rotated over an angle of $\pi/2$. The apprentice is shocked: how could this have happened? He did after all perfectly follow the instructions all along, oh my! But the Chef is unrelenting: 'You are fired! Out through the backdoor you fool!'

Holonomy. What we may learn from this mini-drama becomes clear when we turn the story around. It is apparently simple to find out whether you live in a curved space, without stepping outside into the embedding space; it suffices to just walk around some closed paths and parallel transport a vector along with you, and see wether it is rotated upon return. So each closed path on the manifold induces a map of the tangent space onto itself which corresponds to a rotation. This intrinsic property of a space is called *holonomy* and an important characteristic of curved spaces. For the example at hand we see that the vector is rotated by an amount that equals the solid angle bounded by the loop. The total area of a sphere is $4\pi r^2$, so 4π for the unit sphere. And indeed, the triangle covers the area (or solid angle) of an octant which equals $4\pi/8 = \pi/2$. It is easy to check that this solid angle-holonomy correspondence also holds for other simple closed paths. If we for example extend the triangle by moving the two points

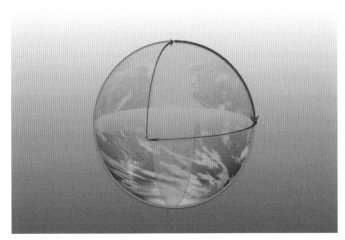

(a) Rotations generate translations on the two-sphere S^2. Triangle on curved space has more than $180°$.

(b) Vectors at a point in a curved space live in the tangent space ($\sim \mathbb{R}^2$) at that point.

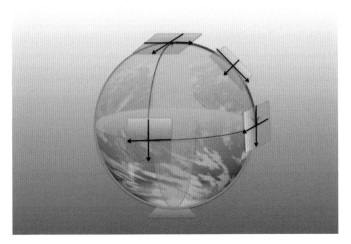

(c) Carrying a frame around a triangle on a sphere.

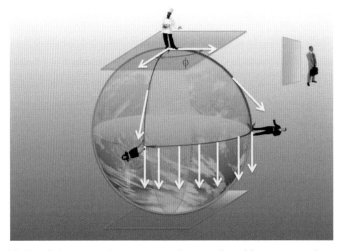

(d) Parallel transporting a vector along a closed loop on a sphere rotates the vector.

Figure I.2.32: *The geometry underlying the tangent bundle of* S^2. Using the equivalence of S^3 with a line bundle over the two-sphere. Moving a point over S^3 is the same as carrying a tangent vector over S^2.

on the equator southwards to the South Pole, we obtain a non-trivial *two-angle* (!). Going around this two-angle will yield a holonomy of π as it should. A more general way to state the result is to say that for any closed loop in any curved space the holonomy equals the net curvature on any surface bounded by the loop, after proper normalization. As the (scalar) curvature of a sphere is a constant that equals 2, the curvature enclosed in the loop is then

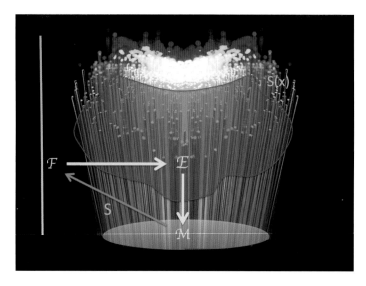

Figure I.2.33: *An optical fiber bundle.* A bundle of optical fibers, each like a finite light ray, isomorphic to the unit interval: $\mathcal{F} = [0, 1]$. The base manifold $\mathcal{M}$ is just a finite disk with a circular boundary. Every fiber can be projected down to a point in the base manifold. This bundle is 'trivial' in the sense that the bundle space is just global product, $\mathcal{E} = \mathcal{M} \times \mathcal{F}$.

equal to two times the solid angle.

Fiber bundles. In a proper description of many physical systems the most basic ingredients are some space(-time) manifold $\mathcal{M}$ that may or may not be curved, and there will be certain physical variables like temperature, a fluid flow, or whatever one is interested in. We assign functions (or fields) to those variables. For the temperature we define a function $T = T(x)$ which is a map from the base manifold to the real numbers: $T : \mathcal{M} \to \mathbb{R}$. For the velocity field this would be a vector field (also called a vector-valued function) $\mathbf{v}(x)$ which you can think of as a map $v : \mathcal{M} \to \mathbb{R}^3$.

Let us now introduce an upgraded setting for the previous paragraph, and start with a big space $\mathcal{E} = \mathcal{M} \times \mathbb{R}^n$. So the space looks very much like a bundle of fibers $F = \mathbb{R}^n$ because above any point $x \in \mathcal{M}$ we have erected a copy of the fiber. Now a function on $\mathcal{M}$ which takes its values in

$\mathbb{R}^n$ can be viewed as taking a cross-section of the bundle. In other words, giving $S(x)$ corresponds to drawing some curved surface above $\mathcal{M}$ that intersects with every fiber only once. Figure I.2.33 gives an intuitive idea of such a fiber bundle. We start with a *base manifold* $\mathcal{M}$, the physical space. In this case the base manifold is a simple two-dimensional disc. Above each point of $x \in \mathcal{M}$ we erect a *fiber* $\mathcal{F}_x$ which is isomorphic to the reference fiber (drawn on the left) and in this case is a finite ray of unit length. The fibers $\mathcal{F}_x$ in $\mathcal{E}$ are transformed images of the reference fiber. In the picture we also show local (x-dependent) map $S(x) : \mathcal{M} \to \mathcal{F}$. Such a map $S(x)$ is called a *section* of the bundle, indeed we obtain a deformed surface above $\mathcal{M}$ which is literally a cross-section of $\mathcal{E}$. In this particular example there is a smooth map from $\mathcal{E} \to \mathcal{M} \times \mathcal{F}$ from the bundle space to the global product of base and fiber, which means that the bundle is trivial.

More generally, if we think of the base manifold $\mathcal{M}$ as the space or space-time manifold, then we usually define all kinds of fields $f(x, t)$ on it. These fields often take values in some vector space $\mathcal{V}$ or an algebra, meaning that we have a map $f : \mathcal{M} \to \mathcal{F}$. A natural setting to describe both the space $\mathcal{M}$ and such a function on it is to extend the manifold to a *fiber bundle* $\mathcal{E}$, which locally for any neighbourhood $U_i \subset \mathcal{M}$ has a direct product structure $U_i \times \mathcal{F}$. The point is now that globally this is not necessarily the case. It may be that a basis cannot be extended smoothly over all of $\mathcal{M}$; In such a situation the fiber bundle framework is very powerful and versatile.

Let us illustrate this difference with another simple example. Consider the case where the base manifold M is a circle, $M = S^1$, and the fiber $\mathcal{F}$ the unit interval $\mathcal{F} = I = \{0 \le y \le 1\}$. The 'trivial bundle' would be a cylinder, corresponding to the global direct product $\mathcal{E} = S^1 \times I$. But we could also identify the fibers as $(\varphi = 0, y) \sim (\varphi = 2\pi, 1 - y)$, in which case we get a *Möbius band*. This band has locally the same structure as the cylinder, which means that if you only were allowed to explore your direct

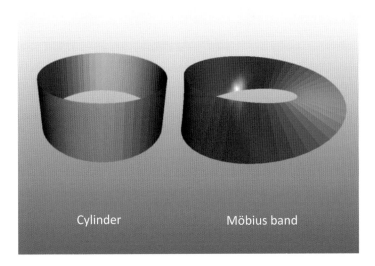

Figure I.2.34: *The Möbius band.* We have depicted the trivial bundle over the circle with the unit interval as fiber, which is a cylinder. The tangent bundle of the circle corresponds to an infinite cylinder: $\mathcal{E} = S^1 \times \mathbb{R}$. On the right we give the topologically non-trivial bundle corresponding to the Möbius band.

neighbourhood, you would not be able to decide whether you lived on a cylinder or on a Möbius band. But globally the situations are very different, walking along the inside, you end up on the outside and vice versa. In other words there is no such thing as an inside or outside as they are smoothly connected. The Möbius band is a non-orientable manifold with a single boundary. We have illustrated the trivial cylinder and the non-trivial, 'twisted' Möbius band in Figure I.2.34. The bundle picture allowed us to clearly set apart two spaces that are locally the same but globally (topologically) different. The cylinder is a two-dimensional flat space in that it needs only one coordinate patch, it has an inside and an outside separated by two one-dimensional boundaries. It is topologically like a disc with the origin taken out; it has no hole and two boundaries. If you live on the inside and your relevant-other on the outside, than that is bad news because you cannot run into each other. Remarkably, on the Möbius band that problem is non-existent.

This simple example gives a hint as to how natural and powerful the geometrical construct of a fiber bundle is. Exactly because for the base space and the fiber there are very many choices, and each of them gives rise to a sub-category of bundles with their own specific properties. You will find that there is a great variety: *line bundles, vector bundles, principle bundles, tangent bundles, frame bundles,* and many others. This world has vigorously been explored by the mathematicians, and they have developed a beautiful and rigorous framework in which many physical applications can be embedded. Books have been written about the subject and it is not our goal to delve too deeply into it, except to explore its relevance to the physics subjects treated in this book.

Tangent bundles.

As we mentioned already, to have parallel transport and have a proper definition of distance on a curved manifold, we need extra ingredients. Having the coordinate patches with transition functions, we can draw continuous curves and parallel transport vectors. With these attributes we cannot only construct a tangent space at every point of our base manifold $\mathcal{M}$, but we can also define what is called the *tangent bundle* of $\mathcal{M}$. The tangent bundle is a smooth $2n$-dimensional manifold $\mathcal{E}$, which consists of $\mathcal{M}$ and all its tangent spaces. It has the structure of a *fiber bundle*, because above every point x of the base manifold $x \in \mathcal{M}$ of dimension n, we have erected a fiber $\mathcal{F}$ which is a copy of the tangent space $\mathbb{R}^n$. This bundle itself is a smooth manifold of dimension $2n$. For flat space $\mathcal{M} = \mathbb{R}^n$ the bundle space would just be $\mathcal{E} = \mathbb{R}^n \times \mathbb{R}^n = \mathbb{R}^{2n}$. And as we saw for the circle, the tangent bundle is just a two-dimensional (infinite) cylinder: $\mathcal{E} = S^1 \times \mathbb{R}$, it is the global direct product and therefore a trivial bundle.

The S^2 tangent bundle. The construction of the tangent bundle of S^2 is more complicated because it is topologically non-trivial. The two-sphere and various local tangent planes are sketched in Figure I.2.35, where we have also

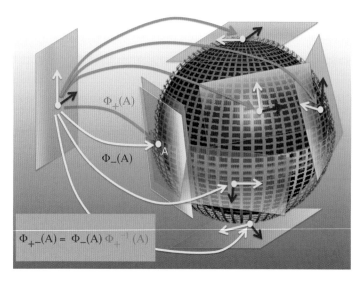

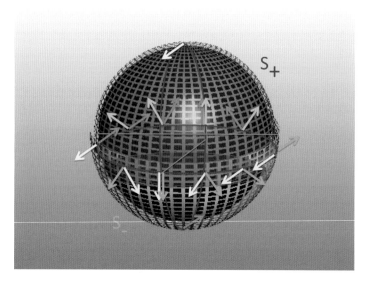

Figure I.2.35: *Tangent bundle of* S^2. The *base manifold* is the two-sphere. The *fibers* are just copies of $\mathbf{R}^2$. We have indicated the *ortho-normal frames* which are rotated with respect to a reference frame on the left. The *structure group* of the otho-normal frame bundle is just the group of rotations in the two-dimensional plane, denoted as $SO(2)$. We have indicated the transition map from the tangent frames referring to the two patches in the point $x = A$.

Figure I.2.36: *Transition map of coordinates and frames.* The two-sphere covered by two coordinate patches $S_\pm$, We have parallel transported a vector from the North Pole along the light blue meridians in S_+ and from the South Pole in S_- to points on the equator. Going around the equator we see that the white vectors rotate clockwise and the pink vectors anti-clockwise by an angle $\beta_\pm = \pm\varphi$. This yields the transition function $\Delta = \beta_+ - \beta_- = 2\varphi$. The topology of the tangent bundle is therefore non-trivial and has winding number $m = 2$.

shown how each fiber is related to the standard plane by some map $\Phi(\theta, \varphi)$. This map basically tells you how the basis for the fiber as vector space in each point on the sphere is rotated with respect to some reference frame. So Φ corresponds to the angle by which the frame is rotated. It means that in general in this construction of the tangent (or simpler: the related otho-normal frame bundle) there is always a rotation group involved. This map is smooth on each patch, and one obtains the transition function to go from the frame for S_+ to one for S_- at a point x in the overlap, by applying the product map $\Phi_{+-}(x) = \Phi_-(x)\,\Phi_+(x)^{-1}$. Now why is this bundle non-trivial? This is the question we turn to next.

To find out whether the bundle is trivial we focus on the transition map or gluing function in the overlap region. The result is depicted in Figure I.2.36. We start by choosing the

white vector (but think of it as a frame) on the North Pole and transport it along the meridians down to the equator, there the transported white vectors are found to make an angle $\beta_+(\varphi) = \varphi$ with respect to the vector at $\varphi = 0$ (parallel transported along the equator to the tangent space at the same point). Subsequently we carry the vector at $\varphi = 0$ on its meridian all the way south, resulting in the pink colored vector at the South Pole. And from there we transport that pink vector upward along all the meridians in S_- again to the equator, yielding the pink vectors making an angle $\beta_- = -\varphi$, with the pink vector transported from $\varphi = 0$. What we have constructed is a globally smooth *section* of the frame bundle. The frames in the overlap region (the equator) on the two patches differ, and are related by a local rotation in the respective tangent planes. We see that the transition function corresponds to a transition angle $\Delta(\varphi)$, which satisfies $\Delta(\varphi) = 2\varphi$. If we walk full-circle around on the equator once then the angle $\Delta(2\pi) = 4\pi$, has gone around twice. This means that the bundle is topologically non-trivial, because it is similar to the non-trivial twist of the Möbius band, but we here have a relative winding number $m = 2$.

Let us lift this discussion to the n-dimensional spheres S^n. The bundle is an example of a frame bundle, this bundle is linked to the group of rotations (denoted by $SO(n)$) that maps all possible ortho-normal frame choices for the tangent spaces $\mathbb{R}^n$ into each other. We cover the sphere by two overlapping disc-like patches, then the overlap is a sphere S^{n-1} times the interval. Then the transition function is a map from the overlap region into the group $SO(n-1)$. If this map is contractible, meaning that its homotopy class is trivial, then the bundle is topologically trivial.

For the two-sphere we had a transition map from the equator with coordinate φ to the frame group $SO(2)$, which is also a circle, parametrized by the angle Δ. These classes of such maps are labeled by the elements of the first homotopy group $\pi_1(SO(2)) = \pi_1(S^1) = \mathbb{Z}$, the integer $n \in \mathbb{Z}$ is often called the winding number. This means that $\Delta(2\pi) = 2\pi n$ and for the frame bundle of the two-sphere we found $n = 2$. This winding number is a topological invariant that characterizes the bundle in question. We can now also answer the corresponding question for the three-sphere, this boils down to a mapping of the two-sphere (the 'equator') into the group $SO(3)$ of three-frames. The homotopy group in question, $\pi_2(SO(3)) = 0$. So the group has only one element, which means that all the maps are contractible from which we conclude that this frame bundle is trivial. And this in turn means that the three-sphere is 'parallelizable.'

There is one other observation we want to make, which links this frame bundle of the two-sphere to the bundle that we studied in connection with the Dirac magnetic monopole.

Let us recall that for the monopole we basically dealt with two vector potentials $A_\pm$ defined on two patches on the two-sphere, linked by a gauge transformation.[5] In other words we considered a map from the equator (S^1) into the gauge group of electrodynamics (which is the group phase group $U(1)$ which also corresponds to a circle: $U(1) \simeq SO(2) \simeq S^1$). We gave the explicit formula for that map $\Delta(\varphi) = \varphi$ in equation (I.1.57), meaning that the winding number for the monopole bundle equals $n = 1$.

The bundle space $\mathcal{E}$ in the monopole case corresponds to the manifold S^3, interpreted as a S^1 or phase bundle over S^2. The bundle is exactly the one described by Hopf in 1931. As we will point out in Chapter II.1, also the quantum state space of a single *qubit* corresponds to such a three sphere.

What we have learned is that the monopole and frame bundle are both realizations of a circle bundle over the two-sphere, but they are topologically distinct because they have winding numbers equal one and two respectively. The bundles with higher winding numbers correspond for example to multiply charged Dirac monopoles satisfying $eg = 2\pi n$. But the most gratifying is perhaps that in spite of their quite different physical origins these two situations could be related within the framework of fiber bundles.

Differential geometry.
In this section we have demonstrated that for most physics applications which involve geometry we need extra structure on the manifold which allows us to properly define functions and their derivatives or integrals, and of vectors and vector fields. The structural ingredients we need are a *metric*, a *connection* or *covariant derivative*, and a definition of the *curvature* tensor. This takes us to the basic definitions of Riemannian or more generally of *differential geometry*.

---

[5] We talk about the concentric spherical shells for a fixed radius larger than zero.

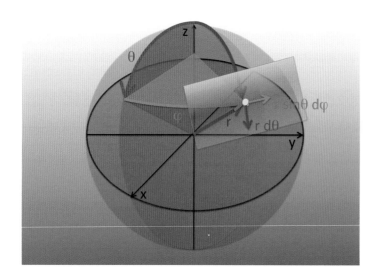

Figure I.2.37: *The geometry of the sphere.* The yellow point has spherical coordinates (r, θ, φ). The length of the equator (red circle in xy-plane) on the sphere equals $2\pi r$. The red and blue arcs therefore have equal lengths $s_r = s_b = r\theta$; with angle expressed in radians $(2\pi \text{ radians} = 360^\circ)$. The green-colored segment of a horizontal spherical disc with radius $a = r\sin\theta$. For the length of the green arc follows $s_g = \varphi r \sin\theta$.

Metric. We introduced the metric with the definition of the line element in equation (I.2.16), which in general reads:

$$ds^2 = g_{\mu\nu}dx^\mu dx^\nu \qquad (I.2.17)$$

The metric is a symmetric 'tensor' with two indices which you can think of as a matrix $g_{\mu\nu}$ depending on $\mathbf{x}$,

The metric also gives a local definition of the length $|v|$ of a vector v^μ in the tangent space at a point $\mathbf{x}$ as follows:

$$|v|^2 = \mathbf{v} \cdot \mathbf{v} = g_{\mu\nu}v^\mu v^\nu = v_\mu v^\mu, \qquad (I.2.18)$$

where in the expressions we have adopted the standard convenient 'Einstein convention,' which says that if in any expression with repeated upper- and lower indices, these are automatically summed over, so, $v_\mu v^\mu \equiv \sum_\mu v_\mu v^\mu$.

For example on a two-sphere with radius r with coordinates (θ, φ) the standard metric has two non-vanishing

components: $g_{\theta\theta} = r^2$ and $g_{\varphi\varphi} = r^2 \sin^2\theta$. The line element ds follows from:

$$ds^2 = g_{\mu\nu}dx^\mu dx^\nu = r^2(d\theta^2 + \sin^2\theta d\varphi^2) \qquad (I.2.19)$$

Looking at Figure I.2.37 it is not hard to see why. You may verify that, (i) for φ fixed the arc or path length on the sphere corresponding to an angular displacement $d\theta$, corresponds to $r\,d\theta$ (as θ runs along a big circle), (ii) for fixed θ, the path length corresponding to the angular displacement $d\varphi$, equals $r\sin\theta\,d\varphi$ (as the φ variable runs along a 'lateral' circle with radius $r\sin\theta$). What this means is the following: if we change the coordinate φ for an arbitrary point on the sphere by an infinitesimal amount $d\varphi$ then the length of the corresponding displacement vector is $ds = r\sin\theta d\varphi$. So the metric tensor locally links infinitesimal changes in coordinates to infinitesimal path lengths in the space.

Path length. The length L_{ab} of the curve $\gamma(t)$ parametrized by t, between two points $\gamma(a)$ and $\gamma(b)$ is naturally defined as the integral:

$$L_{ab} \equiv \int_a^b |v(t)|dt, \qquad (I.2.20)$$

in a different more familiar wording, the distance traveled is just the magnitude of the velocity component along the trajectory integrated over the appropriate time interval. So for example if we choose the lateral green circle (with θ constant) in Figure I.2.37 , we would have $\gamma(t) = \{\theta, \varphi(t)\}$:

$$L = \int r\sin\theta \frac{d\varphi}{dt} dt = r(\varphi(b) - \varphi(a))\sin\theta, \qquad (I.2.21)$$

as it should.

Frames. We like to mention that there is a slightly different formulation for dealing with Riemannian geometry due to Cartan. This formulation is close to the standard form in which gauge theories of the non-gravitational interactions are presented. We start by introducing an ortho-normal basis or frame in the tangent space by writing:

$$g_{\mu\nu} \equiv \eta_{ab} e_\mu^a e_\nu^b, \qquad (I.2.22)$$

where η_{ab} is the usual flat space metric (or inner-product), and the funny objects e_μ^a are the so-called *solder forms* or *'vielbeine'* that convert vectors from the curvilinear coordinate components to the 'flat' components. So for the spherical surface we could simply choose $e_\theta^1 = r$ and $e_\varphi^2 = r\sin\theta$ and all others equal zero. These define what is called a local orthonormal frame $\{e^a\} \equiv \{e_\mu^a \, dx^\mu\}$.

With these definitions the inner product can be rewritten as:

$$\mathbf{v} \cdot \mathbf{w} = g_{\mu\nu}v^\mu w^\nu = \eta_{ab} e_\mu^a e_\nu^b v^\mu w^\nu = \eta_{ab}v^a w^b, \quad (I.2.23)$$

with the flat space vector components defined as $v^a \equiv e_\mu^a v^\mu$.

Connection. Given the metric g or the frame $\{e\}$ we define the so-called metric connection ω, which written in components would read $\omega_\mu{}^a{}_b$, meaning that it is like a space(time) (row) vector and acts like a matrix in '$a - b$' space. This connection is defined by the linear set of equations:[6]:

$$d e + \omega \wedge e = 0. \qquad (I.2.24)$$

Specifying the metric, the metric connection or the set of 'vielbeine' are equivalent characterizations of the manifold. Knowing the frame $\{e\}$, one can solve equation (I.2.24) for the connection in terms of the vielbeine and their derivatives. For the two-sphere the result for the connection is simply $\omega_\varphi{}^1{}_2 = -\cos\theta$. Note that it has two flat indices and therefore it acts like a matrix in flat space. We introduce the connection ω_μ, because it is similar to the gauge potential A_μ in gauge theory. The gauge transformations in the case of general relativity would correspond to *local* orthogonal (or Lorentz transfomations) rotations of the

frame that leave the metric in other words the angles and lengths of vectors invariant,

$$e'^a = \Omega^a{}_b e^b. \qquad (I.2.25)$$

Curvature. To complete this lightning review of non-Euclidean or Riemannian geometry, we have to add a final ingredient, which is the Riemann *curvature tensor* or two-form R , which is the strict analogue of the 'field strength' F in gauge theories. It can be calculated from the connection as follows:

$$R = d\omega + \omega \wedge \omega. \qquad (I.2.26)$$

This Riemann curvature is an object with four indices. We will refrain from descending any further in this myriad of indices except for at least giving the result for the two-sphere. There is basically only one component that is non-zero: $R^1{}_2 = R^1{}_{212}\, e^1 \wedge e^2 = \frac{1}{r^2} e^1 \wedge e^2$. From this Riemann curvature one finds the Gaussian curvature as $R_G \equiv R_{abab} = 2/r^2$. We say that the Gaussian curvature of the sphere is constant. It does not depend where you are on the sphere, it only depends on the radius of the sphere. If that radius becomes large the curvature tends to zero. In other words the space becomes effectively flat.

The main point of this subsection is to show that the analytical structure of differential geometry is highly canonical. It involves three subsequent defining equations: it involves three subsequent defining equations: (i) for the metric (I.2.22) or the frame, (ii) for the connection in terms of the frame (I.2.24) and (iii) for the curvature in terms of the connection (I.2.26). Our aim is *not* to make any real computations but merely to get across that at this level of analysis it is evident that general relativity and gauge theories share an underlying geometric structure. Roughly stated, both involve a connection and a curvature defined in terms involving derivatives of the connection.

The geodesic equation. Geodesics are the paths along which free particles move. We have asked what the shortest path between two points is on a sphere and found it

---

[6]We use the quite compact index free notation because it makes the underlying structure more transparent. With indices the above equation would look quite daunting: $\partial_\mu e_\nu^a - \partial_\nu e_\mu^a + \omega_\mu{}^a{}_b \, e_\nu^b - \omega_\nu{}^a{}_b \, e_\mu^b = 0$.

to be a segment of a great circle. In general that question can be answered by minimizing the path length L_{ab} under variations of the path. From the metric one can directly construct a free particle Lagrangian, which is a function of the coordinates and their time derivatives:

$$\mathcal{L}(x^{\mu}, \frac{dx^{\mu}}{dt}) = \frac{1}{2} m g_{\mu\nu} \frac{dx^{\mu}}{dt} \frac{dx^{\nu}}{dt}$$
$$= \frac{1}{2} m r^2 ((\frac{d\theta}{dt})^2 + \sin^2 \theta (\frac{d\varphi}{dt})^2)$$
$$= \frac{1}{2} m r^2 (v_{\theta}^2 + v_{\varphi}^2) \tag{I.2.27}$$

Minimizing the time integral of $\mathcal{L} \sim |v|^2$ (instead of L_{ab}) one obtains the so-called Euler-Lagrange equations. On the two-sphere one obtains:

$$\frac{d}{dt} (\frac{d\theta}{dt}) - \cos \theta \sin \theta (\frac{d\varphi}{dt})^2 = 0 \,,$$
$$\frac{d}{dt} (\sin^2 \theta \frac{d\varphi}{dt}) = 0 \,. \tag{I.2.28}$$

These are the Newtonian equations of motion for a particle on a sphere in the absence of an external force as discussed in the section on Newtonian mechanics in Chapter I.1. All terms have two time derivatives, among them are the pure 'accelerations' in the θ and φ directions. There is no potential as such and the extra terms that appear are a consequence of spherical geometry. So like in flat space, where a force would typically curve the orbit, and straight lines (describing shortest distances) are obtained by setting the force equal zero, something similar is true in curved spaces where free particles move along *geodesics* and they do independently of their mass or momentum.

Let us check a few simple solutions. For example, if we assume that the velocity component in the φ direction, $\sin \theta d\varphi/dt$ vanishes, we obtain the solutions $d\theta/dt = constant$. These describe a particle moving with constant velocity along any meridian (where $\varphi = constant$). This shows that the meridians are indeed shortest paths. Choosing $d\theta/dt = 0$, on the other hand, gives the solution, $\theta = \pi/2$, $d\varphi/dt = constant$, which corresponds to

the particle moving with constant velocity along the equator, again a 'big' circle or geodesic.

These calculations confirm our previous observations with respect to the Figures I.2.31 and I.2.32, where we saw that the shortest path between two points is always a segment of a great circle. That allowed us to also draw a triangle on the sphere as we did in Figure I.2.32, and what we see is that the triangle has three $90°$ angles. In other words that the sum of the three angles of this triangle is $270°$ which is far more than the $180°$ of a planar triangle. It is amusing to note that if you move the two lower points of the triangle to the South Pole, you get a non-trivial 'two-angle.'

Let us finally note also that all shortest paths from the North to the South Pole, in other words all meridians, are in fact 'parallel,' because they all are perpendicular to the equator. Indeed, in a curved space 'parallel lines' may cross. Boy! Yet another reason why life on Earth is so complicated. My devise would be, be prepared: think global and act local, rather than the other way around. ■ ■

The geometry of gauge invariance

A gauge theory is the prototype model for all fundamental interactions, where the gauge field may either describe the *electromagnetic field* corresponding to the *photon*, or the fields mediating the strong interactions corresponding to 8 *gluons*, or the weak interactions described by the $W^{\pm}$ and Z *bosons*, and finally it may describe general relativity corresponding to the gravitational interaction mediated by the *graviton*. The gauge symmetry principle is therefore a fundamental and universal hallmark of nature. Gauge invariance imposes a strong constraint on the system of fields involved. In particular it completely fixes how the *force carrying fields* just mentioned interact with the *'charge' carrying fields* or constituent particles like the the electon, the muon, the neutrinos or the quarks. On the other hand this physically based gauge principle is deeply linked to the geometry of fiber bundles of which the tangent bundle we discussed is only one example.

The topic of gauge invariance will pop up in this book at regular intervals. Here we give some of the mathematical background of the gauge principle which corresponds to the geometry of fiber bundles. In Chapter I.4 on the quest for the basic building blocks of matter we discuss how the gauge theory approach has led to the standard model of the fundamental interactions between elementary particles. And in Chapter II.6 on symmetries and their breaking we describe in more detail what the equations for gauge theories look like and how they implement the idea of a local gauge invariant dynamics.

The charge degree of freedom. To get a better feeling for the notion of charge and its connection to gauge invariance it may help to explicitly introduce a model for electric charge. Think of particles carrying an extra periodic coordinate β that labels points in some 'internal space' that in this case corresponds to a tiny circle. You may think of β in that sense as an extra charge degree of freedom, and the charge $q = ne$ as a kind of momentum in this internal electromagnetic dimension with coordinate β. The particle carries along a charge-phase factor

$$f_n(\beta, x) = e^{in\beta(x)}. \qquad (I.2.29)$$

If we split this phase factor in its real and imaginary parts by writing it as $\cos n\beta + i \sin n\beta$, we represent the phase factor as a little two-dimensional unit vector making an angle $n\beta$ with the real (horizontal) axis.[7] Note that if we vary β from 0 to 2π, then the phase of the particle with charge number n changes by $2\pi n$, so the corresponding little vector rotates n times as fast.

You may say that the charge-number corresponds to the

---

[7]If you are unfamiliar with the notion of a complex phase factor you might want to look at the *Math Excursion* on complex numbers at the end of Part III on page 630.

'momentum" in the β direction because it is proportional to the beta derivative $-ie\partial_\beta f_n = q\, f$, and as there is no β-dependent potential or force, the β-momentum (= charge) is conserved. The dynamics in beta-space is therefore entirely trivial and that is precisely why nobody talks about it in the first place. But it at least explains the terminology that charge corresponds to an *internal degree of freedom*. I think that it is also quite helpful for getting a better understanding of the notion of gauge invariance. And moreover, if we would treat this little charge-degree of freedom as a quantum particle on a circle, the momentum (= charge) would be quantized as well. It would look like the Bohr model applied to the quantization of charge.

Gauge transformations. The best way to think about (local) gauge transformation is as a position- and time- dependent rotation, not in real space but in some internal vector space, that is carried by each of the matter fields. To clarify this let me return to electromagnetism. Another way to look at the local charge-phase factor we introduced is that it is the phase of a field $\Phi(x) = f_n(x)\phi(x)$ having a charge $q = ne$. In quantum theory a particle with charge $q = ne$ is described by a complex wavefunction $\Phi(x) = f_n(x)\phi(x)$, and $f_n(x)$ represents the local phase of that wavefunction and the function $\phi(x)$ its magnitude. Formally a gauge transformation acts on the fields (in fact on the phase factor) as follows:

$$f_n \to f_n' = U_n f_n \quad \text{with}: \ U_n(\Lambda) \equiv e^{in\Lambda(x)}. \qquad (I.2.30)$$

The transformation U_n corresponds to a unitary representation of the group $U(1)$ labeled by the integer $n \in \mathbb{Z}$. It is unitary because $U^*U = U^{-1}U = \mathbf{1}$. And the gauge group of the theory is therefore naturally called $U(1)$, because a phase factor can be thought of as a (1×1) unitary matrix. If you prefer to talk about the little vector, then you should refer to the gauge group $SO(2)$, the group of rotations in the two-dimensional plane, but that group is the same as (or isomorphic to) $U(1)$ because its elements are also labeled by an angle.

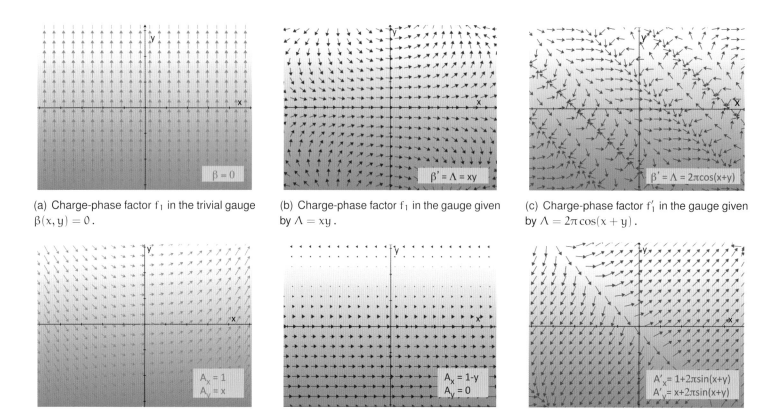

(a) Charge-phase factor f_1 in the trivial gauge $\beta(x, y) = 0$.

(b) Charge-phase factor f_1 in the gauge given by $\Lambda = xy$.

(c) Charge-phase factor f_1' in the gauge given by $\Lambda = 2\pi\cos(x + y)$.

(d) The gauge potential yields $\mathbf{A} = (1, x)$, yields a constant magnetic field in the z-direction.

(e) The vector potential after the transformation $U = e^{i\Lambda}$. With $\mathbf{A}' = \mathbf{A} - \boldsymbol{\nabla}\Lambda$ with the Λ given above.

(f) The vector potential in a gauge with Λ given above.

Figure I.2.38: *Gauge transformations* The effect of two different local gauge transformations on the phase factor $e^{i\beta(x,y)}$ and on the gauge potential $\mathbf{A} = (A_x, A_y)$. All describe the same uniform magnetic field that is directed out of the page to the front.

So, properly speaking, the phase factor $f_n(x)$ of the wave-function is an element of a one-dimensional complex, or two-dimensional real vector space $\mathcal{R}ep$, on which the unitary representation of the gauge group $U(1)$ with label n acts as a transformation. In brief, if I make a gauge transformation $\Lambda(x)$, the phase factor of the field will transform by multiplication with a phase factor $\exp\left(in\Lambda(x)\right)$ and therefore its phase gets shifted by $n\Lambda(x)$. And the gauge potential transforms like indicated in the formula (I.1.48).

What gauge invariance means is that we are free to choose

a frame of basis for the two-dimensional vector space in which unit charge vector $f_n(\beta, x)$ lives, at every point x independently. Very much like the tangent spaces we discussed before. In other words at any point x we have the choice of which point on the circle we call the origin to which we assign the value $\beta = 0$. *Gauge invariance is the statement that the physics does not depend on that local choice.* This implies that the physics doesn't change if we shift β at each point x by an amount $\Lambda(x)$. We have illustrated this in Figures I.2.38, where we have depicted both the phase $\beta(\mathbf{x})$ and $\mathbf{A}(\mathbf{x})$ in three different gauges for a situation in two spatial dimensions. These images underscore the great generality of local gauge transformations, and in spite of looking so different, the magnetic field $\mathbf{B} = \nabla \times \mathbf{A}$ is the same for all three configurations. It is a gauge invariant quantity and corresponds in this case to a uniform field in the positive z-direction.

The reasoning above clarifies the use of the term 'gauging.' If you think of a little pointer moving over a dial, then applying a gauge transformation amounts to redefining the label 'zero' on the dials located at different positions x. It is like calibrating the dials in all of space-time.

Gauge covariant derivative. Let us now consider the following question. I have a space with some electromagnetic fields (or potentials) in it, and I take a charge that sits at $x = x_0$ and move it slowly along some path γ to another point x_1. What will happen? I was careful enough to not disturb the fields, but as the charge interacts with the fields along the way, did something happen to that phase perhaps? Well, certainly, and what will happen is that the phase β will change on its way to x_1. By what amount does it change? And does that change depend on the path I choose? These are the questions that we turn to next.

Let us take small steps at a time, or better even, infinitesimal steps! So, suppose we want to know what the charge-phase would look like at a nearby point, then we can make a linear approximation only keeping the first derivative:

$$f_n(x') = f_n(x + \triangle x) \simeq f_n(x) + \triangle x \frac{df_n}{dx}\Big|_x + \cdots , \quad (\text{I.2.31})$$

but this does not take care of the change in the frame in which the phase is expressed, by which I basically mean the orientation of the real and imaginary axes of f_n at different points x. That basis change is determined by the gauge connection $A_\mu(x)$, which means that we have to replace the ordinary derivative with the so-called *gauge covariant derivative*:

$$\partial_\mu \rightarrow D_\mu \equiv \partial_\mu + iqA_\mu . \quad (\text{I.2.32})$$

The added gauge connection literally connects the frames in neighbouring points. It is not sufficient to just calculate the phase; in order to compare the phases at different points you need to know how the bases at those points are related.

Why the term covariant derivative? It is like the derivative in a co-moving frame, and therefore the appropriate term indeed. This becomes clear if we look at the how this derivative transforms under gauge transformations given that the field transforms as given in (I.2.30) and the potential like that given in (I.1.48) as $A_\mu \rightarrow A'_\mu = A_\mu - \partial_\mu \Lambda$. We find:

$$D_\mu f_n \rightarrow [D_\mu f_n]' = (\partial_\mu + iqA'_\mu)f'_n = U_n[D_\mu f_n] . \quad (\text{I.2.33})$$

which shows that this derivative transforms covariantly indeed, in other words, just like the f_n itself. This is an important observation because one sees that quantities like $|D_t f_n|^2$ and $|\mathbf{D}f_n|^2$ will be gauge invariant and these are terms that appear in the expression for the energy density of the field f_n. And this in turn implies that to get an invariant energy the interaction between the charged field (or particle) has to be of a form involving the gauge-covariant derivative. That is what it means to say that gauge symmetry dictates the detailed nature of the interactions!

Suppose we have a function $h(x)$, imposing that $dh/dx = 0$ implies that $h = \text{constant}$. Something similar can be defined for the covariant derivative. The equation for what is called a *covariantly constant* charge vector reads

$$D_\mu f_n = 0 . \quad (\text{I.2.34})$$

The solution to this equation amounts to expressing a path dependent relation between the phase at two points, corresponding to the parallel transport of the charge-phase along a given curve. Let us look at this statement in more detail.

The gauge connection. To carry the phase factor around we need a somewhat fancy expression involving the gauge connection A_μ. Let me recall the line integral $I(\gamma; x_0, x_1)$ of the gauge field along a curve γ given in (I.1.51) and depicted in Figure I.1.26. To parallel transport the phase along some curve γ going from x_0 to x_1, we need to use not just the line integral $I(\gamma; x_0, x_1)$, but rather its exponential:

$$W_n(\gamma; x_0, x_1) \equiv e^{i\,n\,I(\gamma; x_0, x_1)}. \qquad (I.2.35)$$

This path dependent phase factor carries exactly the frame from x_0 to x_1 so that:

$$f_n(\beta, x_1) = W_n(\gamma; x_0, x_1)\, f_n(\beta, x_0). \qquad (I.2.36)$$

This expression furnishes the general solution to the equation (I.2.34) for the covariantly constant charge-phase f_n. It transports the phase in a gauge covariant way, that is to say in such away that under a gauge transformation we have that

$$W_n \to W'_n(\gamma; x_0, x_1) = U_n(x_1) W_n(\gamma; x_0, x_1) U_n^\dagger(x_0),$$

and this means that in the equation (I.2.36), the combined effect of a gauge transformation on all factors is the same on the left- and right-hand side. The net effect is a multiplication by $U_n(x_1)$ from the left, as it should be according to (I.2.30). So we have answered both questions: how the charge-phase will change and that it does so depending on the path chosen. The gauge 'connector' is nothing but the path dependent phase factor W_n.

Gauge theory and principle fiber bundles. The central concept describing both the gauge potentials and the underlying space-time manifold $\mathcal{M}$ is called a *principle bundle* denoted by $\mathcal{E}$, consisting of a space which locally can be thought of as a direct product of the *gauge group* G and the base manifold $\mathcal{E}$: $G \times \mathcal{M}$.

In Figure I.2.39 we have given a simple example in which the base manifold is a circle $\mathcal{M} = S^1$ parametrized by an angle φ (the red circle). For the group we have chosen the group of rotations in the plane denoted by $SO(2)$, parametrized by an angle Λ making the group space also a

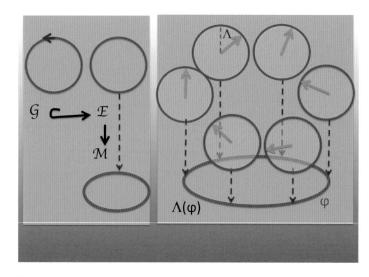

Figure I.2.39: *A principle bundle associated with a gauge group $\mathcal{G}$.* Here the group is the phase group $U(1)$, which is a circle (in brown) parametrized by $0 \leq \Lambda < 2\pi$. The base space $\mathcal{M}$ is also a circle (in red) with $0 \leq \varphi < 2\pi$. Above each point in the base space we have a fiber that is a copy of the group $\mathcal{G}$ labeled by an angle Λ. Choosing a gauge corresponds to choosing a (cross) section of the bundle: a particular choice for $\Lambda = \Lambda(\varphi)$ as indicated on the right.

circle $\mathcal{G} = S^1$ (the purple circle). This group is the same as the phase group $U(1)$, and as we saw this group is actually the gauge group of electrodynamics. Above each point of $\mathcal{M}$ we have a copy of $\mathcal{G}$ with an angle $\Lambda = \Lambda(\varphi)$.

The point is now that any electromagnetic field configuration corresponds to a particular bundle, and choosing to write down the configuration of the potentials explicitly we have to 'choose a gauge' which amounts to choosing a particular cross-section through the fibers specifying a particular choice of $\Lambda = \Lambda(\varphi)$. And this is for example done in the picture on the right-hand side.

Charge carrying fields and associated bundles. Often the gauge field is called the gauge connection, because it connects local coordinate frames at different points with each other. In general a charge carrying field carries a *representation* of the gauge group and these correspond to so-called *associated bundles*, where we have attached a copy of the representation space Rep of the group $\mathcal{G}$, to every point of the base manifold in some smooth way.

Returning to our previous example a field carrying a charge $q = ne$ would described by a complex field say $\psi_n(x)$, which has a magnitude and a charge-phase that again may depend on position, so,

$$\psi_n(x) = \exp(in\beta(x))\rho(x).$$

Gauge transformations on such a field act as a local phase transformation; we multiply the field with the local phase factor $U_n(\Lambda(x))$:

$$\psi_n(x) \rightarrow \psi_n'(x) = U_n(\Lambda(x))\psi_n(x). \qquad (\text{I.2.37})$$

Examples are depicted in the Figures I.2.39, and I.2.40, which give you an impression of the case where $\mathcal{M} \simeq S^1$, $\mathcal{G} \simeq U(1)$. The representations act on the $f_n(\beta(\varphi))$ and the representation space can be depicted by the little charge vector. In Figure I.2.39 you see that the fiber corresponds to the orbit of the charge vector under rotations, and a specific bundle is obtained by choosing a particular gauge which means that above every point of $\mathcal{M}$, you choose a particular vector making sure that the overall configuration is smooth. This is appropriately called *choosing a (cross) section* of the bundle. This leads to for example to the configurations depicted in Figure I.2.40 of a number of smooth closed ribbons. The configuration on the left represents the constant phase $\beta(\varphi) = 0$, corresponding to the connection $A = 0$ of the trivial bundle. The other phase configurations are smooth deformations that correspond to gauge transformations. So all three represent the same physical situation in different gauges. They are *gauge equivalent* configurations. It clearly demonstrates the local character of the gauge transformations, because at any point of the base manifold we can choose a different rotation, as long as the overall deformations correspond to smoothly 'wiggling' the configuration.

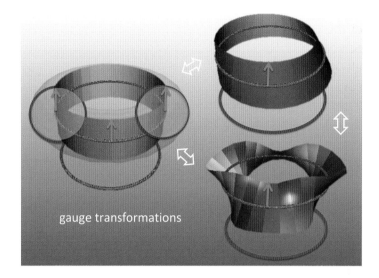

gauge transformations

Figure I.2.40: *Gauge equivalence.* Here we have depicted gauge equivalent configurations of the charge-phase factor $e^{in\beta(\varphi)}$ on a circle. On the left we have the *trivial* configuration $\beta(\varphi) = 0$. Gauge transformations correspond to 'wiggling' the configuration. The configurations above are related by a periodic transformation $\Lambda(\varphi)$ so that $\beta \rightarrow \beta' = \beta + \Lambda$, with $\Lambda(0) = \Lambda(2\pi)$.

Gauge invariant characteristics. You may wonder if it is possible in reality to 'drag' a state vector along a closed loop like we described and whether the resulting phase change can be measured. The answer is yes and the fact is that what I have described is known as the *Berry phase* after the British mathematical physicist who discovered that it was possible to identify it in certain setups with time- or space-dependent Hamiltonians. The effect is also closely related to the much older *Aharonov-Bohm effect* as will be discuss in Chapter II.3. This interference pattern depends on the solid angle that the path $H(\lambda)$ has covered on the sphere.[8] Interestingly the Berry phase is apparently a purely geometric phase depending only on the geometry of the space of Hamiltonians.

---

[8]The path is oriented and the orientation decides whether to take the solid angle ω or $4\pi - \omega$, which with equation (II.3.4) amounts to $R_k(\theta) \rightarrow R_k(-\theta)$.

Other gauge groups. We have in this subsection exhibited the structure of a principle fiber bundle and the vector bundles associated with its representations, but only for the rather modest example of the group $U(1)$. This may have come across as a demonstration of how to crack a peanut with a sledgehammer. We want to stress that the fiber bundle description is quite universal as it is the framework in which most classical physics involving local symmetries can be cast. For example the *Standard Model* involves $U(1)$, $SU(2)$ and $SU(3)$ gauge fields describing the electromagnetic, weak and strong interactions respectively. And the *Grand Unified Theories (GUTs)* that we will discuss in Chapter I.4 have even larger gauge groups like $SU(5)$ or $SO(10)$ involving more gauge interactions.

It means that the fields take a value in a *representation space* which is a vector space $V = \mathcal{R}ep$ which is typically $\mathbb{C}^n$ or $\mathbb{R}^n$. And the corresponding unitary representation of the group works in this space as a linear transformation (say, a rotation). The group can be any compact group like the groups of unitary or orthogonal $(N \times N)$ matrices denoted by $SU(N)$ or $SO(N)$ respectively. The label n on the field refers to the dimension of the vector space on which some irreducible (unitary) matrix representation of that gauge group acts. The *Math Excursion* on groups on page 635 of Part III gives a basic introduction to group theory. As we saw the group $U(1)$ is special in that all representations are one-dimensional, meaning just phase factors.

For the group $SO(3)$ the unitary representations are labeled with a semi-positive integer l, where the group is then represented by $(2l+1) \times (2l+1)$ matrices. This representation acts as a transformation group on a $(2l + 1)$-dimensional vector space. A field in this $SO(3))$ gauge theory will take a value in one of these vector spaces and is said to carry integer spin l. When the spin equals one we have the standard three-dimensional vector but one that lives in a $\mathcal{R}ep = \mathbb{R}^3$ internal space.

For $SU(3)$, the gauge group related to the strong interactions, the quarks and antiquarks transform as 3-dimensional representations (color *triplets* and *anti-triplets*), while the gluons form an 8-dimensional representation. This indeed means that $SU(3)$, the group of 3×3 unitary matrices with a unit determinant, also has a representation by 8×8 unitary matrices, which is *irreducible*, meaning that it cannot be reduced to a lower dimensional (for example three-dimensional) representation. This representation acts on the eight-dimensional vector field, which describes the gluons. A major achievement in mathematics has been that in the early twentieth century all these continuous groups and their representations were classified. The results have found a rich variety of applications in physics as we will show in Chapter I.4 where we discuss the phenomenology of the 'Standard Model.'

In the previous subsection we argued that to describe vector fields on curved spaces one needs to introduce the so-called 'tangent bundle' of the manifold. This means that also general relativity can also be cast as a gauge theory where the local gauge group is the symmetry group of the local structure of space-time. Locally our space-time is flat Minkowski space-time with its translation and the Lorentz symmetries. The corresponding group is called the *inhomogeneous Lorentz* or *Poincaré group*. The field strength in that case corresponds to the local curvature tensor R of the manifold and the connection would be the so-called metric connection ω_μ that we introduced in equations I.2.26 and I.2.24. It is gratifying to see that these phenomenologically so different fundamental interactions that we have encountered in nature share this underlying structure of gauge invariance, mathematically represented by the concept of a fiber bundle. We must add the important fact though, that the physics itself resides in the field equations, being the Maxwell (more generally, the Yang-Mills) and Einstein equations. We return to the Yang–Mills equations in Chapter II.6 on symmetries and their breaking. The bundle picture makes the mathematical setting transparent and clarifies some of the physical features. ■ ■

The physics of information:
from bits to qubits

It would appear that we have reached the limits of what is possible to achieve with computer technology, although one should be careful with such statements, as they tend to sound pretty silly in 5 years.

John von Neumann (1951)

Computation necessarily involves information storage and the manipulation of information on some underlying physical substrate, so far mostly based on semiconductor technology. Information is stored in the states of the system and one can manipulate the states by interacting physically with that system. If the scaling down of basic components is to continue as is predicted by Moore's law, then entering the quantum domain is inevitable. So, there is a quantessence to information as well. This has profound consequences for how we should think about information and information processing. It turns out that quantum computation offers fundamentally different options for tackling certain classes of hard problems.

A bit of information. Volumes are typically measured in liters, gallons, pints or cubic meters; and the unit chosen strongly depends on the local context. For information, however, this does not hold; it is universally measured in *bits*. This canonical character derives from the fact that the introduction of computers was right from the start a global affair. The 'bit' is the smallest unit of information and forms the basis for digital memories and data processing devices. One bit can be represented in many ways, for example like a switch that is on or off, or a single digit binary number being either one or zero, or equivalently as a magnetic spin pointing either up or down, or a number that is either plus or minus one (see Figure I.2.41). If I want to qualify for a discount on a public transportation

Figure I.2.41: *The bit.* Various representations of a bit of information. It is a two-state system such as a switch, a particle that can be in either of two states, or a classical spin that can point up or down.

ticket for example, only one bit of information concerning my age will do. I only have to answer one yes-or-no question: are you younger or older than 65? In answering a single yes-or-no question you provide one bit of information. Generally quantitative thinking is based on working with variables that can be assigned numerical values; we attach numbers to them even though these may be only approximate. Those finite approximations can always be converted to finite base-2 or *binary* numbers, only containing one's and zero's, and any calculations that you would like to do with the original numbers can also be performed in base-2. And we all know that such calculations can be extremely well and swiftly performed by today's digital devices, at least if an efficient algorithm is available.

Information and entropy

State counting, entropy and information. In all information devices the information is carried by a physical sub-

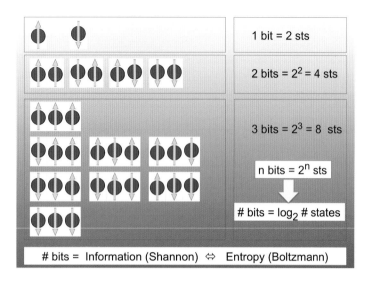

1 bit = 2 sts

2 bits = 2^2 = 4 sts

3 bits = 2^3 = 8 sts

n bits = 2^n sts

bits = $\log_2$ # states

bits = Information (Shannon) ⇔ Entropy (Boltzmann)

Figure I.2.42: *Entropy and information.* Counting the number of states of a digital memory. Shannon defined the *information capacity* of a system in bits as the logarithm of the number of states, therefore information is directly proportional to the notion of entropy in physics as defined by Boltzmann in the nineteenth century.

strate representing a certain number of bits. The amount of information that can be stored in a physical system is determined by the number of distinct states that the system can be in. Let us think of a memory consisting of an array of little magnets that can point either up or down. Then we can count the number of states of such an array of bits as we did in Figure I.2.42. For one bit we have 2 states, for two bits it is $2 \times 2 = 4$ states, and for n bits it is clearly $2 \times 2 \times ... \times 2 = 2^n$ states. This shows that there is a direct relationship between information capacity, i.e. the number of bits, and the number of states. This is an *exponential* relation,

$$n \text{ bits} \Leftrightarrow 2^n \text{states} \quad (\text{exponential relation}). \quad (I.2.38)$$

This implies that the converse relationship between information capacity and the number of accessible states is a

logarithmic one: [9]

$$\# \text{ bits} = \log_2(\# \text{ states}) \quad (\text{logarithmic relation}). \quad (I.2.39)$$

This relationship provides a precise and general quantitative definition of information that forms the very basis of information theory. The relation should remind you of the expression for the *entropy* $S = k \log W$ of a physical system, derived by Stefan Boltzmann, which links the entropy S as a state variable of a macroscopic system to the total number of distinct microscopic states W that correspond to that given macroscopic state, as we discussed in Chapter I.1 in connection with equation (I.1.62). So, entropy quantifies the microscopic diversity hidden in what we see as a single macroscopic state. In information theory, entropy is a measure for information capacity, the information that can be stored.

Entropy and probability. At this point it is interesting to refine this relation between available states and information by explicitly introducing the notion of *probability*. In the previous derivation we have tacitly assumed that given a single macroscopic state, the probability of finding the system in any of the corresponding microscopic states is uniform. With N states that would mean that $p_i = 1/N$ because the total probability should add up to $\Sigma_i^N p_i = 1$. In thermodynamics this distribution would correspond to a closed system at *fixed* (conserved) energy, and where one assumes the equipartion of energy.

---

[9]The information unit bit is linked to the logarithm base-2. If $S = \log_2 N$ this means that $2^S = N$. Thinking binary means that you reason in base-2. If I say a number is 21 in base-10, I make the statement that that number equals $21 = 1 \times 10^0 + 2 \times 10^1 = 1 + 20 = 21$. If I say a number is 21 in base-2, that statement makes no sense because the symbol '2' isn't there. To convert the number 21 in base-10 to base-2, I have to expand the number in powers of 2, so, $21 = 16 + 4 + 1 = 1 \times 2^4 + 0 \times 2^3 + 1 \times 2^2 + 0 \times 2^1 + 1 \times 2^0 \Leftrightarrow 10101$. In base-10 the digits run from zero to 9, whereas in base-2 you only have 0 and 1. So the number 1011 in base two equals $1 + 2 + 8 = 11$ in base 10. This way, all integers can be uniquely encoded in any integer-based number system.

In general though, the probabilities will not be equal and one should introduce a probability distribution $\{p_i\}$ over the microscopic states, as we did in the section on statistical thermodynamics in Chapter I.1. There for a system in thermal equilibrium at temperature T, we introduced a probability p_i which was dependent on the energy ε_i of the microsystem labeled by 'i.' For that case we showed that the expression (I.1.69) for the thermodynamic entropy was first given by Gibbs, and now we see that it corresponds to an information entropy or information capacity (in bits) of the system given by the fundamental expression:

$$S = -\Sigma_i \, p_i \log_2 p_i \, . \qquad (I.2.40)$$

We mentioned already that the entropy of the system, as defined above, is equivalent to its information carrying capacity as it was defined by Claude Shannon. While working at Bell Labs he published in 1948 a groundbreaking paper on the transmission of information, that by many is considered to be the birth of information science. The important contribution from our point of view is firstly that he proved that it was the *unique* solution that satisfied some general constraints on information, and secondly that it applied in a general context that transcended its physical origins as thermodynamic entropy. So, that is where the term *information entropy* originated from.

Let us see what happens if we apply the formula to the two-spin situation where we have a set of four states which we denote as $\{11, 10, 01, 00\}$. We may turn on a weak magnetic field so that, say, the state 11 with both spins up is energetically preferred, for example leading to a distribution: $\{p_{11} = 1/2, p_{10} = p_{01} = p_{00} = 1/6\}$. Then the corresponding information capacity would be $S = \frac{1}{2}(1 + \log_2 6) = 1.79$ bits, which is clearly smaller than the uniform case with all $p_i = 1/4$, yielding $S = 2$ bits. The point I want to make here is that the uniform distribution is the maximally unbiased distribution, and it is that distribution which maximizes the information entropy, precisely because there is no additional constraint on, or in other words, 'additional knowledge' about, the system.

Adding *a priori* knowledge reduces the information content, or the amount of surprise the outcome of measurements could provide. Constraints always reduce the number of allowed states for the system and therefore lower the entropy.

The Landauer principle. Talking about the relation between information and physical entropy it may be appropriate to briefly mention the principle proposed by Rolf Landauer in 1961, which is a particular formulation of the second law of thermodynamics which directly applies to information theory and computation. The principle expresses the fact that erasing information necessarily involves producing heat, thereby increasing the entropy. So, in other words, the principle governs the intimate relationship between information processing and the production of heat. This is of great importance, and it explains why large server parks tend to move up further north to colder environments. The heat produced by computers can certainly be reduced, but the improvements are bounded by the second law of thermodynamics.

We have illustrated the principle in Figure I.2.43. Consider a 'gas' consisting of a single atom in a symmetric container with volume 2V in contact with a heat bath. We imagine that the position of the particle acts as a memory with one bit of information, corresponding to whether the atom is on the left or on the right.

Erasing the information amounts to resetting the device to the 'reference' state $|1\rangle$ independent of the initial state, and therefore reinitializing the system rather than making a measurement. This can be done by first opening the diaphragm in the middle, then moving the piston from the right in, and finally closing the diaphragm and moving the piston back. In the first step the gas expands freely to twice the volume. The particle doesn't do any work, the energy is conserved, and therefore no heat will be absorbed from the reservoir. For that reason this is an irreversible free expansion process by which the entropy S of the gas

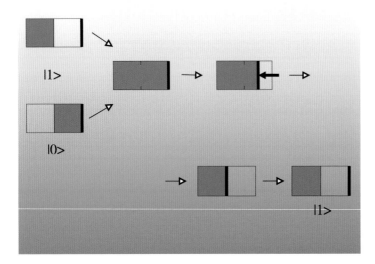

Figure I.2.43: *The Landauer principle.* An illustration of the Landauer principle using a simple 'thermodynamical system' consisting of a single particle in a vessel. See text for explanation of the successive steps.

increases by a factor $k(\ln(2V) - \ln V) = k \ln(2V/V) = k \ln 2$. (The number of states the particle can be in is just the volume; the average velocity is conserved because of the contact with the thermal bath and will not contribute to the change in entropy). In the second part of the erasure procedure we bring the system back to a state which has the same entropy as the initial state. We do this through a quasi-static (i.e. reversible) isothermal process at temperature T. During the compression the entropy decreases by $k \ln 2$. This change of entropy is nothing but the amount of heat delivered by the gas to the reservoir divided by the temperature, i.e. $\Delta S = \Delta Q/T$. Therefore the heat produced ΔQ equals the net amount of work W that has been done in the cycle by moving the piston during the compression. The conclusion is that during the erasure of one bit of information the device had to produce at least $\Delta Q = T\Delta S = kT \ln 2$ of heat. This argument shows that actually the heat computers generate is a necessary byproduct of them destroying information. It directly links the destruction of logical information with the thermody-

namical generation of heat. This is a powerful result as it holds independent of the specific device one is talking about.

To summarize, you could say that 'forgetting' has its price (in heat). And that raises an interesting question about computation in general: can one avoid the heat by doing computation reversibly? The answer to this question was given by Charles Bennet in 1982, and is affirmative. However, reversible computation necessarily employs reversible gates only, but the familiar AND and OR gates (to be discussed shortly) are not reversible because they reduce a two-bit input to a one-bit output, producing at least $kT \ln 2$ units of heat upon acting. A reversible computer doesn't pay the price of heat, but as all information has to be stored, the price of reversible computation is the requirement of ever-expanding memories! Not so cheap either.

Models of computation

Computing is normally done by [a person] writing symbols on paper. [...] I assume that the calculation is carried out on one-dimensional paper, i.e., on a tape divided into squares. I shall also suppose that the number of symbols [...] is finite. [...] The behaviour of the computer at any moment is determined by the symbols which he is observing, and his 'state of mind.' [...] We may suppose [...] the number of states of mind which need to be taken into account is finite. ...the use of more complicated states of mind can be avoided by writing more symbols on the tape [...] Every [simple] operation consists of some change in the physical system consisting of the computer and his tape.

Alan Turing,
On Computable Numbers with an Application to the Entscheidungsproblem, Proc. Lond. Math. Soc. 2: 42. (1937)

Turing machines. Armed with a precise and operational definition of what information is, we should spend some time on computation or the processing of information. What are the basic underlying principles upon which the operation of all our computational devices is based?

We distinguish an input fed to a 'machine' that somehow processes that input leading to the desired result. To achieve this, the computer follows a sequence of instructions according to a certain procedure; an algorithm, or a program to produce the output. In a formal sense one could say that the device computes the output as a function of the input. As we have seen one can always present information in a binary way as a sequence of zeros and ones. So computers basically evaluate a function of the input, corresponding to the output. And a basic question concerning computation is to model this process in its full generality and determine what kind of functions can be calculated.

This is where the notion of a *Turing machine* comes in, which is a formal device satisfying certain specifications that can execute computations in the sense that it takes input and produces the desired output. It is not a machine in the ordinary sense but rather a fundamental model of computation. It does not address the question of the possible physical implementation of the models, of how to make them into a real machines. It cannot care less whether you build it with rods and wheels, or like a fluid system with pipes and valves, or with Lego, or with elementary electronic semiconductor components called transistors.

Turing's starting point was in fact a rather natural and intuitive one based on the notion of an *effective computation*. A computation, procedure, or algorithm is called 'effective' if it satisfies the following criteria:

(i) it is specified in terms of a finite number of exact instructions,
(ii) if the instructions are carried out without errors, the desired result is obtained in a finite number of steps,

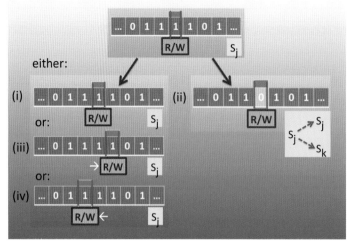

Allowed transitions in time step t -> t+1

Figure I.2.44: *Turing machine transitions.* The four possible actions of the R/W head in a transition: (r) if it writes it cannot move in the same step, and the state may either change or not; (l) if it does not write it can move at most one step either to the left or to the right, but cannot change the state .

(iii) the instructions could in principle be carried out by a person only using using paper and pencil,
(iv) this person does not need any particular insight or ingenuity to carry out the instructions.

Note that there is no restriction on the amount of paper (memory), nor on the time it might take to perform the computation, apart from it being finite. The computation is 'effective' but not necessarily 'efficient.'

The Turing machine can in principle perform any such 'effective computation' and is defined as follows:

(i) it has a (half)infinite tape containing cells labeled by an integer p, each cell contains a symbol α taken from an alphabet $\mathcal{A}$. In the following we will just take the alphabet to be $\{0, 1\}$, meaning that the tape is just a binary string which has a non-trivial input that starts on the left and may end with only zeros on the right.

(ii) a read/write head which is positioned at a given cell where it can read and (re)write the tape if instructed to do so. There are restrictions on what the head at any stage can do.

(iii) At any given time the machine is in some definite internal state S_j which is an element of some finite state space $\mathcal{F}_S$. The program or algorithm corresponds to a table that precisely specifies for every state what transition it has to make if the head reads either a zero or a one. This instruction specifies (a) what the head has to do, and (b) to what state the machine is supposed to go.

(iv) At the start of the computation, the input is the binary string on the tape. The head is located at the $p = 0$ cell and the machine is in the internal state S_0. The program halts if it reaches a final state (the output) where it finds no further executable instructions. So this is how a Turing machine computes a binary output function from some binary input.

From the fact that for any *effective computation* there is a Turing machine, one can prove the existence of a universal Turing machine that can perform all effective computations. This machine defines the set of *Turing-calculable functions.*

This rather intuitive definition of Turing-computability is the subject of the *Church-Turing thesis* which is central in the theory of computation. The Church-Turing thesis states that Turing computability is equivalent to the much more formal definition of computability based on *recursive functions* and *Abacus machines*. We are not going to dwell on these topics as they are really outside the scope of this book. The thesis cannot be proven as it links formal to intuitive notions. It is actually a hypothesis and all that can be said is that no counter example has been found so far.

At this point it is probably helpful to describe a basic version of the machine in some detail. In Figure I.2.44, we have the computer in some state S_j and we show the tape

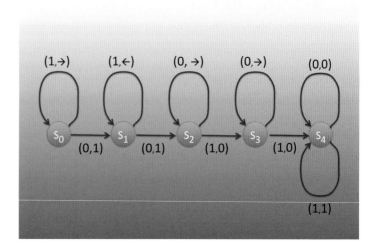

Figure I.2.45: *Turing machine state diagram.* The state diagram for the digital adder described in the text. In this program the machine goes through four states before it halts; in each state the move or write instructions on what to do if the head reads a 0 or a 1 are indicated.

with the R/W head at some position p_t. The program tells the head what to do but the possibilities are very restricted. There are only four possible transitions for the head/machine to execute:

(i) it stays at position p and does not change the entry with $S_j \rightarrow S_j$,

(ii) it stays at position p and does change the entry on the tape, in which case it also may or may not change the state of the system $S_j \rightarrow (S_j \text{ or } S_k)$,

(iii) it moves to the right ($p \rightarrow p + 1$) with $S_j \rightarrow S_j$,

(iv) it moves to the left ($p \rightarrow p - 1$) with $S_j \rightarrow S_j$.

The permitted transitions are schematically depicted in Figure I.2.44.

A Turing machine can also be represented by a finite state diagram. This diagram is a directed network where the nodes are the states S_j and the directed edges represent the instructions. Instructions where the state does not change correspond to lines returning to the same state. The number of arrows leaving the node equals the number of symbols in the alphabet (in our case there are only two).

In Figure I.2.45 we have depicted the state diagram corresponding to a program that can add two positive integers m and n. We should think of the input as the two numbers in *unial coding* (this means that a number k is represented by a sequence of $k + 1$ symbols 1) separated by a 0, with also zeros on the left and on the right. So the input sequence on the tape would look like:

$$000[11...11]_{m+1}0[11...11]_{n+1}000.$$

The head should then walk along the string of symbols starting from the most left 1, and then moves to the right till it hits the in-between 0, changing that 0 into a 1, so that the sequence then looks like:

$$000[11...11111...11]_{n+m+3}000.$$

Next the head should move to the left till it hits the first 0 on the left, then moves right again changing the first two 1 symbols into 0's. The result yields the required sequence representing the desired outcome.

$$000[11...11111...11]_{m+n+1}000.$$

You may verify that this sequence of steps is indeed performed by the machine depicted in Figure I.2.45, by following the sequence step by step.

We see that this simple problem already needs a quite complicated diagram. It is therefore more convenient to work in terms of logical gates, to which we now turn.

Logical gates. A computation is formally the calculation of a function f of many binary variables, so $f(a_1, a_2, \ldots a_n) = b$. The circuit for f should after entering an input of any set of a values return a binary number b. In practice one starts

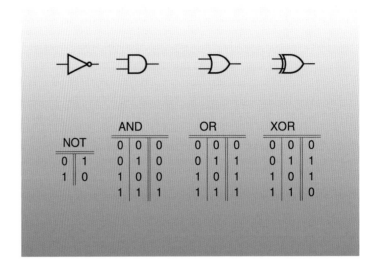

Figure I.2.46: *Logical gates.* The one-bit NOT gate, some two-bit gates, and their logical tables.

with a universal set of simple *logical gates* that compute certain basic functions. By combining many of those in specific parallel and serial arrangements, arbitrarily complicated functions can be composed. Diagrams with logical gates are simpler and more practical than going all the way back to the underlying Turing state diagrams.

The basic gates typically have only one- or two-bit inputs and a one-bit output, like:

(i) the NOT gate inverting the value of a single bit, meaning that if the bit contains a 1, then it is changed to a 0 and vice versa;
(ii) the OR and the AND gate. These are 2-bit gates, they are irreversible because they reduce the information of the 2-bit input to a 1-bit output.

One may prove that the set of these three gates is *universal*, in that they allow you to make machines to perform all the effective computations as defined by Turing. There are many other gates possible and these may be preferred depending on the problem one wants to solve,

Going quantum

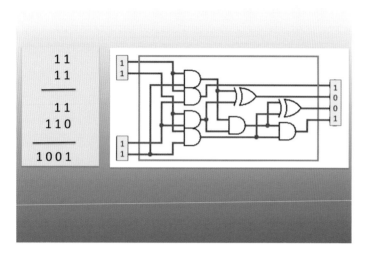

Figure I.2.47: *Multiplication.* A multiplication for two 2-bit numbers 'by hand' and the corresponding digital multiplier schematic composed of six AND gates and two XOR gates. The two lines of multiplication are performed in parallel, and the subsequent additions are sequential, so one therefore needs a total of $2n - 1 = 3$ time steps.

Until recently, most people thought of quantum mechanics in terms of the uncertainty principle and unavoidable limitations on measurement... The appreciation of the positive application of quantum effects to information processing grew slowly.

Nicolas Gisin

Once we have come to appreciate the basic fact that information capacity is directly related to the 'number' of available states of a system, it is immediately clear that if we are to descend to the level of quantum mechanics, we have to think in terms of quantum states. As we will see, quantum states are quantessentially different from their classical precursors, and therefore we should be prepared to go back to the drawing board and define from scratch what we mean by information. The space of states has a completely different structure indeed, and that forced the scientists to start developing what is nowadays called *quantum information theory*.

for example the *exclusive* OR gate also called XOR gate. It returns zero if both input bits are equal and one if they are different. These simple gates compute simple binary functions which can be represented in so-called *truth tables* where the possible input values (the arguments) are given on the left whereas the function value appears on the right. For the basic gates these tables are given explicitly in Figure I.2.46.

In Figure I.2.47 we demonstrate for example how to multiply two 2-bit numbers. We calculate $3 \times 3 = 9$, which in binary terms reads $11 \times 11 = 1001$. On the left we show how this is done by 'hand' with pencil and paper, and on the right how it is done by a logical device consisting of some AND and XOR gates. Using the truth tables it is quite straightforward to follow the lines and put the bit-values on them, and convince oneself that it indeed works

.

It is in that way that a turning point in our understanding of what matter really is on the microscopic level induced a radical change in our basic notion of information. It was the eminent physicist Richard Feynman who maybe for the first time pointed out some of the basic principles in a well-known paper entitled *There is plenty of room at the bottom*. The change did not just affect the abstract, software side of information theory, but also the hardware side. The crucial challenge is nowadays to develop new types of quantum technology that allow us to store and manipulate quantum information. Without exaggeration one may say that this constitutes a new holy grail for experimental physics and engineering.

There are basically two reasons why information will go quantum. The first is that information science has to confront quantum physics at some point because of Moore's

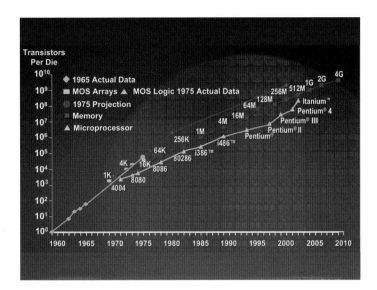

RSA-2048 =

251959084756578934940271832400483985714292821262040320277771378360436620207075955526401852588078440691829064124951508218929855914917618450280848912007284499268739280728777673597141834727026189637501497182469116507761337985909570009733045974880842840179742910064245869181719511874612151517265463228221686999875491824224336372590851418654620435767984233871847744479207399342365848238242811981638150106748104516603773060562016196762561338441436038339044149526344321901146575444541784240209246165157233507787077498171257724679629263863563732899121548314381678998850404453640235273819513786365643912120103971228221207203571

Figure I.2.49: *RSA-2048*. RSA-2048 is a number with 2048 binary and 617 decimal digits. The factorization has not been found yet.

Figure I.2.48: *Moore's law*. This law states the astonishing fact that over the last half a century the power of computing has doubled every 18 months. The continuous downscaling of the basic components forces us to enter the gates of quantum domain. (Source: High Tech Forum)

law. The second is that scientists who looked more thoroughly into the equations governing quantum information made the astounding discovery that for a number of tasks the quantum computer is extremely more powerful than its classical digital counterpart.

Moore's law. This is an empirical 'law' which refers to the spectacular fact that our computational power over the last half a century has increased at an incredible rate: on average it has doubled every 18 months, as you can see in Figure I.2.48. This implies that it has been growing exponentially for more than half a century!. We are now at a stage where a single active component of an integrated digital circuit has a size of about 10 nanometer, very small indeed. Once you realize that atoms are of the size of a nanometer, it is clear that Moore's law has to break down if we don't succeed in entering the quantum domain. In other words the continued scaling down in the size of the hardware components forces us to enter the quantum world

one way or another!

A tough problem: integer factorization. But going quantum also means that we turn something that at first sight looks like a crisis into a tremendous opportunity. Quantum mechanics is so fundamentally different, that it would allow for a quantum computer to solve problems that would be intractable on our classical digital computers.

A famous example is the factoring problem: I give you a very large integer N of n digits which I tell you can be written in a unique way as the product of two other integers M_0 and M_1. I don't tell you what they are, but instead ask you to find M_0 and M_1. This turns out to be an extremely hard problem not only for people but also for very, very big computers. Hard in the sense of time needed to find the answer. Numbers of this type, that can be factorized into two prime factors are called RSA numbers and they have important applications in cryptography.

That may surprise you but let us get a rough idea of why this is so.

A simple way to find the divisors is the method of 'trial division' which goes back to the medieval Italian mathematician Fibonaci. To know whether a number N has a divisor M you start with N and keep subtracting M until after k steps you get a number smaller than M, if that number happens to be zero then M is a divisor of N. You start doing this by choosing $M = 2$ and that takes care of all even divisors. Clearly the next number M we have to check for would be the next prime number but that requires that the list of primes is known. To get a rough estimate what we can do is to check divisibility for all odd divisors. One additional observation that simplifies the search is the fact that if the two prime factors are unequal then one will be larger than $\sqrt{N}$ and the other smaller. We thus have to check the divisor property only up to $\sqrt{N}$. Knowing that apart from the number 2 all prime numbers are odd we have to only search for odd divisors, which leads to a further reductions. An estimate for the maximum number of simple subtractions P^* in such a worst case scheme would give:

$$P^*(N) = \sqrt{N}\left(\frac{1}{2} + \sum_{k=1}^{\sqrt{N}}\left(\frac{1}{2k+1}\right)\right) \qquad (I.2.41a)$$

$$\simeq \frac{\sqrt{N}}{2}\left(1 + \int_1^{\sqrt{N}+1}\left(\frac{1}{x+\frac{1}{2}}\right)dx\right)$$

$$\simeq \left(\frac{n}{2}\ln 2\right) 2^{n/2}. \qquad (I.2.41b)$$

In the last line we have assumed the number N to be a n-bit number, $N \simeq 2^n$, and kept only the leading term in n. The key conclusion we draw from this rough estimate that the core time needed to factorize an n-bit RSA number grows exponentially with n. It is no surprise then that children find factorizing to be much harder than multiplication, and that is why in the pre-calculator-era they had to learn the multiplication tables (which are also factorization tables) from 1 to 20 by heart, like it concerned the first few couplets of a universal human anthem! And with computers we do now the same thing, reading values from tables, whether they like it or not. A realistic example of such a

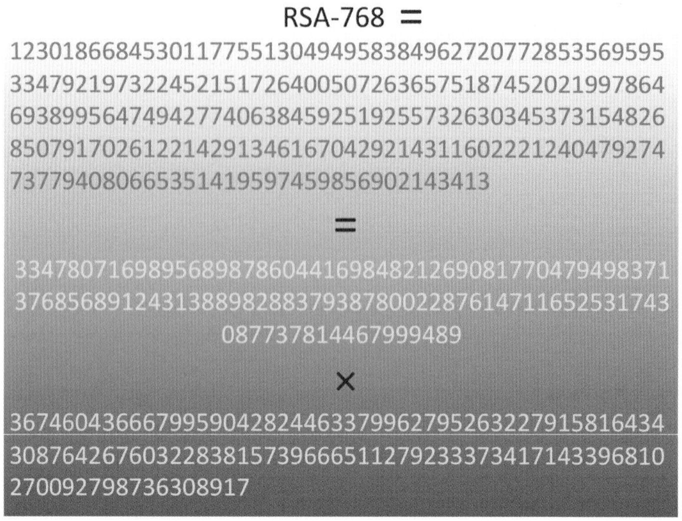

Figure I.2.50: *RSA-768*. RSA-768 is a number with 768 binary and 232 decimal digits. The factorization given below was obtained through a heroic effort by an international collective of experts. It would have taken a powerful super-computer some 2000 years, but they managed to do it in just two years.

gigantic number is RSA-2048 shown in Figure I.2.49, having 617 digital or 2048 binary digits. It is a public challenge to factorize it into two primes, and if you meet the challenge you get US$ 200.000 – unfortunately the number of dollars does not come near N, nevertheless making it worth to give it a try! But wait is that true? We just calculated that the amount of processor time would typically be $t^*(2048) \simeq P^*(n = 2048) \times (10^{-10}\sec) > 10^{300}\,\mathrm{yr}$. this is a clear warning that you have to come up with a rather smart idea.

An example of an integer number that – in a heroic effort by an impressive international collective of computer experts and mathematicians, using a tremendous amount of algorithmic ingenuity and digital power – has been successfully factorized in its two prime factors, is called *RSA-768* with 768 binary or 232 decimal digits. The result is displayed in Figure I.2.50.

Quantum factorization. We concluded that with a classical computer the typical time it takes to factor N in its prime factors grows exponentially with its size n, but the American applied-mathematician Peter Shor proved in 1994 that with a quantum computer the job can be done in *polynomial* time. We will discuss the (quantum) algorithm he constructed in more detail towards the end of Chapter II.4 in Volume II.

The factorization problem is in a strange way asymmetric: finding the integers M_0 and M_1 is kind of exponentially hard, but if you give me those integers, you and I can simply check wether you are right by just multiplying them using a large calculator, in a time of order $t \simeq n$. Factorization is one of the main tools in cryptography, so it is not just a matter of academic interest. It is of prime interest to all those who are concerned about security and safe transactions via the internet, like banks (and their clients), medical services, intelligence agencies and twittering celebrities. In fact, with today's world in a severe state of *cybernation*, all of us are highly dependent on a secure internet!

To see the huge importance of exponential vs. polynomial scaling, suppose an elementary computational step takes Δt seconds. If the number of steps increases exponentially, factorizing a number with n-bit will take $\Delta t\, 2^{an}$ seconds, where a is a constant that depends on the details of the algorithm. We have depicted some of the different computation time behaviors in Figure I.2.51. The take-home message there is the huge qualitative disparity between polynomial and exponential behavior that becomes manifest for large n.

For example, if $\Delta t = 10^{-6}$ and $a = 0.1$, factoring a number with $n = 1,000$ binary digits would roughly take 10^{37} seconds, which is much, much longer than the lifetime of the universe (which is a mere 4.6×10^{17} seconds). In contrast, if the number of steps scales as the third power of the number of digits, the same computation takes $a'\Delta t\, n^3$ seconds, which with $a' = 10^{-2}$ is 10^4 seconds or a little un-

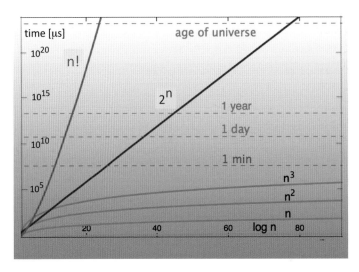

Figure I.2.51: *Computational complexity.* The classes P and NP refer to the growth of time needed to solve a problem of size n. Problems in P can be solved in polynomial time ($t \sim n^\alpha$ for some number α) and problems in NP cannot. These might grow exponentially ($\sim 2^n$) or super-exponential (like the factorial $\sim n!$.) (Source: C. Moore, SFI)

der three hours. Of course the constants a, a' and Δt are implementation dependent, but because of the dramatic difference between exponential versus polynomial scaling for sufficiently large n, there is always a huge qualitative gap in speed that cannot be compensated for by adding more pieces of conventional hardware.

I should add that for the factoring problem as such, the situation is in fact more subtle: at present the best available classical algorithm does significantly better than exponential, it would require $O\big(\exp(n^{1/3}\log^{2/3} n)\big)$ operations, whereas an available quantum algorithm provided by Shor needs $O\big(n^2 \log(n)\log(\log n)\big)$ operations. To give you an impression we give a log-linear plot of the two factorization times in Figure I.2.52, and you can see that the behavior for large n is qualitatively drastically different with slopes tending to 1/3 (classical) and zero (quantum).

Factorization is only one of several problems that could

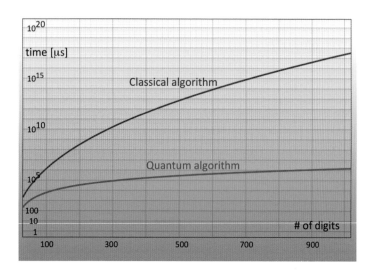

Figure I.2.52: *Factorization algorithms.* A log-linear plot of the estimated time it takes to factor an n digit number with the best available classical and quantum algorithms mentioned in the text.

potentially benefit from quantum computing. The implications of quantum information even go beyond quantum computing, and include diverse applications such as quantum cryptography and quantum communication, which by the way is intrinsically secure.

The quantum leap to such mind-boggling speed-ups arises from two main sources. Firstly from the intrinsically parallel nature of quantum mechanics, which in turn is a consequence of a quantessential feature called the *linear superposition principle*. This parallelism basically derives from the fact that state vectors have many components, and a quantum interaction or operation or gate affects all components simultaneously. Secondly from the existence of so-called *entangled states* that are unique to quantum theory. Particles that are in an entangled state can be correlated in a way which is not possible in classical physics. We will talk in quite some detail about these quantessential notions in Volume II. The actual workings of quantum theory were apparently sufficiently subtle that it took

many decades after the discovery of quantum mechanics before anyone realized that its computational potential was fundamentally different and quite powerful indeed. The huge interest in quantum information and computation in recent years has caused a thorough re-examination of the concept of information contained in physical systems, spawning the field that is referred to as 'quantum informatics.'

Computational complexity. One of the deeper issues in the theory of computation is to try and quantify what we mean by *computational complexity*. Roughly speaking a measure of the complexity of a problem would be the time it takes to solve the problem on a computer running an optimal program (algorithm) for that problem. The time it takes to multiply two n-digit numbers on a computer for example would naively grow quadratically with their size n, because you have to do of the order of n^2 basic multiplications (plus order n additions). You can gain a factor n by parallelizing the algorithm: the multiplications giving the n 'rows' in the standard multiplication chart can be done in parallel, and the subsequent additions have to be done sequentially, as indicated in Figure I.2.47. The classification of complexity is now linked to the functional dependence of the computation time on n.

There is a crucial distinction to be made here. Firstly, there are problems that can be solved in polynomial time, meaning that time is bounded by some simple power law $t \leq n^k$. Such a problem is by definition in the 'polynomial' class P, but one believes that there are many problems that do not belong to P and they belong to a larger set containing P as a subset denoted by NP. Note that NP does not just mean 'not polynomial.' The set NP contains problems of the 'find-the-needle-in-a-haystack' type. These are hard to solve because you basically have to do an exhaustive search of the whole stack and that takes a hell of a lot of time. The distinguishing property for NP is that once you have found an answer it is straightforward to check that your answer is right or wrong. Easy, because a needle is a

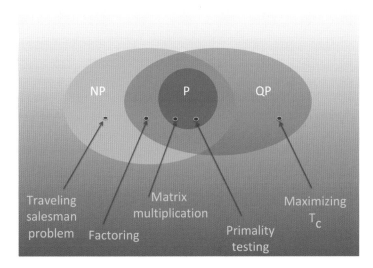

Figure I.2.53: *Complexity classes.* Hypothetical hierarchy of computational complexity classes and some standard problems belonging to them. Note that the integer factorization and graph isomorphism problem are classically believed to be not in P but in NP while in quantum informatics they belong to QP. (Source: M. Freedman et al.)

needle, isn't it? The formal statement is that the answer to an NP problem can be checked in polynomial time.

The hardest problems in NP are called NP-*complete*. The NP complete problems are in an abstract way equivalent, meaning that they can be mapped onto each other in a one-to-one way. If you solve one, you have solved all of them. Integer factoring is believed to be in NP but not in P. Furthermore the problem is *not* considered to be NP-complete; it is believed to belong to an intermediate class. The complexity of complexity theory is that we do not a priori know that a super smart algorithm does not exist to factor large integers into their prime factors in polynomial time, but that we just have not been able to find the algorithm yet, nor have we found a formal proof that such an algorithm does not exist. We find ourselves in a serious *catch-22* situation. Therefore one likes to say that certain problems are 'believed' to be NP-*complete*.

P versus NP. Indeed, the million dollar question really is whether NP in the end is not just *equal* to P! Here we just have to wait for some real or arificial computer genius to strike. That question by the way is considered to be so fundamental, that it appears on the illustrious list of seven Millennium problems of the Clay Institute for Mathematics in the US, which were announced at a meeting in Paris, held on May 24, 2000 at the Collège de France. Just solve it and they will pay you that million dollars!

Clearly the advent of quantum information theory calls for a new complexity classification scheme, with new categories denoted as QP and QNP. And therefore the complexity analysis becomes even more intricate. Whereas factorization is believed to be classically NP it is in quantum QP as we have indicated in Figure I.2.53. Nevertheless, as things stand now, there is still a remote but dramatic possibility that the content of this complexity picture in the end collapses to a single point!

We will return to what a *qubit*, the fundamental building block of a quantum computer, exactly is, as well as to the basics of quantum communication in Part II of the book. Quantum computation as a branch of science nowadays involves sophisticated and highly specialized subfields of experimental physics which are beyond the scope of this introductory book. We want to restrict ourselves to the quantessence after all. One quantessential conclusion we want to draw here is that information will go quantum not too long from now. Or, to quote Nelson Mandela: 'It's always impossible until it's done.'

Quantum physics: the laws of matter

[The homeland] looked strange to us returned soldiers...The civilians talked a foreign language. I found serious conversation with my parents all but impossible.

Robert Graves, Goodbye to All That.

Understanding the deep structure of matter has led to a new conceptual basis for all of physics. A basis that governs the laws of new fundamental particles and force fields but also of new phases of condensed matter, of chemistry and finally the laws of quantum information.

Surprisingly, this section is the shortest of this chapter the reason is simply that we still have a whole book in front of us on the subject. Quantum theory has the names of many great scientists associated with it, and not just because of the saying that success always has many parents. Roughly speaking one distinguishes three generations of quantum physicists. The first generation consists of people like Max Planck who coined the idea that energy of heat radiation be quantized, Albert Einstein who, following Planck, postulated the existence of a particle of light, which he called a photon and explained the photoelectric effect using this new particle, and finally, Niels Bohr, the great Danish physicist whose model for the atom proved it to be a tremendous breakthrough. A second generation consists of great names like Erwin Schrödinger, Werner Heisenberg, Paul Dirac and others, who managed to give a mathematical foundation for the theory and derive its fundamental equations. Many other luminaries like Wolfgang Pauli, Max Born, Enrico Fermi and John von Neumann greatly enhanced our understanding and interpretation of the theory (see Table B.1 on page 645 of Part III).

After the Second World War a third generation took the stage, with the development of quantum field theory as the most outstanding fundamental contribution. Great physicists like Richard Feynman, Julian Schwinger and Sin-Itiro Tomonaga completed quantum electrodynamics shortly after the war, and during the sixties and seventies a long list of distinguished scientists constructed the Standard Model of elementary particles and fundamental forces (see Table B.3 on page 647 of Part III).

Parallel to these developments many new research directions opened up such as quantum chemistry, quantum con-

densed matter theory, quantum material science and quantum optics (see Table B.2 on page 646 of Part III). We would also like to mention the fundamental progress in our theoretical understanding of quantum principles that these three generations and generations after them have left us with. This book is of course completely devoted to these matters and we will discuss what the central ideas of quantum theory are and how counter-intuitive and therefore unbelievable these ideas must have appeared at the time of their inception. You might experience some of that same uneasiness as you read along. As a matter of fact quantum physicists all around the globe have acquainted themselves with the theory to such a degree that most of them have developed some kind of 'quantum intuition.' And yet, in spite of that they are still regularly taken by surprise with what nature is telling them.

The development of quantum theory is one of the most astonishing achievements of twentieth century science to which a large number of gifted characters have contributed in the period of time encompassing the two world wars. It paved the way for a multitude of technological advances and even now we feel that the era of quantum technologies has only just started. This is exemplified by the promising developments where quantessential principles are exploited to create a totally new type of information science, involving quantum computing, quantum teleportation and quantum cryptography. Such is the power of truly new fundamental insights in the workings of nature: what at first appears as pastimes for absent minded eggheads, ends up as core ingredients of radical innovations and new technologies. Innovations that have offered new options for society, and often have deeply affected the human condition.

This book is quite voluminous, but that should not surprise you once you realize that – as is in full display in the tables at the end of the book – so many Nobel prizes have been awarded in this incredibly prolific field of science.

Further reading.

On relativity:

- *Very Special Relativity: An Illustrated Guide*
  S. Bais
  Harvard University Press (2005)

- *Exploring Black Holes: Introduction to General Relativity*
  E.F. Taylor and J.A. Wheeler
  Addison Wesley (2000)

- *General Relativity*
  R.M. Wald
  University of Chicago Press(2010)

- *Gravity: An Introduction to Einstein's General Relativity*
  J.B. Hartle
  Cambridge University Press (2021)

On the physics of geometry:

- *Flatland: a Romance of Many Dimensions*
  E.A. Abbott
  Penguin Group (2020)

- *The Geometry of Physics: An Introduction*
  T. Frankel
  Cambridge University Press (2011)

On the Physics of Information:

- *Introduction to the Theory of Computation*
  Sipser
  Cengage India (2014)

- *The physics of information*
  F.A. Bais and D. Farmer
  Chapter in *Philosophy of Information*
  P. Adriaans and J. van Benthem (Eds)
  Elsevier Publishers (2008)

Chapter I.3

Universal constants, scales and units

Is man the measure of all things?

Physicists have come to appreciate the existence of certain universal constants of nature like the velocity of light, Newton's constant, the elementary charge, Planck's constant etc. These are numbers that cannot be calculated from first principles. They have to be obtained from measurements and their values set the scales that characterize our universe. First we show how these constants can be used to define a complete and consistent system of units. In the second section, we take a step back and ask whether these constants are really universal, or just the parameters that appear in our theories and therefore only reflect the present state of science. In the third section, we play around with these constants to explore to what extent these natural scales mark the domains of validity of particular theories. We conclude by describing the Planck system of 'natural' units and discuss its interpretation. Indeed, the arguments presented in this chapter suggest that man is not the measure of all things, rather the arguments constitute a modest plea to bid farewell to anthropocentrism.

Isn't it a pity that we have lost many of those good old home and kitchen units, such as the thumb, the ell, or the foot, the knifepoint, the stone, the cloud, the crate, the walking hour, or horse power? The 'foot' is an example of where man was taken as the measure of all things; in fact

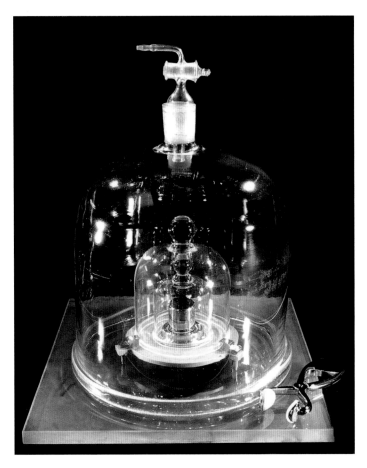

Figure I.3.1: *The international prototype of the kilogram.* Up to 2019, this was the standard of mass, kept under three glass bells in the *Bureau International des Poids et Mesures* in Paris. (Source: Wikimedia)

it was in the middle ages around 1100 that King Henry I decreed that *his* foot would be the unit of length. A nice illustration of the amusing fact that even only *one* man could be the measure of all things, with the clear disadvantage that that unit undoubtedly changed over time and furthermore one may assume that he took this 'standard foot' with him in his grave. Since the era of the Enlightenment we have been 'decimalized,' as the powers of ten are naturally built into our common number system and our metric unit system, and they are now by far superior, not least because they are pretty much shared globally. However as you know there are many remnants that don't fit in. I am not just talking of astronomers or atomic physicists claiming that they only live 10^{-13} *parsecs* or 10^{13} *angströms* respectively from their work, because such jargon is presumably rather a measure of their 'professional deformation,' or should I say devotion? A brief history of time may clarify what I mean.

On time

It's about time. In spite of the globally accepted metric supremacy, there remains ample room for exceptions. Think of our units of time for example. As you know, these are mostly dictated by the dynamics of our solar system, with the *year* that refers to the earth's rotation around the sun, while the *month* is set by the moon's rotation around the earth and the *day* is fixed by our rotation around the axis of the earth. In fact the system of time divisions was primarily inspired by the geometry of the circle, which has 360 degrees, approximately one degree per day. The circle exactly encloses six adjacent equilateral triangles with all angles equaling 60 degrees, and when you cut this partition in half – which one can do with only ruler and protractor – you would account for the division of a year in twelve months. The solar system's periodic motions serve as a celestial clock, with the almost natural choice of 24 hours to the day. It is better to think of twelve hours for the day

and twelve for the night, which is a division believed to go back to the Egyptians who did their arithmetic in base 12. From the hour down, the minute and the second are then counted in the base-60 numbering[1], and below the second we talk mili- and nanoseconds and we unanimously convert to base-10 numbering. At opposite end of the scale we think also in powers of ten centuries and millennia. So, indeed, our common time units are quite archaic and convoluted.

Unifying the incommensurate. The numbers given to us by Mother Nature are far from accurate because they may vary. Moreover, they inhibit implementing the geometric precision we just alluded to, because there is no physical reason why the units of year, month and day should have anything to do with each other as they refer to entirely different dynamics which are almost completely decoupled. And that's of course why the year is approximately $365.2422...$ days. To put it in perspective, it is like decreeing that from now on there are approximately $9.893...$ cents to the dime and 9.734 dimes to the dollar! Such incommensurate units would lead to a lot of problems at the check out, I am sure!

To arrive at an orderly bookkeeping of time it took nothing less than a pope – Gregory XIII to be precise – to decree in 1582, much like a well-trained engineer, that we should make successive approximations. First we put 365 days in the year, but to make up for the other decimals we add one day – let's pick the 29th of February – every four years, and call that a *leap year*. That brings us up to 365.25 days per year on average. Now the next step in our approximation is made by skipping one *leap year* at the turn of the century, which brings the leap day contribution down by a factor $1/25$ so we drive at 365.24 days per year on average. In the next step, we don't skip every 400 years

---

[1]The base-60 or *sexagesimal* number system goes back to the Babylonians as far as about 3100 BC. They later even introduced a positional notation marking for empty places (like our zeros) to keep track of additional powers of 60.

which gives us a score of 365.2425.The subsequent corrections are accounted for in a rather ad hoc manner by the introduction of what are called *leap seconds*.

We see the disparity and feel the tension between nature's innate rhythm and the strictly rational recipes we would like to impose. It reminds us of that funny story of a governor of a southern state in the US, who thought he could render his community a great service by decreeing that the number π from then on would be set equal to 3 in order to simplify life! But as the number π is defined as the ratio of the circumference to the diameter of a circle, there is not much room for decreeing anything about it. With the millennium debacle still fresh in our minds, when lots of computer software went haywire because of hardwired calendar settings which couldn't handle the number 2000, we may have to anticipate future troubles simply because the trivial accounting of the Gregorian calendar has not been implemented correctly.

It is amusing to learn that the decimal metric system, which goes back to the French Revolution, was also originally intended to cover the measurement of time. In 1793 apparently the French Republican Calendar was introduced, with weeks of 10 days, lasting 10 hours, with 100 minutes to the hour, and 100 seconds in one minute. This caused massive protests, not in the least by the church authorities, who felt they were losing influence and didn't want to reshuffle their Holy days, which were shared anchor points for people's sense of time. It was only in 1805 that Napoleon decided to abandon the system.

The system of time units is, like our DNA, the outcome of a contingent sequence of improvements that for the case at hand co-evolved with us humans. Our common units of time unmistakably reflect the subsequent stages of human scientific awareness and technological advancement.

Reinventing the meter

An optimal system of units should be complete and consistent, but also precise. This implies that the most advanced measurement of the universal constants of nature, or combinations thereof, have to be used to define units. According to the *Système International (SI) of units*, it distinguishes 7 *base units* and more than twenty *derived units*. The 7 (independent) *base units* are: the *second* (time), the *meter* (length), the *kilogram* (mass), the *ampère* (current), the *kelvin* (temperature) the *mole* (amount of substance) and the *candela* (luminosity).

The measurements by which these units have to be defined should not only be precise, but should also be relatively easy to reproduce, so as to make it easier to share the system of units in a practical way. These criteria are ever more relevant, as many of our daily activities depend on a great precision of measurement that makes our devices work, think for example of using the Global Positioning System (GPS). These criteria also make it mandatory that the system of units has to be upgraded from time to time so as to take advantage of the newest scientific and technological advances, not unlike the operating systems of our computers.

Let us return to our brief history of time, and see what happened to the definition of the *second* as a unit of time in the course of time. We started with time units inspired by the heavenly mechanics and the observations thereof. It may surprise you, but indeed, up to 1960 the second was defined as 'the fraction $1/86400$ of the mean solar day.' The exact definition of 'mean solar day' was left to astronomers. Apart from the fact that the rotation of the earth has irregularities, the measure itself was ad hoc. In 1967, it was finally switched from an astronomical to an atomic time standard as it is both far more precise and much easier to reproduce.

When the Saints go marching in... Given the plain fact that the human length is of the order of a meter, their weight is in the range of kilograms, their hart ticks at the rate of seconds we should not be surprised that we have ended up with something nice like the metric SI *(Systeme International d'unités)* – or MKS (Meter-kilogram-second) system as the measure of measures. And with it come the *prefixes*, the formal powers of ten, from picoseconds to terabytes and beyond. This metric thinking suggests that scientists have lifted their quantitative thinking entirely to the rational norm.

But alas, it is exactly in their ranks that irrational alternatives flourish. Extensive use is made of *derived units* that pay tribute to their ancestors and perhaps – who knows – one day to themselves. Experts thus actively employ the *Newton, Joule, Pascal, Coulomb, Watt, Farad, Ångström, Tesla, Gray, Henry, Fermi, Ohm, Siemens, Weber, Hertz, Oersted, Becquerel, Rydberg, Curie, Fahrenheit, Röntgen, Stokes, Millikan, Gray, Sievert,* and whatnot. What's in a name, you may wonder. However, note that *we should have typeset these names in lower case*, to avoid any suggestion that they might refer to individuals. After all, the force of 3 Newtons is quite something else than 3 newton. If only we could have 3 Newtons! It reminds me of the disclaimers made in the preface of some classic novels: 'all similarities with persons alive or dead are purely accidental.'

Count your blessings though: in the nineteenth century, just to communicate about temperatures, one had to convert between a rich variety of what I would like to call *tribal scales*. Not only the familiar the degrees *Fahrenheit, Celsius* and *Kelvin*, but also degrees *Réaumur, Rømer, Rankine* and *Wedgewood*! Fortunately there is only one nature,

meaning that whatever units you happen to invent, they always can be converted to more sensible ones. So, referring to obscure units is more a matter of name-dropping highly-esteemed colleagues, than using double standards. □

Today the *second* is defined as:

the duration of *exactly* 9192631770 periods of the radiation corresponding to the transition between two hyperfine levels of the ground state of the Caesium-133 atom.

This we may write as an exact defining equation:

$$\nu_{Cs} \equiv 9,192,631,770 \text{ s}^{-1}. \qquad (I.3.1)$$

This definition of the second refers to the frequency associated with the radiation that is transmitted if the Caesium atom makes the transition between two well-defined quantized energy (hyperfine) sub-levels. You could say that a Caesium clock gives about 9.2 billion ticks a second. That quantity can be measured with great precision, meaning that if you compare the outcomes of a great many carefully performed measurements, the spread of outcomes will be extremely small. In other words it is the spread of these measurements which determine the number of significant (reliable) digits. By defining the second as a *fixed* number times a physical observable, the number of significant digits in the definition of the unit equals that of the best possible measurements. The central point here is that the units inherit the precision of the measurements and they therefore necessarily co-evolve with the state of the art in experimental physics, without the need to redefine the units all the time.

You may not be surprised to hear that at present physicists are in the process of developing devices which will allow us to define the unit of time by a factor 100,000 times more precise', by using so-called *femto second lasers*, that deliver tiny pulses about 10^{15} per second. This technique uses a so-called *frequency comb*, produced by a pair of frequency locked optical lasers. It is a quantum optical device for which the Nobel prize was awarded in 2005 to the American physicist John Hall and his German colleague Theodor Hänsch. Indeed the definition of time is getting outdated all the time and a switch to the new quantum optical standard is to be expected in ten years' time.

In quantum theory many observable quantities like energy levels, currents, fluxes, charges and so on turn out to be quantized, meaning that they only can take on discrete values, exactly equal to integer multiples of certain combinations of universal constants. This 'quantization' property allows them to be measured with extreme precision and that makes them particularly suitable for defining units. We should devise definitions for a set of base units linked to the universal constants of nature so that we can measure the best, and then use those to define the other derived units.

Also in that vein the unit of length, the *meter*, was redefined in 1983 as:

> the distance traveled by light in vacuum in *exactly* $1/299792458$ of a second.

Another way to say it would be to state that,

$$c \equiv 299792458 \ \mathrm{m/s} \,, \qquad (\mathrm{I.3.2})$$

again exactly, no decimals to be added! This definition together with the definition of the second then *defines* the meter. We need no longer refer to the *International Prototype Meter* kept at the *Bureau International des Poids et Measures* in Paris, as the distance between two marks on a Platinum-Iridium bar that was kept at the freezing temperature of water.

Now, it may come as a surprise to you that the definition

of the *kilogram* as the unit of mass was up to 2019 linked to an artefact, the *International platinum-iridium kilogram* kept at the aforementioned *Bureau* in Paris, and shown in Figure I.3.1. It comes across as indeed somewhat archaic, and fortunately this artefact has been replaced by a more adequate and operational definition involving Planck's constant, again referring to precise measurements of quantum behavior.

The definition of ampère also used to be somewhat cumbersome and hard to implement. It was defined as:

> the constant current which, if maintained in two straight parallel conductors of infinite length, of negligible circular cross-section, and placed 1 meter apart in vacuum, would produce between these conductors a force equal to 2×10^{-7} newton per meter of length.

Imagine entering the store and asking for two infinite wires of zero cross section: 'Oh yes, Sir, uh, let me see, oh no, it's not in the catalogue. I am really sorry Sir. And by the way, Sir, may I ask also you to be so kind as to leave my store immediately please.'

As to the notion of temperature, the definitions were linked to phase transitions in matter systems, as for example the Celsius degree which was defined as 1/100 of the temperature difference between the boiling and freezing temperatures of water under 'normal' conditions. Since 1954, the kelvin has been defined as exactly equal to the fraction 1/273.16 of the thermodynamic temperature of the triple point of water, which is the point at which water, ice and water vapor co-exist in equilibrium. That is a very useful definition because for water at a specific pressure, the triple point always occurs at exactly a temperature of 273.16 K. Yet also there it was agreed to couple the definition with a universal constant – the Boltzmann constant k – which links energy and temperature according to the formula $E = kT$. The new 2019 definition reads:

The kelvin, symbol K, is the SI unit of thermodynamic temperature; its magnitude is set by fixing the numerical value of the Boltzmann constant to be equal to exactly 1.380649×10^{-23} J/K [joules per kelvin].

As a matter of fact the most accurate measurements of k (about one part in a million) have been obtained by acoustic thermometry, which relies on the fact that the speed of sound in a gas is directly dependent on its temperature.

Can we change? Yes, we can! What has happened over the last half-century is that we have been replacing units defined by certain sacred artefacts kept in highly-esteemed institutions, with units based on precision measurements of certain universal constants or combinations thereof.

The diagram depicted in Figure I.3.2 gives a comprehensive scheme of the newly proposed definitions of the base SI units. The proposal was prepared by the *Comité international des Poids et Mesures* and was officially adopted in 2019. This is quite a substantial upgrade, much like the upgrades of your computer software, except that I would guess that here we talk about version 26 or so, because the first versions go back to about 1875. The base units are represented as colored nodes, and the fundamental constants of nature used to define them correspond to the surrounding brown nodes. The grey arrows indicate how the definitions are hierarchically linked to each other. There are seven fundamental units, and therefore seven constants are needed to fix them. The proposal is interesting in that these seven constants are given exact values when expressed in the base units, and therefore this guarantees a consistent set of definitions if we follow the arrows in the appropriate way. To understand how a unit is defined you look at the arrows coming in to the corresponding node and see where they come from. One arrow comes from an adjacent constant of nature and possible others come from

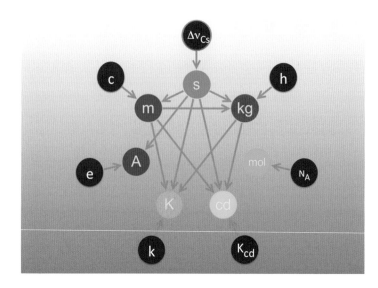

Figure I.3.2: *New SI-Units* The update of the definition of the base SI units adopted by the *Comité international des Poids et Mesures* in 2019. The brown nodes represent integers defining the constants and the arrows indicate the dependencies in the definitions. You start by defining the *second* in terms of the frequency of the ground state Caesium hyperfine transition. Then you move on to the *meter*, the *kilogram* and the *ampère*, all of which involve one additional constant, and then you move on to the *kelvin* and *candela*. (Source: Emilio Pisantly, on Wikipedia.)

units that have been defined before.

Let us consider the definition of the ampère A. We start with the gray arrow coming from the elementary charge e, that arrow represents the exact value of e in terms of A:

$$e \equiv 1.602176634 \times 10^{-19} \text{ A s}.$$

The other arrow comes from the 'second,' which is the unit we already defined in terms of the caesium frequency, and therefore A is defined in terms of the observed values of e and ν_{Cs}.

For the kilogram the prototype is not longer used, but reference is now made to the exact value of Planck's constant h:

$$h \equiv 6.62607015 \times 10^{-34} \text{ kg m}^2 \text{ s}^{-1},$$

which now also involves the meter (referring to c and second) and second (referring to ν_{Cs}). So the definition of the kilogram relies on the measurement of the constants h, c and ν_{Cs}.

The remaining question is how, and in what combinations, are these constants determined experimentally. For example magnetic flux Φ that pierces through a two-dimensional superconductor happens to be quantized directly in terms of fundamental constants: $\Phi = n\phi_0 = nh/2e$, from which the *Josephson constant* $K_J = 2e/h$ can be measured extremely precisely. On the other hand, in a so-called quantum Hall system, the Hall-conductivity, which is a transverse conductivity, is quantized in units $\sigma_H = ne^2/h$ that allow for a precise determination of the *Von Klitzing constant*, $R_K = h/e^2$. Measuring these two constants yields an accurate determination of the fundamental constants e and h. Another important observable defined in terms of fundamental constants, which can be measured very precisely, is the *fine structure constant* α,

$$\alpha = \frac{1}{4\pi\varepsilon_0}\frac{e^2}{\hbar c}. \qquad (I.3.3)$$

Indeed the choice of universal constants forms a fair reflection of the depth and precision to which science has managed to descend, and the way they are used in the definition of SI units strikes the optimal balance between precision and reproducibility.

How universal is universal?

Universality is a beautiful, ambitious, but also vulnerable concept, because how do we know whether some constants of nature are universal or not? In mathematics we know such numbers exist, but in physics it is harder to define and establish universality. One should at least require that such would-be universal numbers are the same throughout the (our) universe. But how do we know they are or are not?

Universal constants are – if not God-given – at least Mother-Nature-given-numbers. They happen to be equal to what they have been found to be in human experiments. Their values are believed to be universal, that is, independent of space and time. As you know too well, that doesn't hold for all Mother-Nature-given-numbers, like todays value of your body-mass index for instance, or the viscosity of some expensive French Cognac. If I use phrases like 'the same everywhere and for all time,' I in fact mean everywhere and for all time in our universe, or even better, just nearby in our universe in our present age. Because if we happen to live in a *multiverse* – and there is no fundamental reason why not – then one of the clues about multiverses is that in each separate universe the laws of physics could be quite different. They would represent very different points in the space of possible theories that we have come up with so far. This would imply that there might be entirely different sets of universal constants or known constants could take different values.

Fundamental constants as model parameters. A more pragmatic approach would be to postulate that the universal constants are the numerical input parameters that appear in our theories, such as the masses of elementary particles and the strengths of the fundamental forces. The latter, like Newton's gravitational constant and the electron charge, are also called *coupling constants* because they set the strength of the forces between particles carrying mass and/or charge. The very fact that they appear as input parameters means that they cannot be calculated within that theory; their value can only be determined through experiment. And for all we know these numbers are completely independent.

In mathematics we have universal numbers that are absolute as they can be rigorously defined. The number π for example is defined as the ratio of the circumference of a circle and its diameter. It is a dimensionless number that cannot change and is absolute within the framework of mathematical axioms. One might be tempted to link the dimensionless ratios of physical universal constants to an expression in terms of the universal numbers of mathematics only, much like Plato in his cave would have liked it. In spite of the fact that there is quite an industry actively pursuing these ideas, I consider that somewhat premature. I can only envisage such a step as a final one where the ultimate unified physical theory would be obtained. But nobody promised us such a paradise in the first place so let's go back to the parameters in our current fundamental physical theories.

Reducing the number of fundamental constants. From the perspective of physics it makes complete sense to ask how fundamental these would-be fundamental constants really are. Over time, physical theories get more and more unified in their description of physical phenomena, implying that fewer theories with a smaller number of parameters suffice to account for the same or an even larger body of experimental data. This means that the number of independent fundamental constants has to decrease because we discover relations among them.

Think for example of Maxwell's theory unifying the description of electricity, magnetism and light into a single framework. That theory has in fact three fundamental constants (i) the dielectric constant of the vacuum ϵ_0 featuring in the Coulomb law that gives the force between two electric charges (ii) the magnetic permeability of the vacuum μ_0 featuring in Ampère's law that gives the force between two current carrying wires and (iii) the velocity of light c. Now it turned out that there is a relation between these constants that follows on from Maxwell's equations, that relation is just $c = 1/\sqrt{\epsilon_0\mu_0}$, and it is this relation which allowed us to write the Maxwell equations (I.1.26), with only the velocity of light appearing in them. This is a nice illustration

of the fact that the more unified the perspective, the lower the number of independent fundamental constants. This insight forces us to accept that our universal constants are not so universal after all, and it makes us wonder where this game will end.

Where do we stand? Constants that at present are considered to be universal are for example the strength of the gravitational and electric forces G_N, and $e^2/4\pi\epsilon_0$, the velocity of light c, Plank's constant $\hbar$, and Boltzmann's constant k. These constants are *dimensionful*; they are not pure numbers like π, because they have some units linked to them, like c has units *length/time*. That may disappoint you because we are talking about universal constants and they change already if we go from measuring lengths in meters to lengths in inches and the like.

But the good news is that they, exactly because they have units, provide universal – Mother Nature given – links between those different types of units. Such links allow you to eliminate specific units, for example we can use c to convert to units where spatial distance is measured in seconds, $\mathrm{light\ seconds}$ to be precise. A distance of one light second is defined as the distance a light pulse would travel in one second, so generally the distance d in meters corresponds to a distance d/c in $\mathrm{light\ seconds}$. This is what we discussed extensively in the previous section. The sun is eight light minutes away while the Andromeda galaxy 2.5 million light years. Planck's constant h appears in the fundamental relation linking energy and frequency postulated by Einstein reading $E = h\nu$, and has units $\mathrm{joule \times second}$, the velocity of light links mass and energy ($E = mc^2$) but also space and time as we saw. Boltzmann's constant links temperature to energy through the relation defining the thermal energy $E = \frac{1}{2}NkT$. Having all these relations we could do away with all conversion factors, meaning that you can choose units in which the universal constants (h, c and k) would become equal to unity, and then measure everything in powers of *only* joules (energy) *or* only meters (length) *or* only $\mathrm{seconds}$ (time). We will come back to this system of 'natural units' shortly.

Time dependence of fundamental constants? The comments made so far suggest that we take a more pragmatic stand on this question of universality. On a deeper level the value of many would-be universal constants could for example depend on some underlying, hitherto unknown dynamical mechanism, which typically means that they are probably *not* constant in space and time. Instead they are like fruit or peanut butter, in that they have an expiration date. They turn from external input parameters of the old theory into calculable output parameters of the underlying new theory. They move from the pool 'fundamental' to the pool 'effective.' But if this is the way it works it suggests that we should go out and measure whether there are universal constants that do actually vary in time and space. We know for example that the fine structure constant $\alpha = e^2/4\pi\hbar c$ sets the scale for the separation of lines in the atomic spectra, and one could try to make observations of the spectra emitted from atoms that are very, very far away in the universe and check whether the fine structure constant was exactly the same or different at the time the signal was emitted. Experiments of this nature were proposed by John Barrow et al. in 2002. The results of such experiments have so far not confirmed the idea but did produce some upper limit on the relative shift of α of 10^{-17} per year in 2008.

The narrow window of opportunity for life. It is the set of values that these constants of nature have, which turns out to be essential for *our* universe to be what it is. How do we know? Can we go to other universes to check this out? No, not quite, but having reliable theories in which these numbers feature allows us to ask what would have become of our universe if the parameters had had different values. The result of such an exercise is quite surprising not to say startling: it is only in a very narrow window of parameter values that a universe like ours, with its structural complexity and diversity as expressed through the chemistry of life for example, would be possible. We have touched upon

 What to do if somebody tells you that they weigh 10^{52} Hertz? If you befriended a music lover and they tell you that their mass is 10^{52} Hertz (1 Hz = 1 inverse $second$), then you might want to call them crazy, but if they know about universal constants what they say may make complete sense. You can always go back and restore the more familiar units by multiplying with a particular simple combination of fundamental constants. In this case you start with inverse seconds and want to get back to kilograms: $M = 10^{52}[second^{-1}] = M \times h$ [joule] $= M \times h \times c^{-2}$ [kg]. So, the upshot is that the combination hc^{-2} converts [sec^{-1}] into [kg]. The numerical factor involved equals $6\times10^{-34}/9\times10^{16} = 0.66\times10^{-50}$ [sec kg]. So having a mass of 10^{52} Hz is actually quite OK. Indeed, units are a matter of convention; if somebody on a market ordered 50 $troy$ $ounces$ of Gouda Cheese, you would not be surprised if I told you that this person was an English jeweler honeymooning in Amsterdam, would you? □

some of these aspects in the section about Big Bang cosmology. And others will be mentioned in a section on the ascent of matter in Chapter III.1.

Turning the argument around one could say that choosing the values of the universal constants at random, the chance to end up with an inhabitable universe would be vanishingly small. We expect universes equipped with fancy observers like ourselves to be extremely rare. Lucky us! The *anthropic principle* – a philosophical principle – refers exactly to the attempt to apply the arguments just presented in the opposite order. It tries to derive the structure of our actual universe solely from the fact that we, *homo sapiens*, are here. In a qualitative sense this is of course an interesting question, but as a quantitative approach it strikes me as naive and doomed. Think of the calculation from quantum first principles, of the anomalous magnetic moment of the electron, which agrees with experiment to twelve significant decimal places! It is hard to imagine getting such precision out of a qualitative approach like the anthropic principle. To understand the universe you need to use far more facts from nature than our mere existence.

Theories outside their comfort zone

Scientific progress can be measured by how effective our theories are. The more physics we explain with the fewer theories, the better. In this section we are going to play some heuristic games with numbers. The observed numerical values for our universal constants tell us what the relevant scales in nature are. At the same time these numbers provide insight in the domains of validity of some of the well-established theories. Surprisingly, naive reasoning and dimensional analysis leads to suggestive qualitative insights with respect to fundamental physics. These arguments underscore the value of heuristics. We have listed some of the fundamental scales with the formulas related to them in Table I.3.2 on page 147.

Domains of validity. Given the values of the universal constants, it is enlightening to cook up other numbers from them which in turn can be interpreted as *characteristic scales* that play a significant role in our universe. Such scales not only follow from the observed values, but also from assumptions underlying the theories in which they appear as parameters. This number cooking game often involves extrapolating the 'laws of nature' to uncomfortable extremes and exactly for that reason this game can yield some information on what the *domain of validity* of such theories really is.

Some devil's advocate, a malign adversary or even a bright student may within the context of a certain model come up with some well-defined, yet, really nasty questions. Questions, which the theory may fail to answer correctly, or may cause the theory to get stuck in a recursive loop that points to a profound confusion or persistent contradiction in our current understanding. Contradictions of a type that faithful teachers sometimes hide, ignore, or even deny. Yet, there always appears to be a moment of truth when it is no longer possibly to deny that the theory fails to give a straight answer to a straightforward question, not even in principle. That is why such Q&A sessions are worth pursuing in spite of their heuristic if not speculative nature. Fortunately many of the theorists I met in my life were always willing and – even eager – to randomly 'shoot the breeze' and ask creative 'what if' questions.

This freedom to let the collective mind wander should be cherished as it is at the heart of scientific progress. And scientific progress is basically about pushing the limit on the ranges of the validity of theories further and further. After each turning point or paradigm shift, the new theory usually provides clear-cut quantitative restrictions on the domain of validity of the old theory; that is why we can speak of scientific progress in the first place[2].

The virtue of heuristics

All we need is the back of an envelope.

Do electrons love or hate each other? We have so far discussed some aspects of the classical theories and some of the salient features of the relativity and quantum domains. And we have commented on the universal constants of nature that we have measured and that feature as external input parameters in our models, like the strength

---

[2]Some devil's advocates therefore argue that particular religions, as systems of knowledge, lack an internal mechanism or stimulus through which they might learn about their limited domain of validity. It is my opinion that the imperative of open questioning and self-improvement sets science apart in the history of human endeavors.

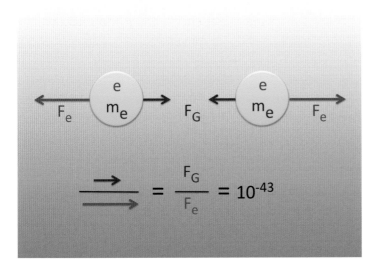

Figure I.3.3: *Interacting electrons.* Two electrons in outer space repel because of their equal charges and attract because of their masses. Yes, and they do fly apart!

of certain forces and the masses of certain fundamental particles. Combining such numbers and the simple laws in which they appear gives interesting information about the characteristic scales that we observe in nature. That information is at best qualitative and heuristic, but it does provide useful insights about the expected domain of validity of our theories.

In this subsection we limit ourselves to the electromagnetic and gravitational force and what we can conclude from them with respect to the scales that we should associate with them, then we will add some quantum wisdom to it. These two forces are remarkable in that they both have an infinite range and the laws describing them are so-called 'inverse square laws.' For the gravitational force between two masses we have Newton's law, while for the electric force between two charges we have Coulomb's law:

$$F_G = -G_N \frac{m_1 m_2}{r^2} \quad \text{and} \quad F_e = \frac{1}{4\pi\epsilon_0} \frac{q_1 q_2}{r^2}. \quad (I.3.4)$$

One might ask: Is there a way to compare these forces? Yes and no; they talk about essentially different things like

masses and charges, so it's like comparing apples and pears. However, it is not as bad as that because nature has given us particles that have both mass and charge – they are both apples and pears so to speak – and these allow us to compare the strengths of the two forces in a meaningful way. In Figure I.3.3 we show two electrons which have charge e and mass m_e. They attract because of their masses and they repel because they have equal charges. If they met in outer space they would experience two opposite forces, so the key question is: will they pair up or fly apart? To get the answer, we have to take the ratio of the magnitudes of the two forces,

$$\frac{F_G}{F_e} = \frac{4\pi\epsilon_0 G_N m_1 m_2}{q_1 q_2} \simeq 10^{-43}. \quad (I.3.5)$$

This shows that the gravitational force is phenomenally weaker than the electric force. Note that this ratio does not depend on the distance; it is a fixed number. How sad for the electrons, it is not only hard to stay together; it would even be extremely hard to meet in the first place. The order of magnitude of this number holds for any fundamental particle which carries both mass and charge, though the actual number could differ of course.

An electromagnetic size: how big is an electron? Given the force between two charges one can calculate the interaction energy of two charges that are separated by a certain distance. One may also define what is called the *self-interaction energy* of a particle due to the force field. This electrostatic self energy is the energy it costs to build up a charge e on a sphere of radius r, and is of the order of $e^2/4\pi\epsilon_0 r$. Building up a charge means that you bring in infinitesimal amounts of charge from infinity and calculate the interaction potential. Equating that potential energy to its mass energy $m_e c^2$ according to the famous Einstein formula yields the *classical electron radius* in terms of its mass:

$$r_e = \frac{e^2}{4\pi\epsilon_0 m_e c^2} = 2,8 \times 10^{-15} \text{ m.}$$

This expression is directly obtained from combining certain

constants of nature known from experiments with naive dimensional analysis, and begs for an interpretation even though it would be heuristic. It certainly is a size one can naturally assign to a charged particle as it reflects the energy of the total electric field carried by a charge on a sphere of radius r_e. Note that the electromagnetic size of a charge grows with charge but decreases with increasing mass. So the lightest particle having a certain charge yields an upper-bound for the electromagnetic size of such a charge. Note the paradoxical nature of this classical reasoning, it would produce an infinite potential if one would assume the particles to be point like. This fact stood out as a fundamental limitation of the classical theories in the description of a charged particle, and as we'll see in Volume III, Chapter III.4, quantum field theory provided an essential new perspective on this question that exploited the sophisticated notion of *renormalization*. Anyway, according to the reasoning we have followed so far, a particle of zero charge could still be considered point-like.

A gravitational size: know your horizons! As for a neutral particle electromagnetic considerations are void, so one could maybe make use of the gravitational interaction to set a scale, and assign a classical gravitational radius to any mass m. One repeats the argument and replaes Coulomb's law by Newton's gravitational law, ignoring for the moment the sign difference[3], so the potential energy of a mass m at radius r would be $E \sim G_N m^2/r$, and equating this to the mass energy $E = mc^2$, we get $r_g \sim G_N m/c^2$. This relation sets a scale for the applicability of classical Newtonian gravity, and indeed, remarkable enough it is (up to a factor 2) equal to the *Schwarzschild radius* of a particle of mass m defined as:

$$R_s = \frac{2G_N m}{c^2};\qquad (\text{I.3.6})$$

that is $\sim 10^{-57}$ m for the electron. This is an excruciatingly

small number, far outside of the scope where our physical intuition has any experience, let alone any bearing. It's like somebody getting up and starting to talk to you about what they are planning to get done in the next one billionth of a second! Stay normal please! The Schwarzschild radius is where the gravitational horizon around a black hole with mass m is located, and according to the general theory of relativity, there is no information that we, as outside observers, can obtain about the interior of the black hole. Talking about a particle's properties beyond that scale is problematic. If you would send a willing observer to check out the interior they would not be able to report back to you, as they are doomed to a not so gracious exit facing the singularity at the origin.

No escape: apocalypse you! To clarify this peculiar property of black holes, it suffices to repeat the thought experiment that the French mathematician Pière-Simon Marquis de Laplace described in 1796, and that lead him to the notion of the *corps obscur*, which in modern parlance is just a black hole[4]. You probably are familiar with the notion of *escape velocity*, if you throw this book straight up in the air it will under most circumstances drop on your head some time later. Yet, if you throw it with a speed of more than 11 kilometers per second, then it would never return. As you see it is not so simple to get rid of a book, they tend to stick around. Far away it would still feel the gravitational force caused by the mass M of the Earth, but it can escape because the kinetic energy would be larger than its gravitational binding energy to the earth. Equating the kinetic energy and the binding energy gives the equation for v_{esc}, we obtain:

$$mv_{esc}^2/2 = mG_N M/r \;\Rightarrow\; v_{esc} = \sqrt{2G_N M/r}.\quad (\text{I.3.7})$$

Note that this velocity does not depend on the mass m of the book, so anything you throw up with a velocity exceeding 11 km/s will be gone for ever. You see that the

---

[3]The sign would translate in the statement that the the potential corresponds to the energy needed to gradually bring the mass to infinite radius.

[4]A British natural scientist, John Mitchel, had already made a similar argument in 1783. He called the objects *dark stars*.

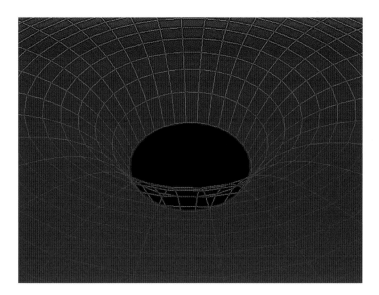

Figure I.3.4: *A black hole.* General relativity tells us that if we put a lot of mass in a tiny volume that mass will collapse under its own weight and form a black hole. Black, because its escape velocity exceeds the speed of light and – at least classically – no information can escape. A virtual sphere called the *event horizon* will form outside of the mass, and its radius corresponds to the Schwarzschild radius (I.3.6).

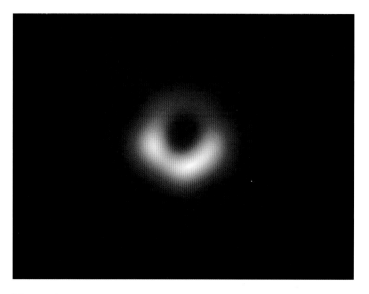

Figure I.3.5: *A black hole picture.* This is a real picture of a black hole in the galaxy M87 about 5×10^{20} km away. It measures 4×10^{10} km across, and has a mass corresponding to 6.5 billion solar masses. The picture was captured by the Event Horizon Telescope (EHT), a network of eight linked telescopes on Earth.

escape velocity would increase if we would decrease the radius of the Earth while keeping its mass fixed. And indeed, knowing that the velocity of light was approximately 300.000 km/s. Laplace basically asked himself the question: to what radius do we have to shrink the size of the Earth in order that the escape velocity would become equal to the velocity of light? And beyond that radius, he argued, even light would not be able to escape from the Earth's surface – the Earth having the size of a marble by the way. No light signals could be sent to some far away observer, at least they would not get very far. The Earth would be black: a black hole so to speak. Though this tiny Earth would be invisible, you would still be able to probe its presence gravitationally. If the Sun were a black hole, you wouldn't be able to see it but the planets would move in their orbits all the same. Going back to the formula (I.3.7), you'll also agree that an object with *any* given mass M will

have an event horizon once its size is small enough. With black holes one tends to think of super massive objects like heavy stars. After having burned up their nuclear fuel they would collapse under their own gravitational attraction in a supernova event. The compact object staying behind would indeed be a black hole. Astrophysicists have in the meantime identified large numbers of them. They also are located at the center of galaxies. One suspects the presence of giant black hole gobbling loads of stars for breakfast. At first nobody could think of compactifying a chunk of matter like the Earth to within a radius smaller then its horizon of less than a centimeter. The concept of a black hole was so totally inconceivable that it was discarded as a brilliant fiction of the mind – clearly an artefact of fancy mathematics. The idea was that a condensed state of matter, like the space inside of a stone or a lead block, would be 'filled up' completely. It would only be only compressible to a limited extent, which seemed evident from just experimenting with it. There would be no room for such extreme collapses was the prevailing opinion, which was even held by influential astrophysicists like Sir Arthur Eddington.

In fact the story went the other way around. With the advent of the quantum understanding of the deep structure of matter, it was that intuitive idea that matter fills space, which turned out to be a fiction of the mind. Quantum theory taught us exactly the opposite, that matter *is* mostly empty space. The mass of a stone is carried mostly by the tiny nuclei inside the atoms and the spacing between those nuclei is about a million times larger than their size. Removing that space, you could in principle compress the Earth to the size of a meter across – the density would then correspond to the density of a neutron star. Astrophysicists have systematically studied the processes of stellar evolution, including their dramatic ending. A star will, depending on its mass, end up as a compact object, like a white dwarf, a neutron star, or a black hole. Most black holes observed have masses between five and several tens of solar masses, and the lightest known black hole has a mass of around 3 solar masses.

A second comment to make is that small masses also have a horizon, which makes it possible to study mini black holes in order to find out to what extent they could be produced and would be stable. Maybe also these hypotheticals – fictions of the mind – will be found one day in spite of them being 'invisible.'

The age of our universe. Before continuing our black hole adventure where science is running into at least one of its own horizons – if not a brick wall – we briefly return to the other side of General Relativity (GR) connected with the Friedmann cosmology, which we discussed quite extensively in the previous chapter. The question we want to address is a question that has puzzled humankind already for millennia, but at the same time it is also a question that children start asking when they are in elementary school.

Did the world always exist, or was there a beginning – a moment of creation? And if so, when was that? Such questions that everybody encounters at some point in their life create a demand for answers, and where there is demand, economists tell us that there will be supply. And so there was!

There is a great history of estimating the age of the universe. The early estimates from a smart clergyman who managed to argue from The Scriptures that the week of creation was about 4000 years ago are well known. The story is that the Bishop James Ussher around 1650 came even with a precise date: Sunday 23 October 4004 BC! What you can say about the history of would-be answers is that there was an overall trend to ever increasing numbers.

It is interesting to recall the involvement of the great biologist Charles Darwin who estimated the age of the earth by using geological arguments combined with the time needed to have the complexity of life evolve, to be a few hundred million years. This estimate was heavily criticized by Lord Kelvin who argued that the age of the sun, based on the state of knowledge – or ignorance – of the day, could not be more than say 20 or 30 million years. His knowledge typically comprised Newtonian gravity, chemistry and thermodynamics, and his ignorance was hidden in the fact that he didn't know that he didn't know. The unknown unknowns concerned the whole field of nuclear physics, because there was none in those days. And to understand the age of the Sun you have to understand the nuclear processes that keep the Sun shining. This was an exemplary scientific debate, where Darwin got much closer to the correct answer for reasons that are clear now. In the second half of the twentieth century the astronomers entered the game using a variety of observational and calculational methods. This caused the numbers to go up dramatically into billions of years. Fortunately the results also started to converge.

Let us try to make a crude estimate of the age of the universe starting from the Friedman equation (I.2.9). For simplicity we assume that the universe is flat ($k = 0$) and has only matter in it. The matter density drops inversely with the volume, so:

$$\rho_m = \rho_{crit} \frac{\Omega_m}{a^3}.$$

with ρ_{crit} is the critical energy density and Ω_m the present relative matter constant. The equation then simplifies considerably and we get:

$$\sqrt{a}\frac{da}{dt} = H_0\sqrt{\Omega_m}. \qquad (I.3.8)$$

As you can check by differentiating, the solution is $a = \beta t^{2/3}$ where β is some constant. This yields for the Hubble parameter $H(t) = 2/(3t)$. Evaluating this for t_0 we obtain $H_0 = 2/(3t_0)$, resulting in the estimate,

$$t_0 = \frac{2}{3H_0} \simeq 9.3 \times 10^9 \; yr,$$

where we have used the value $H_0 = 70 kms^{-1} \; Mpc^{-1}$. This crude calculation thus shows that the age of the universe is of the order of the inverse Hubble parameter. The best value available today, extracted from the 2018 data of the Planck space telescope is:

$$t_0 = (13.781 \pm 0.020) \times 10^9 yr.$$

Note the amazing precision here, which shows the tremendous progress in the field of observational cosmology! This means that the Hubble parameter is a fundamental observable as it sets the scale for the age of the expanding universe.

Going quantum

The quantum size of a particle. So far we used the equations of classical physics and relativity, which involved the fundamental constants G_n, e, and c. What happens if we include some of the basic quantum relations? This would add Plank's constant h (or its reduced version $\hbar = h/2\pi$, denoted as 'h-bar') into our deliberations.

A nice starting point is the expression that Louis de Broglie[5] in 1923 proposed for the wavelength λ of the 'matter wave' associated with a particle of mass m moving with velocity v or momentum $p = mv$, which simply reads $\lambda = h/mv$. Combining this formula with Einstein's dictum that nothing can move faster than light implying that $v \leq c$, we arrive at a 'minimal wavelength'

$$\lambda_c = \frac{h}{mc}, \qquad (I.3.9)$$

for a quantum particle, which is called its *Compton wavelength*. The Compton wavelength for the electron is $2.43 \times 10^{-12} \; m$, which on a heuristic level can be interpreted as a measure for the 'quantum size' of the electron. For scales much larger than the Compton wavelength we can safely consider the electron as a well-defined localized 'particle' whereas when we approach the Compton wavelength we have to take its wavy nature into account and treat it quantum mechanically. In other words also in quantum theory the notion of a point particle breaks down beyond a certain scale. A rigorous way to define the Compton wavelength is to say that it equals – following Einstein – the wavelength of a photon whose energy equals that of the rest energy of a particle: $E = hc/\lambda = mc^2$. This is certainly true but less straightforward to interpret.

Alternatively we may invoke Heisenberg's uncertainty relation $\Delta x \, \Delta p \geq \hbar/2$, which in words amounts to the statement that in a given quantum state of a particle the uncertainty in the outcome of a position measurement times the uncertainty in the outcome of a momentum measurement equals at least h-bar over two. And if we then interpret mc as the maximum uncertainty in momentum that leads to the Compton wavelength as the minimal uncertainty in

---

[5]In fact I should have said: Louis-Victor-Pierre-Raymond, the 7th Duke of Broglie!

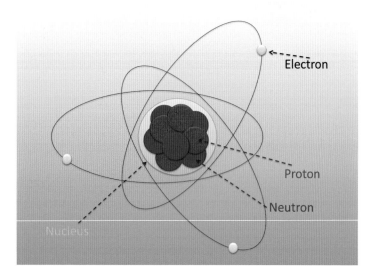

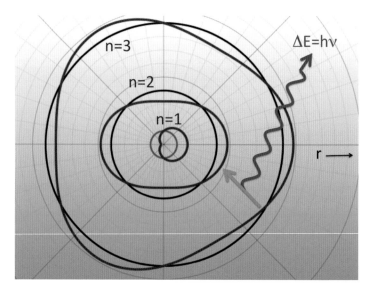

Figure I.3.6: *The Rutherford model of the atom.* The canonical picture of the atom proposed by Ernest Rutherford, with a positively charged nucleus consisting of protons and neutrons, with some negatively charged electrons orbiting the nucleus. It is a symbolic representation, which is misleading in two ways. The relative sizes are totally out of proportion, since the size of the orbits is about 100,000 times larger than the size of the nucleus. So if you take the nucleus as depicted in this figure the electron orbits would be about a kilometer in size! Furthermore, in the stationary states of the atom, the electrons are not at all localized like point particles. The states rather correspond to the 'standing' wave patterns proposed by Bohr as indicated in the next figure. They represent the smeared out probability distributions for finding the electron at a given location.

Figure I.3.7: *The Bohr atom.* This model has *quantized orbits*, satisfying the constraint that the electron wave would fit an integer number of times on the orbit. This condition $n\lambda = 2\pi r_n$ leads to states with quantized energy and angular momentum. The radii of the successive orbits scale quadratically ($\sim n^2$).

position of the particle. As we will see later this scale is directly linked to the width of the 'wave packet' representing the electron in quantum theory. And with a quantum leap in vagueness you could argue that minimal uncertainty in position indicates the effective size of the quantum equivalent of a particle.

Heuristics and reasoning by analogy is a dangerous game but can be enlightening and yields a rough sense of the scales involved with little work, not more than that. Therefore very useful!

An atomic size: the Bohr radius. There is one more quantum scale that we should mention at this point. It is the first quantum estimate of the atomic size called the *Bohr radius*. In 1911 Rutherford had shown that the atom has an almost point-like positively charged nucleus with the electrons orbiting around it. This brought Niels Bohr to his famous atomic model that, with its simple but radical starting point, immediately led to an astonishingly deep insight in the line structure of atomic spectra. Indeed, it is one of the most outstanding results of early quantum theory. The argument used the wave character of the electron (say De Broglie's formula) to quantize atomic orbits, and thereby also its energy levels. From these energies the frequencies of the lines in the spectra could be calculated directly.

Bohr used the idea of *particle-wave duality*, and put it into practice by assuming that the stationary electron states in the tiny atomic environment would correspond to standing waves on a supposedly classical orbit. That wave should not destructively interfere with itself and therefore Bohr demanded that the electron wave would fit an integer number of times on the orbit of the electron, which led him to the 'quantization condition': $n\lambda = 2\pi r$ with $n = 1, 2, 3, \ldots$. If you now use the relation of De Broglie between momentum and wavelength you get $p = h/\lambda = nh/(2\pi r) = n\hbar/r$. A straightforward exercise in Newtonian mechanics shows that in order to have a circular orbit you need a central force $F_c = ma = mv^2/r$, which in this case is provided by the Coulomb force F_e of equation (I.3.4). So, from the equation $F_c = F_e$ one finds the possible radii r_n :

$$\frac{mv^2}{r} = \frac{p^2}{mr} = \frac{n^2\hbar^2}{mr^3} = \frac{e^2}{4\pi\varepsilon_0 r^2},$$

from which Bohr derived the quantization rule:

$$r_n = a_0 n^2; \text{ with } a_0 \equiv r_1 = \frac{4\pi\varepsilon_0 \hbar^2}{me^2} \sim 5.3 \times 10^{-11} \text{ m},$$

where the constant a_0 in honor of its creator is called the *Bohr radius*. In Figure I.3.7 we have sketched the periodic electron waves for the first few orbits.

It is no surprise that the quantization of the orbits implies that other physical quantities are also quantized, notably the energies and the angular momentum. To start with the latter, for a circular motion we have that the angular momentum $L = rp$, and just substituting the quantized value for p given above, one gets $L = n\hbar$, showing the basic integer quantization condition for orbital angular momentum, which indeed has the dimensions $[\text{kg m}^2/\text{s}]$ of angular momentum. Substituting the radius in the expression for the total energy $E = E_{\text{kin}} + E_{\text{pot}} = p^2/2m + V_{\text{Coul}}$, one finds that the energy is quantized as

$$E_n = E_1/n^2, \tag{I.3.10}$$

where the ground state energy is given by:

$$E_1 = \frac{me^4}{32\pi^2\varepsilon_0^2\hbar^2} \simeq -13.6 \text{ eV}. \tag{I.3.11}$$

We see that the energies of the hydrogen atom are negative (meaning that they are bound states) and that for large n the states pile up towards $E = 0$. An essential feature of the model which, also depicted in Figure I.3.7, is the proposition that when an electron makes a transition from a higher to a lower orbit, the energy difference ΔE will be carried away by a photon that has a frequency $h\nu = \Delta E$. We return to the Bohr model and its relationship with the observed atomic line spectra in the section on atomic structure in the next chapter.

Further gaming with fundamental scales. Returning to typical length scales related to the electron, we have so far cooked up three sizes: (i) the classical electromagnetic size (= the classical electron radius) $r_e \sim 10^{-15}$ m, (ii) the gravitational radius (= the Schwarschild radius) $R_s \sim 10^{-57}$ m, and (iii) the quantum scale (= its Compton wavelength) $\lambda_c \sim 10^{-12}$ m. One thing these numbers clearly suggest is that in worrying about the size of the electron we should first take into account quantum effects, before entering into profound debates on the meaning of its classical electromagnetic or gravitational radii.

What else can we do with these length scales? We could take their ratios and try to interpret them. We can for example define the dimensionless ratio of the (i) and (iii). This number (up to the factor $h/\hbar = 2\pi$) is denoted as α and called the *fine structure constant* $\alpha = e^2/4\pi\varepsilon_0 \hbar c$; it is indeed a pure number and equals $\alpha \simeq 1/137$. This constant is a clean measure of the interaction strength of the electromagnetic interaction in (relativistic) quantum theory, which is not so surprising because the fundamental constants e, c and $\hbar$ feature in it.

Another dimensionless ratio one can take is the Compton wavelength over the Bohr radius, giving an idea as to what extent the electron would fit in the atom. One finds that $\lambda_c/a_0 = 2\pi\alpha$, which is again proportional to the fine structure constant. This indicates that the two scales are not vastly different, particularly if one takes into account that the electron in the Bohr-atom is non-relativistic and the Compton wavelength an underestimate for its quantum size. This underscores once more that we should treat the problem of atomic structure with quantum theory.

We could also define a gravitational fine structure constant as $\alpha_g = Gm_e^2/\hbar c$, which would equal $\alpha_g = 1.75 \times 10^{-45}$. The ratio of these two 'structure constants' show, which also equals the ratio of (iii) and (i), bring us back to the intrinsic difference in coupling strength that we mentioned before: the gravitational attraction of two electrons is weaker than their electromagnetic repulsion by some 43 orders of magnitude.

A quantum bound on processing speed. The uncertainty relations allow one to construct heuristic quantum bounds on various dual observables like momentum and spatial extent, or energy and time. The former yielded the Compton length, and the latter allows us for example to set an ultimate bound on processing speed. If we take the energy corresponding to a mass $E = mc^2$ and relate that energy to a fundamental frequency according to $E = h\nu$ and interpret this frequency as the number of logical operations per second, we arrive at the formula proposed by Seth Lloyd in a 2000 paper for the maximal number of transitions N^* per unit mass per unit time.

$$N^* \simeq \nu = c^2/h .$$
(I.3.12)

Putting in the numbers one arrives at the ultimate processing speed of a 'one kilogram laptop' as some 10^{50} logical operations per second. To give you an idea of what this means typical estimates for the human brain yield 10^{15}, while the most powerful super computers run at $10-100 \times 10^{15}$ flops. These comparisons are rather misleading because of the very different structure of these 'machines;' the brain has a relatively low clock speed of about $100 \mathrm{Hz}$ but works in a highly parallel mode.

Nuclear forces: the story of weak and strong. Later on in the book we will discuss two other forces which are not

of the inverse square type: the strong and weak nuclear forces They differ in an essential way in that they effectively only act over small distances – meaning, small compared to the size of an atom – and that is why we don't see or feel them. These forces can be approximated by a inverse square law, which is cut-off at a certain characteristic scale, called the strong and weak scales respectively. The effective potential of a weak or strong charge corresponds to the so-called *Yukawa potential*:

$$V_Y = g_Y \frac{1}{r} e^{-r/\lambda_c} .$$
(I.3.13)

We see that the inverse $1/r$ potential standard for gravity and electromagnetism with a strength g_Y is multiplied with a negative exponential of the distance. The interaction potential is said to be *screened* and becomes vanishingly small past the typical scale λ_c, appearing as an additional fundamental parameter in the theory. Such screening effects make the interactions effectively *short range*. The particle's experience would be comparable to driving in a dense mist or calling each other in the crowd, the interaction between entities is only effective at short distances. We have depicted the Yukawa potential in Figure I.3.8. The interpretation of the characteristic scale λ_c is, that it is inversely proportional to the mass m_c of the particle that is mediating the nuclear force, like the photon mediates the electromagnetic force. The natural relation between a mass and a characteristic length is the quantum scale or Compton wavelength of the particle as pointed out before.

To complete this short interlude on the nuclear forces, let us just give you the scales involved. The strong nuclear scale is in the first approximation associated with the exchange of so-called *pion* particles, their masses are of order $m_\pi \simeq \frac{1}{10} m_p$, yielding a length scale of approximately $10^{-14} \mathrm{cm}$, which typically is the size of a nucleus. For the weak nuclear force the mediating particles are the W and Z bosons with masses $M_W \simeq 100 m_p$ and consequently the weak force has a tiny range of the order of

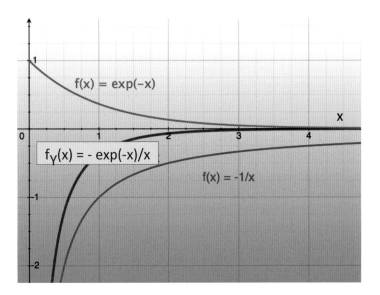

Figure I.3.8: *The Yukawa potential.* The purple curve is the product of a $(-1/x)$ potential in blue (like the one of electromagnetism or gravity) and an exponential suppression factor $(\exp -x)$ in red. What results is an attractive potential for the weak and strong interactions, which is effectively short-range because of the exponential cut-off.

$$\lambda_W \simeq 10^{-17} \text{cm} .$$

At this point we may also mention that setting the mass of the mediating particle to zero we get back to the formulas of electromagnetism and gravity (the blue curve in Figure I.3.8). This confirms our earlier claim that these long range force fields are associated with the exchange of massless particles such as the photon and the graviton. In that case the potential is a simple power law reflecting the scale free nature of the long range interaction. The power law potential exhibits therefore what in modern parlance is called a *long* or *fat tail*, which refers to the behavior clearly visible on the right in Figure I.3.8 where the blue power law curve is much larger than the exponentially suppressed purple and red curves.

Where the quantum collective rears its head. We started in Chapter I.1 by summarizing the fundamental theories of classical physics, and we have indicated in this chapter how quantum theory enters to indicate the boundaries of the domain of validity of the classical theories of mechanics, gravity and electromagnetism. It will not surprise you that the theory of statistical or thermal physics has also an intrinsic parameter that tells you when quantum phenomena should be expected to become relevant in multi-particle systems such as gases and liquids. The interesting thing here is that these phenomena even occur in 'ideal' systems where we ignore inter particle interactions. The central observation is again based on a simple dimensional argument. If one considers an ideal gas of massive atoms in equilibrium at some temperature T, then the average *thermal energy* per particle is $E_{th} = 3kT/2$. So we can define a *thermal momentum* p_{th} through the relation:

$$\frac{p_{th}^2}{2m} = \frac{3kT}{2} . \qquad (I.3.14)$$

Next we use the De Broglie relation to define a *thermal wavelength* as $\lambda_{th} = h/p_{th} = h/\sqrt{3mkT}$. This length scale depends on h and defines the size of the wave packets related to the thermal excitations of the particles in a gas. For the case of particles in a gas at room temperature the thermal wavelength is typically of the order 0.1 *ängström* or 10^{-11} meters. When does this scale become relevant? It clearly matters if it becomes of the order or larger than the typical inter-particle distance d, which is determined by the particle number density n defined as $n = N/V$. Classical considerations (even in the absence of interactions) should break down if:

$$\lambda_{th} \geq d \;\Rightarrow\; \frac{hn^{1/3}}{\sqrt{3mkT}} \geq 1 . \qquad (I.3.15)$$

The conclusion is that we enter the quantum domain at high density and/or low temperature. As we will discuss later on, this is intimately linked to spectacular quantum phenomena like superfluidity, (super-)conductivity, and Bose-Einstein condensation. A rough indication of some examples where the quantum laws are inescapable can be found in table I.3.1.

Table I.3.1: Thermal wavelengths and domains*

System	T[K]	λ_{th}/d	domain
Air at room temperature	300	0.006	classical
Liquid nitrogen (^{4}He)	77	0.10	classical
Liquid helium (^{4}He)	4	1.16	quantum
Electrons in copper	300	18.9	quantum

*R. Baierlein, Thermal Physics, Cambridge Un. Press (1999).

Natural units ©1898 Max Planck

We conclude by discussing a system of natural units introduced by Max Planck. The price to pay is to give up anthropocentricity, at least on the level of units.

Can we please finish this endless talk about units? Yes, we can! It was already pointed out by Max Planck how to do this in the *Fünfte Mitteilung*, *Über irreversible Strahlungsvorgänge*, to the *Preussische Akademie* in 1898[6]:

> Alle bisher in Gebrauch genommen physikalischen Maßsysteme, auch der sogenannte absolute C.G.S.-System, verdanken ihren Uhrsprung insofern dem Zusammentreffen zufälliger Umstände, als die Wahl der jedem System zu Grunde liegenden Einheiten nicht nach allgemeinen, notwendig für alle Orte und Zeiten bedeutungsvollen Gesichtspunkten, sondern wesentlich mit Rücksicht auf die speziellen Bedürfnisse unserer irdischen Kultur getroffen ist.

In the *Mitteilung* he devised a system of units that deserves the qualification *natural* like no other. These *Planck*-units are all directly linked to the simple universal constants that we discussed before:

- the gravitational constant G_N with units $[kg^{-1}m^3s^{-2}]$,
- the speed of light $c \sim [m\ s^{-1}]$,
- Planck's constant[7] $\hbar \sim [kg\ m^2s^{-1}]$
- and Boltzmann's constant $k \sim [kg\ m^2s^{-2}]$.

Some juggling with dimensions leads quite unambiguously to the following natural units: the Planck-unit of length or the Planck length,

$$l_p = \sqrt{\frac{\hbar G_N}{c^3}} = 1.62 \times 10^{-33}\ cm;$$

the Planck mass,

$$m_p = \sqrt{\frac{\hbar c}{G_N}} = 2.18 \times 10^{-5}\ g;$$

and the Planck time,

$$t_p = \sqrt{\frac{\hbar G_N}{c^5}} = 5.39 \times 10^{-44}\ s.$$

If we include the Boltzmann constant k as another fundamental constant, we may add the Planck unit of temperature:

$$T_p = \sqrt{\frac{\hbar c^5}{k^2 G_N}} = 1.42 \times 10^{32}\ K.$$

Divine units indeed! Imagine, adopting these as the units of length, mass, time and temperature amounts to setting all the above expressions in terms of the fundamental constants equal to one, which implies that we have to set $\hbar = c = k = 1$ in all formulas and calculations! What a relief for the students who have to remember them. I am afraid though that in the real world of construction and electrical engineers these units would be despised

---

[6]English translation (by author): All physical systems of measurement, including the so-called absolute CGS system, which have hitherto been used, owe their existence to accidental circumstances, in that the choice of the units on which each system is based does not depend on general points of view that necessary hold for all places and times but takes only in consideration the special needs of our earthly culture.

---

[7]In Planck's original paper this or better *his* constant was actually called b and not $\hbar$.

except in the rare instance where one is involved in building universes[8]. This is precisely the case because using these divine units would involve such huge conversion factors that you would lose a common sense of scale.. On the other hand, dragging along all these fundamental constants all the time makes formulas far less transparent and that clutters the mind. I challenge the entrepreneurial readers to choose natural units for the rest of this chapter, which means that you set the universal constants everywhere equal to one. You will find that the resulting formulas become stunningly simple indeed.

Ahead of the crowd. The natural units beg for an interpretation and maybe it is just that they mark the domain of validity of the theories of Einstein and/or quantum theory. Or better, they mark a domain where quantum and relativity typically meet. Problems at the Planck scale involve phenomena where quantum gravitational effects have to be included. And if we do not have a complete understanding of what the quantum theory of gravity is, our calculations will be unreliable to say the least, and may give unsatisfactory answers to sensible questions. Referring back to the scales we discussed before we see that for a fundamental particle with a mass equal to m_p, the Compton wavelength and the Schwarzschild radius become roughly equal since:

$$\hbar/m_p c = G_N m_p / c^2.$$

This expresses the fact that for a particle with a mass of the order of the Planck mass the quantum uncertainty in its spatial extent is the same as its 'gravitational' uncertainty. This gravitational uncertainty is due to the strong gravitational field which causes that it is impossible to extract information on the outside of that tiny horizon about what happens inside. The equal sign in the above equation, inspired by matching uncertainties, basically makes the bold hypothesis that both uncertainties are somehow

due to the same underlying mechanism. Such a mechanism would have to be accounted for by a would-be theory of quantum gravity.

It is worth remembering that heavy objects have a Compton wavelength that is negligible for example for the earth we get that $\lambda_\oplus = h/m_\oplus c \simeq 10^{-67}$ cm, while its Schwarzschild radius still is a respectable $R_\oplus = 0.9$ cm. And because both are so much smaller than the actual size of the object Earth, it is not in terrestrial physics that this fundamental contradiction will leave any mark. For the electron the situation is the opposite, $\lambda_e = h/m_e c \simeq 10^{-12}$ cm (indeed its non-local character manifests itself on the atomic scale), while the Schwarzschild radius is an excruciatingly small $R_e = 2G_N m_e/c^2 \simeq 10^{-57}$ m. The conceptual conflict between relativity and quantum theory as encountered at the Planck scale signals the crisis our notion of space-time suffers in the light of the quantum postulates. On the other hand, one might hope that also this crisis will be the seed for a new fundamental paradigm.

Black holes

> The question is not whether black holes 'exist'. They exist as classical objects. The question is, what is the quantum mechanical equivalent? It is well possible that in quantum mechanics black holes are no longer strictly distinguishable from more conventional forms of matter.
>
> Gerard 't Hooft, *Physica Lecture* (1995)

It is widely believed that black holes are rather esoteric, far-fetched, out of this world, nerdy gadgets and therefore not so relevant. Wrong! It has become ever more clear that they are the principal key to a new and much deeper understanding of what gravity and thus space-time are really about. It introduced the concept of *information* into physics in a fundamental way. Indeed, some people say that

---

[8]Surprisingly, quite a few engineers appear to do so in their spare time. I would rather have engineers constructing universes, than philosophers building airplanes!

Figure I.3.9: *Information loss?* Does information get lost forever when it falls into a black hole? Detail of the remarkable sculpture *Le Nomade* in Antibes (France) created by the Spanish sculptor Jaume Plensa

'black holes' are for the theory of gravity, what the 'hydrogen atom' was for quantum theory. Gravity's fundamental properties and problems really show up in the unexpected intricacies of black hole geometry. There is more to gravity than dropping a teaspoon on the floor, or keeping the moon in orbit. We have already seen in the previous section the peculiar property of horizons predicted by GR. But just saying that there is a horizon is not sufficient. When you start thinking about it seriously, a lot of hard questions come your way, questions that probe the deeper grounds of GR and go beyond it. This section touches upon the remarkable research by many of the brightest brains of recent generations, attempting to bridge the gap between curved space-time and quantum theory. This appears necessary to get a complete and consistent picture of these miraculous outposts of reality. Yes, horizons mark an important frontier, but to what?

Stephen Hawking: Quantum black holes are not black!
We have discussed the essential feature of GR that ev-

ery mass M has a Schwarzschild radius R_s associated with it. If the size of the massive object is smaller than its Schwarzschild radius, then there will be a *horizon* around the mass located at R_s. It is called a horizon because if a chair or for that matter Shakespeare's collected works fall into the black hole through their gravitational attraction to its mass, then once they pass the horizon, there is no possibility for them to return. Falling into a black hole there is a point of no return. And the points of no return form by definition the horizon. That raises the question what happens to all that stuff disappearing in the black hole. Einstein's theory says without further ado that it disappears in the 'singularity' located at the origin. But that is not what a far away observer sees, because they can not look beyond the horizon. They only see the books approaching the horizon at an ever slower rate. Here a strange complementarity of perspectives arises, because for the infalling 'Hamlet' or 'Midsummer night's dream' nothing special happens as they would smoothly sail though the horizon. From that moment on their fate is decided, they will be swallowed by the singularity; no pardon can be granted, there is just no escape!

So, altogether the physics of black holes was for a long time highly enigmatic, but also unsatisfactory, strangely incomplete and paradoxical to say the least. On the one hand, Einstein's theory inescapably posed their existence, but on the other hand failed to answer many of the basic questions it posed. From the 1970s, fundamental breakthroughs have been achieved in our understanding of black holes. Indeed it turned out that quantum theory had to come in to rescue and resolve some of the bizarre contradictions that black holes confronted the physicists with. Actually it was both quantum theory and information theory that played essential roles. It has become clear that a deep understanding of how black holes work on quantum level could provide the essential keys to a broad understanding and interpretation of what a consistent quantum theory of gravity may ultimately look like.

Black hole thermodynamics

> It is natural to introduce the concept of black hole entropy as the measure of information about the black hole interior.
>
> Jacob Bekenstein (1972)

At first there was the development of a 'thermodynamics of black holes' by Jacob Bekenstein and Stephen Hawking. Subsequently Hawking made the seminal discovery that when quantum processes are taken in account, the black hole is no longer black! Quantum processes that take place at the horizon and which are not allowed by classical physics mean that the black hole will lose energy due to radiation coming of the horizon. Hawking was able to calculate the spectrum of this radiation and that turned out to exactly be the black body spectrum explained by Planck's quantum hypothesis. It means that the mysterious object changed from a black hole into a radiating black body. The black hole is rather like a black ball kept at a certain temperature – appropriately called the *Hawking temperature*, T_H. Let us try to get a grasp of the main components of the argument by recalling some basic concepts:

(i) the thermodynamic relation due to Clausius between heat produced and entropy

$$dQ = TdS; \qquad (I.3.16)$$

(ii) the Boltzmann definition of entropy in terms of the number of states

$$S = k \ln W; \qquad (I.3.17)$$

(iii) the Schwarzschild radius

$$R_s = \frac{2G_N M}{c^2}; \qquad (I.3.18)$$

and (iv) the Planck length,

$$l_p^2 = \frac{\hbar G_N}{c^3}. \qquad (I.3.19)$$

Figure I.3.10: *Information on the horizon*. An artist's impression of bits of information on the horizon of a black hole. The information capacity would be one *bit*, or rather *nat*, per square Planck length.

We start with the observation that classically, nothing can come out of the black hole, so if you drop an object with a certain energy and entropy into the black hole, the only thing you may observe is that the mass increases (and therefore the Schwarzschild radius), but the information content would be lost forever. The idea now is to associate the mass-energy Mc^2 with the heat term in equation (I.3.16) and the area of the horizon A with the entropy term on the right.

Let us talk about spherical black holes, than $A = 4\pi R_s^2$. To convert this area into some entropy, let me define a Planck area a_p, which we will choose as $a_p = 4l_p^2$. The comment here is that the Planck length is the smallest length scale that is physically meaningful, which means that this Planck square is the smallest physically accessible area (as I am giving a heuristic argument I allowed myself to put in the extra factor 4 for convenience). This means that we assume that a single Planck square corresponds to one *nat* of information[9],

$$S = k \frac{A}{4l_p^2} = k \frac{Ac^3}{4\,\hbar G_N},\qquad (I.3.20)$$

which is exactly the expression first written down by Bekenstein and Hawking. In this perspective a black hole would look more like a spherical digital memory as indicated in Figure I.3.10.

This is a surprising result, because, as entropy is associated with the number of degrees of freedom of the system, you would expect that in three dimensions the entropy within a volume bounded by some horizon would grow proportional to the volume and not to the area. This suggests that this rather fictitious, mathematically defined surface will somehow acquire an important physical interpretation if we take quantum processes into account.

Hawking temperature.

> Quantum mechanical effects cause black holes to
> create and emit particles as if they were hot bodies.
>
> Stephen Hawking (1975)

Next, we want to find the temperature of the black hole as a thermodynamic system. The internal energy is given by $U = Mc^2$ and the entropy S is given by the previous equation. That equation allows us to calculate:

$$\frac{dS}{dM} = \frac{dS}{dR_s}\frac{dR_s}{dM} = \frac{8\pi R_s^2}{M}\frac{c^3 k}{4\,\hbar G_N},\qquad (I.3.21)$$

which relates a change in mass with a change in entropy. We may obtain the temperature by using the first law of thermodynamics $dU = dQ - dW$ where the last term on the right-hand side is absent because a black hole doesn't

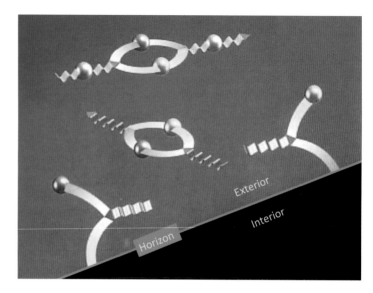

Figure I.3.11: *Pair creation at the horizon.* In a vacuum one always has quantum fluctuations in energy. As a consequence of Heisenberg's uncertainty principle virtual particle anti-particle pairs will be created. Normally these have to recombine but on the horizon there is the possibility that one member of the pair falls in the black hole and the other escapes. This is the microscopic origin of the Hawking radiation.

do any work, while for the first term we will use the expression of (I.3.16). This yields the following expression for the internal energy:

$$dU = d(Mc^2) = \frac{\hbar c}{4\pi R_s k}\,dS.$$

from which the temperature follows,

$$T_H = \frac{\hbar c}{4\pi R_s k} = \frac{\hbar c^3}{8\pi G_N M k}.\qquad (I.3.22)$$

This is indeed the temperature Hawking derived in his famous paper from 1975, and which was therefore named after him.

We only took the shortest and easiest route which suggests the result, but Hawking really proved that a black hole would radiate as a black stove at that temperature.

---

[9]With N states the information entropy is $H =^2 \log W$ [bits], the thermodynamical information entropy is defined by $S/k = \ln W$ [nats]. We choose the nat-unit because we want to make the link to the natural logarithm appearing in thermodynamics.

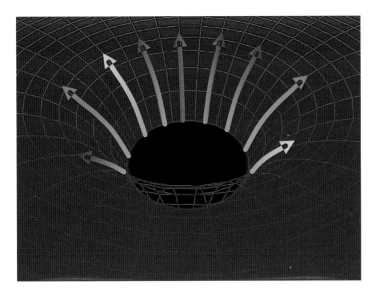

Figure I.3.12: *Hawking radiation.* A black hole is not black as depicted in Figure I.3.4, but rather as depicted here: a black body at a Hawking temperature T_H, emitting thermal radiation.

The idea was simple but brilliant and the calculation notoriously hard. The starting point of the original derivation was the production of *virtual particle – anti-particle pairs* in the gravitational field near the horizon. He basically calculated the probability that one of the two would fall in, then they could not recombine, and the other particle would have to 'become' real and would be able to escape. The quantum black hole would indeed start radiating and would lose energy. Talking in terms of pictures, we should thus replace the image of the classical black hole of Figure I.3.4 with the quantum version of Figure I.3.12.

Power emitted and life time estimate. The total power emitted by a black body, is given by the radiation law of Stefan Boltzmann (the 'other' Boltzmann) which states that the emitted power would be proportional to the temperature to the fourth power and of course also proportional to the surface area, $P \sim AT^4$, which using equation (I.3.22) implies that the power emitted would be *inversely* proportional to the second power of its mass $P \sim M^{-2}$. The black hole loses mass because of the Hawking radiation but the

more mass it has lost the more it radiates. The final stages are therefore more like an explosion. A black hole would not be black anymore; on the contrary, left on its own in outer space it would *evaporate* until nothing, or may be only some unknown type of remnant, would be left! From the power dependence on the mass, we can make a rough estimate of the life time τ of a black hole, with the following calculation:

$$\int_{t(M_0)}^{t(0)} dt = \int_{M_0}^{0} \left(\frac{dt}{dM}\right) dM \sim M^3 . \qquad (I.3.23)$$

The conclusion is that the life time of a black hole would grow with its mass to the third power.

To put this discussion of black hole evaporation in perspective let us mention that the Hawking temperature for a solar-mass black hole would only be 60 nano Kelvin. Such a black hole presently located somewhere in our universe would absorb far more radiation than it would emit, because the universe itself has at present a background temperature of 2.7K. This in turn is a consequence of the cooling of the universe by expansion, and is in fact a leftover from the hot Big Bang. So the Hawking radiation phenomena is profound but hypothetical in so far as there is little hope of being able to directly observe it. Consequently, though considered by many to be one of the great discoveries of twentieth century physics, Hawking was not eligible for a Nobel prize.

Surface gravity. The beauty of Hawking's discovery is that it strongly suggests that it is the horizon where the interesting physics of a black hole really takes place. But at the horizon we are still far away from the singularity and space time is smooth. This suggests that we should try to link the emerging temperature of the horizon to a local gravitational concept. The natural candidate would be what is called the 'surface gravity,' which is basically the gravitational acceleration denoted by g at the horizon. We mean the 'universal' gravitational acceleration Galilei was talking about. Indeed, an observer located at the horizon has to be accelerated to stay there. Just like we are at rest at the earth's surface. The reason we are not freely falling is because the Earth's surface accelerates us radially outward by exerting a normal force. The gravitational acceleration or surface gravity at the horizon is just given by (minus) Newton's law: $g = GM/R_s^2$. Substituting the Schwarzschild radius and comparing with the Hawking temperature we find that the relationship between the Hawking temperature and the surface gravity is strikingly simple:

$$T_H = \frac{\hbar g}{2\pi ck} \, .\qquad (I.3.24)$$

It appears that what matters is the transformation from the frame of the observer, freely falling into the black hole for whom nothing special is going on, to the accelerated frame of the observer at rest near the horizon.

Accelerated observers and the Unruh effect

The above suggests that we should look at the world according to an accelerated observer. This yields another interesting, even more basic link between the structure of space-time and entropy/information known as the *Unruh effect*. Let us first establish that an accelerated observer perceives an horizon. If you transform flat Minkowski space to an accelerated frame you get the so-called Rindler coordinates which is depicted in Figure I.3.13. The world lines of the accelerated observers are time-like hyperbolae. To be precise you should say that the world lines correspond to observers who experience a 'constant force,' because with $F = ma$ and the fact that the mass in this formula is the relativistic mass increasing with the velocity, the effective acceleration becomes smaller so that the velocity never exceeds c, as the figure shows. And that is exactly why the horizon is there. The future light cone of any point beyond the horizon (like the yellow arrow in the dark region) does not intersect with the world line of the accelerated observer and therefore cannot be observed.

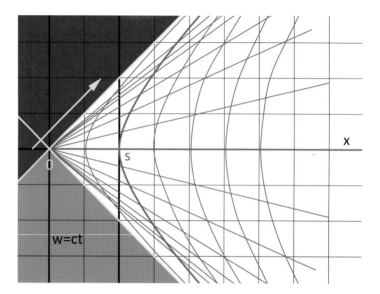

Figure I.3.13: *Accelerated observers.* A space-time diagram for an accelerated frame of reference. The parameter $s = c^2/g$ is the inverse of the acceleration g. The world lines of observers initially at rest on the x-axis are time-like hyperbolae that asymptotically approach the light cones. The white region is the *Rindler space-time* and has a future and past horizon. Light signals emitted from points in the dark region travel along straight lines under $45°$, these do not intersect any world lines and therefore can never be observed by the accelerated observer.

This suggests that also in this case including quantum processes à la Hawking will turn that horizon into a black body with a temperature given by the very same formula (I.3.24), linked to the acceleration $g = c^2/s$ of the observer. This remarkable result is known as the Unruh effect, named after William Unruh who first presented the calculations leading to the formula (I.3.24) in 1978. The proof for this case of an accelerated observer amounts to a rather straightforward (quantum) calculation. We start in the rest frame with a quantum field describing some species of scalar particle. The field is in a zero energy state, usually called the vacuum. In this state no particles are present, and that is what the observer at rest perceives. If then we make the transformation to an accelerated frame, the transformed distribution for the density of states corresponds to a thermal energy distribution. This means that the accelerated observer will perceive a highly excited state with many particles present. The spectrum obtained corresponds exactly to the Planck spectrum, the direct consequence of the quantization of energy. This is the spectrum that was hailed as one of the nails in the coffin of classical physics! This calculation by the way beautifully illustrates the relativistic proverb: 'truth is in the eye of the beholder,' and in particular depends on his frame of reference.

Pair creation of charges. In this context it is illuminating to think of the original Hawking argument. Consider a simple two-dimensional $(x.t)$ space-time where one may introduce a constant background electric field, say $E_0 \approx F_{01}$ in the positive x-direction. This – in two space-time dimensions – corresponds to a Lorentz invariant background energy. In such a background field there is a certain quantum probability that charged particle anti-particle pairs can be created. Clearly these pairs would split up, the positive charge moving to the right and the negative charge to the left. They would experience a constant force $F = \pm eE$ and therefore accelerate, and both would correspond to ideal 'Rindler observers.'

The situation is depicted in the space time diagram of Figure I.3.14 with the two particles accelerating in opposite directions, with their velocities asymptotically approaching the speed of light. They are causally separated from the moment of their creation. The probability of the pair creation depends on the threshold energy which corresponds to the sum of their masses, $2mc^2$, and the electrostatic energy of the pair depending on their distance d. The remarkable result is that the spectrum corresponds exactly to a thermal distribution matching the Unruh temperature.

One other quantum aspect of profound interest in this example is the fact that in the quantum state in which the pair is created, the particles are entangled. The information of one member of the pair is inaccessible to the other

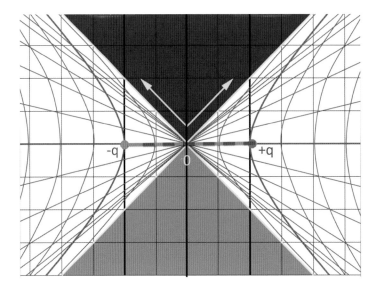

Figure I.3.14: *Pair creation.* In a background electric field, a particle anti-particle pair might be created spontaneously and the members of the pair would accelerate in opposite directions, being causally disconnected from their inception, each living in its own Rindler bubble. However in the quantum world the pair would be entangled which leads to a situation where each of them is dealing with a so-called mixed state.

because it is hidden behind a horizon. This manifests itself in that each of the particles perceives being in a mixed or 'thermal' state with a characteristic entanglement entropy. We will return to these concepts in chapter II.1 but want to mention them already here.

The fate of information. Thermal radiation is completely random (thus maximally uncorrelated and unconstrained) and therefore has maximal entropy. Here we arrive at a familiar point where by solving one question we pose the next one. The idea that quantum processes preserve all entropy and therefore information leads to a non-trivial upgrading of the *information-paradox*: If we throw the entire Encyclopedia Brittanica in a black hole it will be converted into pure thermal radiation according to Hawking. Clearly that cannot be the case, where did all the correlations present in the incoming state go?

If we take a step back, we could compare the formation of a black hole (putting more and more mass on a star, until it becomes a black hole), and its successive evaporation, with a more familiar process (proposed by Sydney Coleman) where we know that quantum processes conserve both energy and entropy. Imagine a piece of coal at zero temperature in a pure state where by definition $S = 0$, that gets irradiated with a fixed amount of high entropy radiation, which we assume is absorbed completely. It brings the coal into an excited state at a finite temperature. As a consequence the piece of coal starts radiating, it will eventually return to the zero temperature state, with zero entropy. As the process of absorbing the initial radiation and emitting the outgoing radiation is a quantum process, it follows that the emitted radiation should have exactly the same entropy as the incoming radiation. And therefore no information could have gotten lost!

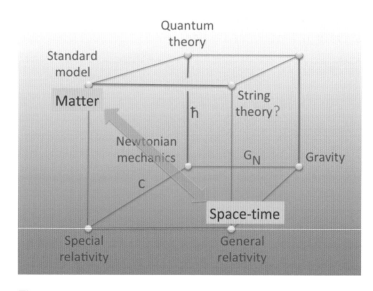

Figure I.3.15: *The magic cube.* Universal constants and the domains of validity of some fundamental theories.

The black hole instability. The conventional narrative is that by throwing an encyclopedia into a black hole, all information would be lost. With the appearance of quantum theory at the horizon, however, our view has radically shifted in the sense that the real physics of black holes is the quantum physics taking place at the horizon. Consequently the question of what happens to the information in the quantum context needs to be critically re-evaluated.

The quantum principles tell you that if you were able to really perform the full quantum calculations including the detailed effects of entanglement, which we haven't discussed yet, then in that case you could in principle recover the entire incoming state. In other words, in the quantum domain it is extremely hard to really get rid of information, it may be hiding, but it still should be out there somewhere. By the way, to people having a Facebook account, this story may sound unpleasantly familiar.

In principle black holes may exist for any mass, hence one may also consider microscopic black holes to rid oneself of the many astrophysical complications that are irrelevant in

this context. The statement is that mini-black holes would evaporate very rapidly and therefore be very short-lived. In other words these mini black holes are states of matter that are bound gravitationally, but are unstable, just like many other massive 'bound states' happen to be. This instability gives rise to a finite life time, and the formation and decay process is a quantum process, often referred to as a 'resonance.' In such quantum processes information is preserved, much like the other conservation laws that physics obeys, like the conservation of energy, angular momentum and charge. So, Hawking's crucial discovery has in the end led to a fundamental overhaul of our concept of black holes. And as a consequence the present view is therefore that quantum theory supersedes general relativity in that information has to be preserved somehow. Yet, at this moment, a fully quantum mechanical account of the formation and subsequent evaporation of a basic black hole, which is the litmus test for claiming an understanding of quantum gravity, has not yet been achieved. Though with the advent of string theory as a serious candidate for such a theory, the perspective on black holes has progressed in impressive ways as we will indicate towards the end of the next chapter. But the fact remains that science at any stage is just 'work in progress.'

The magic cube

The magic cube of turning points. Our story of scientific progress and hope, linked to the successive identification of fundamental constants of nature, is depicted in the 'magic cube' of Figure I.3.15, which is a cube in the space of ideas. The magic cube has classical Newtonian physics on the back lower edge with the laws of mechanics (like $F = ma$) on the left, and his law for gravitation on the right. The constant G_N linking the two appears as the universal constant setting the scale for the strength of the gravitational interaction. The bottom square is the relativity plane where the fundamental constant c (or better $1/c$) is added. The boundary of the domain where Newtonian physics is valid is reached as velocities become of the order of the velocity of light. The Newtonian limit corresponds to $1/c \to 0$. Newton's gravitational force law is instantaneous and therefore incorporates the notion of 'action at a distance'. This notion is incompatible with special relativity, where information and thus disturbances cannot propagate faster than the velocity of light. So special relativity vetoes instantaneous non local interactions. This conflict was then brilliantly resolved by Einstein's theory of gravity, the theory of general relativity.

The vertical dimension opened up with the advent of quantum theory through the universal constant $\hbar$. The classical (non-quantum) limit corresponds to $\hbar \to 0$. The vertical square on the left-hand side includes the modern unified quantum theories for all known forces and matter, except for the gravitational force. The top plane would include a quantum theory of gravity like string theory which so far has not been able to generate predictions that could be tested by experiment. A string theorist may argue that if you had started by postulating string theory, you would

Table I.3.2: Some fundamental sizes and scales.

Notion	Formula	Size [m]
Class. electron radius	$r_e = \dfrac{e^2}{4\pi\epsilon_0 m_e c^2}$	$\sim 10^{-15}$
Compton wavelength	$\lambda_c = \dfrac{h}{mc}$	$\sim 10^{-12}$ (e^-)
Strong nuclear scale	$\lambda_\pi = \dfrac{h}{m_\pi c}$	$\sim 10^{-15}$
Weak nuclear scale	$\lambda_W = \dfrac{h}{m_W c}$	$\sim 10^{-18}$
Bohr radius	$a_0 = \dfrac{4\pi\epsilon_0 \hbar^2}{m_e e^2}$	$\sim 10^{-10}$
Schwarzschild radius	$R_s = \dfrac{2G_N m}{c^2}$	$\sim 10^{-2}$ (Earth)
Planck length	$l_p = \sqrt{\dfrac{\hbar G_N}{c^3}}$	$\sim 10^{-35}$
Age of the universe	$t_0 = \dfrac{3}{2H_0}$	$\sim 10^{10}$ yr
Thermal wavelength	$\lambda_{\text{th}} = \dfrac{h}{\sqrt{3mkT}}$	$\sim 10^{-11}$ gas 300 K

have predicted gravity and the other interactions. Such theories unify the notions of matter and radiation with that of space-time. The magic cube illustrates how inconsistencies led the way to fundamental paradigm shifts. Such are the blessings of the inconvenient truths that keep popping up along the winding road of science.

Conclusion. In this chapter we have celebrated the 'back of the envelope' philosophy and advocated for the virtue of heuristics and approximations. In science the 'truth' is a moving target, elusive like a holy grail because science is by definition 'work in progress.' And if your work is in progress the notion of truth makes you feel extremely uncomfortable. Every new theory or model is just the next – more sophisticated – working hypothesis. But, as we have shown in this chapter, there is – as every engineer can tell you – a certain pleasure as well as value in playing with the numbers given to you, and applying some dimensional analysis to them. A purist may call it 'recreational physics.' And indeed, that's what we were concerned with so as to get an idea of the relevant scales that are linked to the specific values of *our* 'universal' constants. This game has provided us with some surprisingly deep insights about where quantum effects will rear their heads.

Further reading.
On scales in nature:

- *Mr Tompkins in Paperback*
  George Gamow
  Cambridge University Press,
  Reprint from 1939 and 1944 editions (2012)

- *Knowledge and Wonder*
  Victor F. Weisskopf
  MIT Press (1979)

- *In Praise of Science: Curiosity, Understanding, and Progress*
  Sander Bais
  MIT Press (2010)

On black holes:

- *Gravity's Fatal Attraction: Black Holes in the Universe*
  Mitchell Begelman and Martin Rees
  Cambridge University Press (2020)

- *The Little Book of Black Holes*
  Steven S. Gubser and Frans Pretorius
  Princeton University Press (2017)

Chapter I.4

The quest for basic building blocks

If, in some cataclysm, all of scientific knowledge were to be destroyed, and only one sentence passed on to the next generations of creatures, what statement would contain the most information in the fewest words? I believe it is the *atomic hypothesis* (or the atomic *fact* if you wish to call it that) that *all things are made of atoms – little particles that move around in perpetual motion, attracting each other when they are a little distance apart, but repelling upon being squeezed into one another.*

R.P. Feynman (1961)

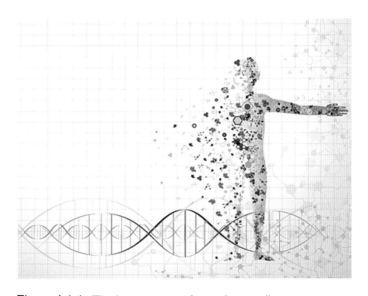

Figure I.4.1: The human quest for understanding nature.

A splendid race to the bottom

The notion of what the basic building blocks of nature are has repeatedly shifted over time. Every time when a new layer of structure is uncovered a new set of 'basic' building blocks is postulated. That way we turned from chemical elements to atoms, from atoms to the understanding of nuclear structure, and from nuclear structure to the elementary subnuclear particles we know today.

Three levels of simplicity. In Figure I.4.2 we have indicated the subsequent paradigm shifts with respect to the fundamental building blocks of matter. It depicts the frontier of knowledge at three typical moments in the past cen-

tury, which one could call 'three levels of simplicity.' The first is the level of atoms. The second, nuclear level stands out for its simplicity with only the electron, proton and neutron making up the atoms. The electromagnetic binding of the electrons to the nucleus was provided by the photon while the protons and neutrons were believed to be held together by a nuclear force that was mediated by the *pion*. But this picture is misleading because I left out the 'zoo' of other nuclear particles to be discussed, of which the proton, neutron, and pion are only the most basic and relevant. Finally, at the next level there is the Standard Model of quarks, leptons and force-mediating particles. The figure provides a bird's eye view of the path of science that brought us ever deeper into matter, and that path is what we are going to run through fast in this section, and explore in more detail in the remainder of this chapter.

The periodic table: atoms. Around 1900 the *chemical elements* were considered the basic building blocks of all matter. Neatly catalogued by the Russian chemist Dmitri Mendeleev in the *periodic table* that he proposed in 1869, the table that has decorated most high-school chemistry-classrooms ever since. These elements are the smallest entities carrying well-defined chemical properties, and as such are indeed the basic building blocks of all of chemistry. The strict order present in the periodic system hinted at an underlying organizing principle that – as we know now – is nothing but the *atomic structure* with a nucleus in the center and electrons 'orbiting' around it, the structure that was uncovered by Ernest Rutherford in 1908 and was so successfully described by the new quantum theory. As we explained in the introduction, quantum physics basically entered our thinking at the atomic level. In this part of the book, and this chapter in particular, we will – as advertised – go down from the atomic level to the physics of the *nuclei* and the underlying structure of elementary *particles.*

Matter matters: nuclei. Once it was realized that the atoms were composite and therefore not truly fundamental, physics turned to the study of the atomic nuclei, which led us to a picture on even smaller scales where we distinguished the *proton* and *neutron* as the building blocks of the nuclei, and of course the electron needed to complete the atoms. And to understand the binding of protons and neutrons in the nucleus a relatively light particle type was identified, the *pion*, that was assumed to be the carrier of the strong nuclear force. It was assumed to play the same role as the photon did for the electromagnetic interactions. Furthermore, it was discovered that the free neutron was in fact unstable; through the so-called β-decay process it would decay into a proton, an electron and another funda-

mental particle that had to be postulated to save energy and momentum conservation. This elusive particle was called the *neutrino*, a remarkable particle with somewhat ghostlike properties in that it was for a long time believed to have neither mass nor charge, and therefore extremely hard to detect directly.

What doesn't meet the eye: the nuclear particle zoo.

> If I could remember the names of all these particles, I'd be a botanist.
>
> *Enrico Fermi*

During the 1960s and 1970s experiments demonstrated the existence of an ever-growing list of so-called elementary nuclear particles which was referred to as the *particle zoo*, a term expressing a mild form of despair. Instead of bringing the number of fundamental building blocks back to an ever smaller number, that number seemed to grow without limit. All of these nuclear particles were called *hadrons*. One class consisted of fancy brothers and sisters of the proton and neutron, collectively denoted as *baryons*. A second class contained a large number of relatives of the pions, and those were called *mesons*. Feynman, in one of his popular lectures, quipped that the business of particle physics basically boiled down to a fancy equivalent of smashing watches into a wall, in an attempt to find out what was in them and how they worked.

Law and order regained: the eightfold way. All these new baryons and mesons turned out to be composite as well. It was quite a mess until Murray Gell-Mann (and independently George Zweig) in 1964 created order by applying a beautiful symmetry principle, which Gell-Mann called *the eightfold way*. This term added a spiritual dimension to elementary particle physics as it alluded to the teachings of Buddha, in particular a fragment from the first sermon after his enlightenment, which reads:

> And what, monks, is the middle path, by which

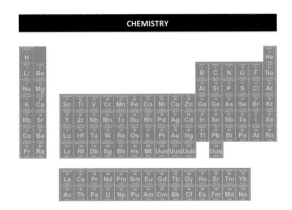

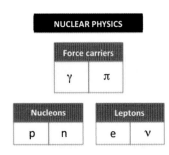

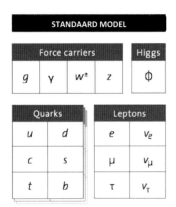

(a) **Anno 1900.** Mendeleev's iconic periodic table of the chemical elements. The elements are ordered by increasing atomic mass in subsequent lines, and the columns give elements which have similar chemical properties. This structure is a direct consequence of applying quantum mechanics to the atom.

(b) **Anno 1950.** The building blocks of nuclei are the proton and the neutron, and together with the electron they make the atoms. While the electromagnetic force is carried by the photon denoted as γ, the strong nuclear force was believed to be carried by particles called the pion, denoted by $\pi_{\pm}$ and π_0. The neutrino had to be included to account for nuclear β–decay.

(c) **Anno 2000.** The constituent and force particles of the Standard Model. The quarks and leptons form three families of constituent particles of which only the top row is stable and used to make ordinary matter of the sort listed in the periodic table. Notice that the Higgs particle has a special place in the scheme of things.

Figure I.4.2: *Three levels of 'simplicity.* Three successive levels of reductionism spanning a century of quantum physics. The basic building blocks (a) of chemistry, (b) of nuclear physics and (c) of subnuclear particle physics. The atomic nuclei are built from protons **p** and neutrons **n** which each consist of three quarks, with $\mathbf{p} = (\mathrm{uud})$ and $\mathbf{n} = (\mathrm{udd})$. So the first element hydrogen $^1\mathrm{H}$ for example has a nucleus consisting of a single proton, while the the second element helium $^4\mathrm{He}$ has a nucleus made up of two protons and two neutrons.

the one who has thus come has gained enlightenment,
which produces knowledge and insight,
and leads to peace, wisdom, enlightenment, and nirvana?
This is the noble eightfold way, namely,
right understanding, right intention,
right speech, right action, right livelihood,
right attention, right concentration,
and right meditation.

Budda, sermon

The eight 'rights' mentioned correspond to the corners of the octagon that fits in the big wheel, as shown in Figure I.4.3.

The 'eightfold way' *à la* Gell-Mann is based on a mathematical group of symmetries known as $SU(3)$.[1] Now, this

---

[1]$SU(3)$ is the group of rotations in three-dimensional complex space. Indeed, there is one sentence that always applies to quantum whatever: things become complex! If not in the real sense than at least in the mathematical sense. Numbers, parameters, functions, spaces, transformations, all of it turns complex when you go quantum! You need a tolerance for 'complexification' to avoid *quantum allergy*.

elegant scheme served not only as a meticulous book-keeping device, and just like Mendeleev's system the eight-fold way also made definite predictions for the existence of certain particle types that were discovered subsequently. More importantly, however, was that the $SU(3)$ structure hinted at the existence of yet a new layer of fundamental particles. Particles from which all known types in the particle zoo could be assembled. Gell-Mann coined the name *quarks* for these new basic building blocks, referring to a – by now famous – quote from the novel *Finnegans Wake* by James Joyce:

Three quarks for Muster Mark!

Sure he hasn't got much of a bark

And sure any he has it's all beside the mark.

But O, Wreneagle Almighty, wouldn't un be a sky of a lark

To see that old buzzard whooping about for uns shirt in the dark

And he hunting round for uns speckled trousers around by Palmerstown Park?

Hohohoho, moulty Mark!

James Joyce, Finnegans Wake

The pronunciation of this elusive particle's name is 'quork' rather than 'quark', which presumably is the one intended by Joyce as it rhymes with Mark and bark. Irish friends I trust have explained to me that the first exclamation is paraphrasing a typical order in a pub: 'Three quarts (of beer) for Mister Mark!' In German 'quark' refers to a dairy product, and one would interpret it like: 'Three quarks for Master Mark!' It probably is no accident that Gell-Mann in his later life turned to the study of linguistics and in particular to phonetics, in an attempt to trace back the evolution of languages and in some sense reconstruct the 'mother' of all languages. He always had an exceptional fascination and talent for language, as he spoke about twenty of them, and I remember him always taking extreme care to make sure he pronounced the rather unpronounceable names of – in my case, Dutch – colleagues like 'Gerard 't Hooft or 'Peter van Nieuwenhuizen' perfectly, followed by an exegesis of its meaning and origins!

Figure I.4.3: *The eightfold way.* In Buddism the 'eightfold way' refers to a very basic principle that brings the eight primary teachings together. It was unfolded in Budda's first sermon after his enlightenment. Presumably it was the symmetric geometry of the above 'wheel of wisdom' that must have suggested the term to Gell-Mann.

To be or not to be: quarks. According to this scheme the quarks carried a new quantum number which is nowadays called *flavor*. In the original theory there were three 'flavors,' *up, down* and *strange*, denoted by the letters u, d and s. Later on additional flavors were discovered – *charm, top* and *bottom*, denoted by c, t and b – to make a total of six. This would mean that the symmetry group would be the much larger group $SU(6)$. The fact is that the last three quark types are much heavier particles and very unstable, so they do not play a prominent role in 'ordinary' physics. The physicists say that the $SU(6)$ flavor symmetry is 'broken' to the much smaller Gell-Mann $SU(3)$.

The nucleons (and in fact all baryons) consist of three quarks: the proton for example corresponded to (uud) and the neutron to (ddu). The mesons like the pion would consist of quark anti-quark pairs. From this assignment it is not hard to see that these quarks have to carry fractional electric charges: you have two equations for two charges q_u and q_d, and if you solve them you find that $q_u = 2e/3$ and $q_d = -e/3$.

Splendid unification: the Standard Model. After these new basic building blocks were postulated, it took almost another decade before the real theory for the binding of quarks into the other nuclear particles was developed and the idea of quarks really caught on. What kept the quark idea from general acceptance was the question of 'to be or not to be,' in the sense that these elusive quarks were not observed as free particles. With their fractional charges they would have been easy to identify. For some reason they apparently could not be knocked out of the protons or neutrons. They lived in peaceful coexistence with their 'not being there' so to say. Later we understood that this *confinement* or *imprisonment* property of quarks was a consequence of the nature of the so-called 'color-force' between them. This new fundamental, strong nuclear force between quarks indeed exhibited the desired feature that it imprisons the quarks in threesomes (the *baryons*) or in quark-antiquark pairs (the *mesons*).

It was not until the 1970s that a slow paradigm shift carried us to the Standard Model of quarks and leptons and of the particles that mediate three of the four known fundamental forces. This Standard Model has in the meantime been confirmed in impressive detail by a large number of experiments performed at the major particle accelerators all over the world.

Fatal attraction: forces yield structure

A description of nature does not stop with the inventory of building blocks or basic constituents. One also likes to know why the building blocks stick together the way they do. What we need to know in other words are the forces between the constituents, and how they act. Because it is

Figure I.4.4: *Gravity at work.* The solar system with its seven (in fact nine) planets moving in bounded elliptic orbits around the Sun. (Source: Getty images)

through interactions between constituents that new structures emerge. This is an all-important ingredient of building models of the world at any level, and we will start with a pedestrian expose, which will deepen along the way in the book. Attractive forces acting between particles may lead to the formation of bound states between the constituents and thus to the formation of structure. Bound systems are only stable when the attractive force is balanced by a repulsive force at small distances. The phenomenon of gravitational binding in Newtonian physics is most familiar. Here we show that our naive classical intuitions fail when talking about the atomic binding of electrons to nuclei caused by the electromagnetic force, and of the nuclear binding of protons and neutrons in the nucleus. We got stuck but quantum mechanics came in to rescue us.

The Earth orbits the Sun in a slightly elliptic orbit: this binding is caused by the attractive gravitational force as described in the section about Newtonian mechanics. The first question is: why don't we drop into the Sun as the force is attractive all the way in? The force-law corresponds to an infinitely deep gravitational potential well; and so why does the Earth not fall down? Deep wells may provoke deep thoughts. The reason that the Earth doesn't drop in is that it has a tangential velocity, and that velocity induces a outward directed so-called *centrifugal force* that balances the gravitational attraction. More precisely, that tangential velocity component implies that the Earth – Sun system has a certain non-vanishing *angular momentum*, because as you remember $\mathbf{L} = \mathbf{x} \times \mathbf{p}$ and it is the $\mathbf{p}$–component perpendicular to $\mathbf{x}$ that matters. Newton's dynamical laws decree that angular momentum is conserved, basically because the force is directed to the Sun, i.e. in the radial direction, and therefore that force cannot change the tangential component of the velocity.[2] The expression for the energy of a particle in the gravitational field can be written as:

$$E(r) = \frac{p_r^2}{2m} + \frac{L^2}{mr^2} - \frac{G_N mM}{r}. \quad (I.4.1)$$

The first term contains the radial motion, while the tangential components give rise to the second term, where L is the magnitude of the angular momentum that is a fixed number for each orbiting planet. The last term is the Newtonian gravitational potential. We note that the second term is positive and acts as a repulsive term for decreasing r, while the last is attractive. We have depicted them separately, as well as their sum in Figure I.4.5. The resulting purple curve has a minimum that corresponds to a situation where the radius is fixed and the motion is circular, and the velocity entirely tangential $(p_r = 0)$.

Turned the other way around, one may ask what would happen if we put the Earth at rest at a certain distance from the Sun and let go, then clearly a disaster would be inevitable as the Earth would drop straight into the Sun.

***

[2]There is something far beyond the scope of our present *exposé* to worry about, however, if we include Einstein's relativity the system would start to radiate gravitationally, which means that the bound system would lose energy and therefore in the end would collapse anyway. This effect of energy loss due to radiation has been observed in spectacular detail in a certain double (neutron) star systems.

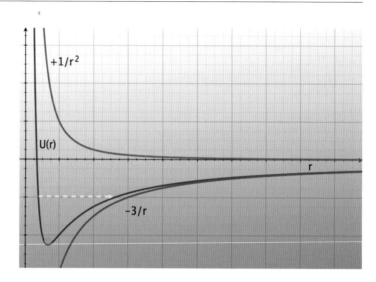

Figure I.4.5: *Balancing attraction and repulsion.* The radial potential $U(r)$ correspons to the last two terms of equation (I.4.1) and represents a central force field which drops off as the inverse square of the radius. The terms are drawn separately as well as their sum for a particular choice of the parameters. The shape of the potential with a repulsive and an attractive part is universal in situations where we have both bound states with $E < 0$, and scattering states with $E > 0$. The $E = 0$ case represents the parabolic orbit. In the minimal energy (orange dot) the radius is fixed and the motion is circular. If the energy is higher, the orbit can be elliptical (yellow dashed line) with two turning points at different radii.

With $L = 0$ there is no *angular momentum barrier* to save the system from collapse! The potential would correspond to the blue curve in the figure. Well this presents us with a puzzle from a principle point of view, if we take the naive approach and consider the idealized situation where we treat the Earth and Sun as point particles. Then the Earth while approaching the Sun would feel an ever stronger attractive force giving the Earth an ever-growing acceleration and speed! And by falling in, the Earth would gain an 'infinite' amount of energy, and as its speed would be limited by the speed of light it would acquire an unlimited amount of mass.

What actually happens in such radial approaches may certainly be violent as we know from falling meteorites hitting us from time to time, but due to the finite size of the objects colliding the acceleration towards the center is stopped and the kinetic energy is converted into structural damage, debris flying around, and heat.

Infinities call for new physics. What these examples teach us is that other, non-gravitational physics takes over and saves the day. This is often the cavalier way physicists wave their hands about the singularities in their theories that keep pestering them, and that most non-physicist audiences are most curious about. It must be said that the physicists have been unreasonably successful with this pragmatic approach. As far as we know nature *is* non-singular, and the moment it threatens to become singular, it usually amounts to a wake-up call to go and search for new physics and new theories that avoid the singularities and thereby save serious science from demise.

This is exemplified by applying the gravitational force to the different case of a radially collapsing star. If we look at an extremely massive star, the gravitational attraction directed to the center and is kept in balance by the repulsive force, caused by the outwardly directed pressure generated by the nuclear burning processes in its core. However, as we'll discuss later on, the amount of nuclear fuel is finite and even a massive star will one day stop shining, after which a gravitational collapse to some compact object is unavoidable. Depending on the mass of the original star, this final state can be a white dwarf, a neutron star or a black hole. In the first two cases a new repulsive force working at smaller inter-particle distances halts the collapse and allows for a new balance thereby avoiding the singularity. The most dramatic possibility is the formation of a black hole. But a black hole is surrounded by a horizon that keeps us from knowing what happens to the mass inside and whether there is anything singular going on. A horizon seems to save the day, or better the horizon masks our ignorance about what precisely is going on! Putting things behind the horizon sounds like the sci-

entific equivalent of sweeping things under the carpet. Yet, that is apparently the way in which nature prefers to keep some of its secrets. This property is referred to as *Cosmic censorship*.

In the previous chapter we mentioned the direction in which progress is made to handle this problem. It is again by shifting the attention from the singularity in the origin to a deeper quantum mechanical understanding of what a horizon really is. In principle black holes come in all sizes and a Planck-mass black hole would have a horizon as well, and could therefore be considered as the 'hydrogen atom' of quantum gravity. We just don't know yet how this works precisely, as we have no fully consistent quantum theory of the gravitational force. But taking the essential idea of Hawking radiation from the horizon as a guiding principle, black holes would be unstable states of matter, bound to somehow evaporate completely. And that would turn the embarrassment of its singularity in some kind of red herring. For the moment however, black holes remain in the category of 'unsolved problems'.

The quantum stability of matter. In the case of colliding ordinary objects it is the much stronger electric force that keeps the balance, and prohibits the infinite energy gain of two point particles colliding gravitationally. But what if we have two point particles with opposite charges, say a positively charged proton and a negatively charged electron, which make up the familiar hydrogen atom? Now both forces are attractive, and yes there can again be an angular momentum barrier, or better a repulsive core due to the angular momentum that dominates over the attraction for small distances. But what about the lowest state where the angular momentum would be zero.

Classically the same 1/r singularity – as it is called – would certainly rear its head again, and maybe you would expect a mini-blackhole to form. No, this is certainly not what happens, and yes, there is other physics – quantum physics to be precise – that saves the day. The lowest quantum state with zero angular momentum turns out to be perfectly stable and well behaved. It has a wavefunction that corresponds to a spherically symmetric probability distribution for the electron to be at a finite distance from the nuclear core. It is one of those 'life saving' manifestations of the *Heisenberg uncertainty relation*. This relation does not allow a quantum particle to just sit at the bottom of a 'quantum bowl'; being at rest and completely localized is a no-go. Heisenberg prohibits a particle from falling down to the origin. This result is all-important because what it means is that quantum theory guarantees atomic stability. Stability means that the energy of a quantum system is somehow bounded from below. The atom can radiate away electromagnetic energy by emitting photons until it gets down to a lowest angular momentum and lowest energy state which is perfectly regular and stable.

Having made this victorious claim I should sit back for a moment and scratch my head. What about an atom with more than one electron? Just take any. Would this atom not decay into a state where all electrons descend to their lowest possible, so-called, ground state, one may ask? Certainly if we ignore the electric forces between electrons. But is this what we see happening?

The answer to this well-posed question is a fully-fledged 'No'! We see that different atoms behave quite differently from a chemical point of view, and that fact is at the root of all diversity in nature. How could that ever be if all electrons would be sitting in the same state? This disturbing shortcoming of naive quantum theory is resolved by an additional – at first sight magical – quantessential principle, that prohibits particles like electrons to occupy the same state! When Wolfgang Pauli introduced this *exclusion principle* it was certainly a rather ad hoc rule, a veritable *deus ex machina*. But it did in one blow bring theory back into excellent agreement with the observations. According to this principle you should think of electrons a bit like people at a pop festival in desperate need of a toilet. The simple truth is that a 'seat' is either free or occupied and there is

no in-between; if occupied, you have to go and look for the nearest free seat, which may be way out. Electrons are permanently involved in playing some game like 'musical chairs.' A notable aspect of this mutual exclusion is that it only concerns exclusion of the same type of particles, not particles of a different type. Moreover not all particle types are subject to the exclusion principle. The particles which are like electrons are called *fermions*, while the particles that are not, like the photon, are called *bosons*. We will return to this topic in a forthcoming section. First we turn to a more detailed description of the atom.

Atomic structure

One of the early icons of quantum theory is the Bohr model of the atom that we discussed in the previous chapter. It makes it clear in a transparent way how a rather simple but radical idea that can be directly implemented leads to a very non-classical behavior, explaining qualitatively the physics we are observing. This heuristic device was then turned into a mathematical precise framework by Heisenberg, Schrödinger, Dirac, Born and many others. This work revealed a complete set of quantum numbers labeling the states including the spin of the electrons. To complete the model of the atom Pauli's exclusion principle also had to be invoked The study of the atom taught us what quantization really means, and at the same time raised the intricate epistemological questions that haunted the theory and its practitioners for almost a century thereafter.

The Bohr atom: energy quantization

In the subsection on the Bohr-radius on page 134 of the the previous chapter, we introduced the Bohr model for the atom with its characteristic quantized orbits depicted in Figure I.3.7, and its quantized energy levels. In this section we want to look at these quantized energy levels and point out how they are related to the observed discrete line spectra of light emitted by atoms. The connection that Bohr established was that if an atom makes a transition from some excited state to a lower one, it would emit a photon with a frequency given by the Planck – Einstein relation, so $\Delta E = h\nu$. Conversely, an atom could absorb a photon if its frequency matched the energy for an electron to move up. The schematic of such processes is given in Figure I.4.6, where it is also indicated that for the hydrogen atom the transitions to the ground states have frequencies that correspond to the ultraviolet, while the transitions to $n = 3$ correspond to the infrared end of the spectrum. So only the transitions to the $n = 2$ levels are in the visible domain. Clearly having a simple model that could account for these discrete line spectra was a major success for the early quantum physicists. These line spectra can be considered as an atomic barcode, if you hand it to me I can tell you which atom you were looking at.

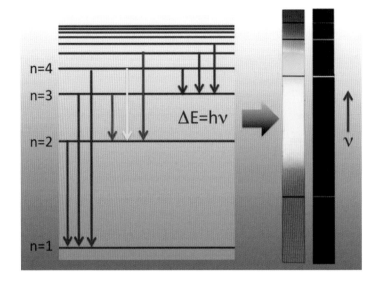

Figure I.4.6: *The origin of light.* If the electron makes a transition between the energy levels, the fixed energy difference ΔE translates into the photon frequency; $\Delta E = h\nu$. This determines the color of the lines of the spectrum, which can be observed in absorption (left) or in emission (right).

The Schrödinger atom: three numbers

After the Bohr model was introduced in 1913, it would take another thirteen years until Schrödinger and Heisenberg published their fundamental equations for quantum physics. The first called the theory *wave mechanics* and the second *matrix mechanics*, but in fact they were fully equivalent descriptions of the quantum states and their observables, as was later shown by Dirac. The Schrödinger equation is a wave equation in three dimensions, that could be solved exactly for simple atoms and that yielded the full spectrum of atomic states with all its quantum numbers. It went much further than the Bohr model, but to a certain extent it incorporated the same simple idea in a full three-dimensional model for the atom. In the Schrödinger picture the states correspond to wavefunctions $\psi(x)$ that are defined over all of the position space, $x \in \mathcal{X} = \mathbb{R}^3$. And from the wavefunction of a state the related proba-

bility distribution of where to find the electron can be derived.

The equation: a guided tour.
So, let me step back and try to give you an idea what the Schrödinger equation is about, and what it looks like. Let us call it a 'guided tour.' In an operational, maybe even opportunistic, sense, going from classical to quantum mechanics, is mathematically speaking not that hard. Once you accept that momentum is represented as a spatial derivative operator, $\mathbf{p} = -i\hbar\boldsymbol{\nabla}$, and the energy or Hamiltonian as a time derivative $H = i\hbar\, d/dt$, one can translate the classical functions into corresponding quantum operators or equations just by substitution. For example:

$$E = \frac{\mathbf{p}^2}{2m} + V(\mathbf{x}) \quad \rightarrow \quad i\hbar\frac{d}{dt} = -\frac{\hbar^2}{2m}\boldsymbol{\nabla}^2 + V(\mathbf{x}),\quad (I.4.2)$$

on the left we have the Newtonian expression of the energy and on the right we have the Schrödinger 'wave operator', which when we let it work on a (wave) function $\psi(x, t)$ yields the *Schrödinger equation* in all its glory:

$$i\hbar\frac{d\,\Psi(x, t)}{dt} = \left(-\frac{\hbar^2}{2m}\boldsymbol{\nabla}^2 + V(x)\right)\Psi(x, t)\,. \quad \text{(I.4.3)}$$

For now we don't want to get too deep into the mathematics of the equation but let us at least make some observations which are not so hard to digest:
(i) The equation expresses a simple truth, namely that the energy (operator) generates the time evolution of the system.
(ii) Quantum states are described by wavefunctions Ψ that satisfy this equation.
(iii) The wavefunction is complex meaning that it has a phase factor in it, and it describes a probability amplitude.
(iv) Squaring the amplitude gives the probability density $p(\mathbf{x}, t)$ for finding the electron in a small volume element $d^3\mathbf{x}$ around the position x and at a time t. We defined $p(\mathbf{x}, t) = |\Psi|^2$, so that the overall phase of the amplitude drops out. It doesn't affect the probability, which is where the physics is.
(v) Indeed, the notion of probability apparently enters already on this basic level in the theory, where we are still talking about the state of a single particle.

The quantization. Of great importance are the so-called *stationary states*, meaning that the physical properties do not change in time. You would think that the wavefunction has to be time independent in that case but that is not quite true. What is true is that the time dependence has to sit in the phase factor $\phi(t)$ which is going to drop out anyway in the probability density. The answer is to write Ψ as a product of a phase factor which depends on t only, and a time independent wavefunction $\psi(\mathbf{x})$ that describes a time independent stationary state. We write

$$\Psi(\mathbf{x}, t) = \phi(t)\psi(\mathbf{x}) = e^{-iEt/\hbar}\,\psi(\mathbf{x})\,, \quad \text{(I.4.4)}$$

and substitute it in the Schrödinger equation. If you take the derivative, you get that the time dependence drops out

completely and you are left with a nice time independent equation for $\psi(x)$:

$$\left(-\frac{\hbar^2}{2m}\boldsymbol{\nabla}^2 + V(\mathbf{x})\right)\psi(x) = E\,\psi(x)\,. \quad \text{(I.4.5)}$$

where E is the constant energy value of the stationary state ψ. The crucial point here is that you *first* have to solve the equation to find out which values of E make quantum sense. It turns out that only specific values give a solution for which the square of ψ gives an acceptable probability function. This means that the solutions have to be *square integrable*; the integral over all of space of the absolute square of the function has to be finite. This integral can then be normalized to one to obtain an appropriate probability density. This type of mathematical problem is called an *eigenvalue problem*; the values E that occur in equation (I.4.3) are called *eigenvalues* and the corresponding functions $\psi(x)$ are called *eigenfunctions*. This really is the stage at which the *quantization* 'takes place' in the Schrödinger approach, and the eigenvalues are often called *quantum numbers*. Hopefully this helps you to also imagine what people mean when they talk about 'quantizing' some (classical) system. They perform the substitutions as we did in equation (I.4.2) and then look for the eigenvalues and the corresponding eigenfunctions characterizing the quantum states of the system. ■

A free quantum particle. Let us consider the simple case where $V(\mathbf{x}) = 0$ that corresponds to a free particle. The solutions are periodic plane waves:

$$\psi_{\mathbf{k}}(\mathbf{x}) \simeq e^{i\mathbf{k}\cdot\mathbf{x}}\,. \quad \text{(I.4.6)}$$

The meaning of the vector $\mathbf{k}$ (which appears here as a vector of free parameters defining the solution) becomes clear if we substitute the solution in equation (I.4.5) with $V = 0$, which yields:

$$E_{\mathbf{k}} = \frac{\hbar^2|\mathbf{k}|^2}{2m}\,. \quad \text{(I.4.7)}$$

This is just the classical expression for the kinetic energy once we use the fact that the momentum is given by $\mathbf{p} =$

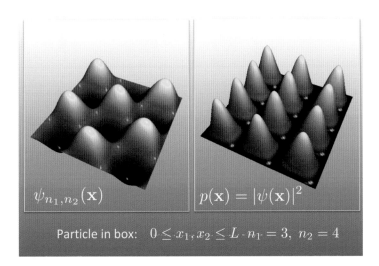

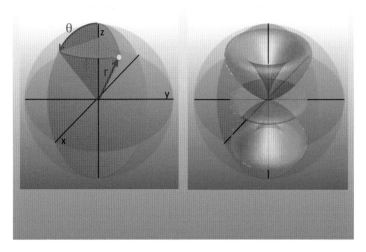

Figure I.4.7: *Quantum particle in a box.* A state of a two-dimensional quantum particle in a box of length L. The wavefunctions $\psi(\mathbf{x})$ have to vanish on the boundary, and are of the form

$$\psi_{n_1 n_2} \sim \sin(n_1 x_1 \pi / L) \sin(n_2 x_2 \pi / L) \,.$$

We have plotted the wavefunction ψ and corresponding probability density p for finding the particle corresponding to quantum numbers $n_1 = 3$ and $n_2 = 4$.

Figure I.4.8: *Spherical harmonics.* The spherical coordinates r, θ, and φ of the (yellow) point $\mathbf{x}$ are defined on the left. On the right the angular distribution $\rho_{l,m}(\theta, \varphi) = \left| Y_l^{\,m} \right|^2$, for a state with quantum numbers $l = 3$, $m = 1$ is plotted.

$\hbar\mathbf{k}$. There is an annoying technical complication here, if you calculate the probability density for the particle, you find $p(x) = |\psi|^2 = 1$, which is unacceptable because it cannot be normalized to '1'. If you take the integral over over a constant non-zero probability density then you would find the total probability to be be infinite! The way out is to put the particle in a box, say a cube of size L, so that the wavefunctions have to vanish on the boundary where $x_i = L$. This in turn means that the momentum values become quantized: $p_i = \hbar k_i = \pi \hbar n_i / L$ with integer-valued n_i. The space of admissible momenta corresponds therefore to an infinite three-dimensional cubic lattice, where the energy levels grow as the length of the momentum vector squared: $E_{\mathbf{n}} \sim \mathbf{n}^2$.

In Figure I.4.7 we have depicted a particular solution for a two-dimensional particle in a box, where the wavefunctions

that satisfy the boundary conditions are of the form:

$$\psi_{n_1 n_2}(\mathbf{x}) = N \sin(n_1 x_1 \pi / L) \sin(n_2 x_2 \pi / L) \,, \qquad (I.4.8)$$

with N a normalization factor. In the figure we plotted the wavefunction and the corresponding probability density function for the case $n_1 = 3$, $n_2 = 4$. Note that this wavefunction describes a one-particle state, but that that particle has a rather outspoken preference for certain positions which sit on a periodic lattice inside the box. We will in Volume II go much deeper into what this probability interpretation of the wavefunction exactly means. For example, looking at the figure the obvious question: 'Where is the particle?' begs for an answer. As it turns out that answer is far from obvious!

The hydrogen atom. Let us return to the question of what the states look like for an atom. With the nucleus in the origin the electron moves in the spherical Coulomb field caused by the positive charge of the nucleus. The potential has a rotational symmetry, which means that it is ad-

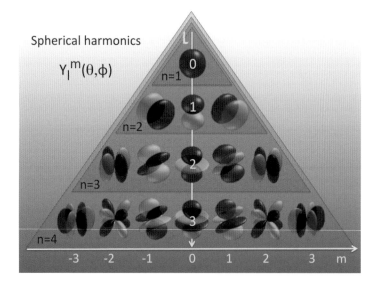

Figure I.4.9: *What the quantum states of hydrogen look like.*
The angular dependencies of the hydrogen wavefunctions corresponding to the so-called spherical harmonics $Y_l{}^m(\theta, \varphi)$ where n, l and m are the discrete quantum numbers which label the state. Each state can hold at most two electrons, one with spin up and one with spin pointing down. The first quantum number n labels the energy level corresponding with a triangle in the Figure. At each level we have states where angular momentum l runs from 0 to $n-1$ along the vertical axis and for each l the component m runs horizontally from $-l$ to l.

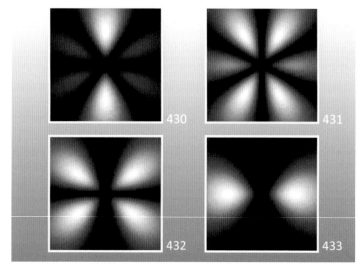

Figure I.4.10: *Charge distributions.* Light color indicates high probability. The charge or electron probability distribution in the xz-plane shows the θ and r dependence. Depicted are the $n = 4, l = 3$ states, with $m = 0, ..., 3$. These states correspond to the states on the bottom line of the previous figure. The shapes of the probability distributions are all-important for understanding the chemical binding properties.

vantageous to rewrite the Schrödinger equation in terms of a radial (r) coordinate and two angular coordinates (θ, φ) (see Figure I.4.8). The equation then basically separates into three independent equations depending again on certain discrete quantum numbers. The radial quantum number $n = 1, 2, \ldots$ linked to energy level is basically the orbital quantum number introduced by Bohr. And the energy eigenvalues E we just discussed are quantized like $E \sim 1/n^2$. The angular dependence of the states introduces two more quantum numbers: $l = 0, \ldots, n-1$ and $-l \leq m \leq +l$, both of which are related to angular momentum. The wavefunctions corresponding to the states are usually written like $\psi_{nlm}(r, \theta, \varphi) = R_{nl}(r)Y_{lm}(\theta, \varphi)$ where the radial and the angular dependences are separated. In Figure I.4.9 we have depicted the angular de-

pendencies by plotting (the real part) of the functions $Y_l{}^m$ for all admissable l and m values up to principle quantum number $n = 4$.

Degeneracies. It turns out that the states $\psi_{nlm}(x)$ are highly degenerate, meaning that different states will have the same energy. For every energy level (labeled by the quantum number n) there are a total of $2n^2$ different angular momentum states which all have the same energy. In Figure I.4.9 these degenerate states correspond to the angular (l, m)-states within each triangle labeled by n. The extra factor two comes from the two possible electron spin states that will be discussed shortly. Plotting this discrete spectrum one would get a three-dimensional discrete lattice filling a triangular pyramid (or is it a nicely decorated Christmas tree?). These degeneracies are not accidental: they are the consequence of certain symmetries in this problem. These symmetries lead to certain conserved quantities and these in turn lead to degeneracies in the energy spectrum. We will return in more detail to this topic in Chapter II.6.

Lifting degeneracies. These degeneracies corresponded exactly to the observations that the Dutch physicist Pieter Zeeman made some 25 years earlier (almost simultaneous with Planck's quantization hypothesis). He discovered that by turning on a magnetic field the degeneracy of the different angular momentum eigenstates was lifted, which is reflected in the splitting of the spectral lines corresponding to one energy level into many different lines. So you could count the multiplicity of the degeneracies. For the discovery of this 'Zeeman splitting' he shared the Nobel prize with Hendrik Antoon Lorentz in 1902.

With the Bohr model in mind it is intuitively not too hard to interpret these splittings. Clearly Bohr had only used circular orbits but if we think of negatively charged electrons orbiting the positively charged nucleus, these would create a magnetic moment like a circular electric current would do. This magnetic moment would be proportional to the angular momentum of the electron state. What caused the Zeeman effect was that the different magnetic moment or angular momentum states would acquire an extra energy contribution from the interaction of that moment with the external magnetic field. And interpreted this way, his measurements showed direct evidence for the quantization of the component of the angular momentum along the magnetic field in integer multiples have quantized values $m\hbar$, where for given l there was naturally the restriction $-l \leq m \leq +l$. Needless to say that none of these quantization rules can be understood from a classical point of view.

This splitting, which could be completely accounted for within the framework of the Schrödinger or Heisenberg equation, is called the *normal* Zeeman effect. However, Zeeman did actually discover an additional quantessential

feature in the spectra, which is referred to as the *anomalous Zeeman effect*, to which we turn next.

The discovery of spin

> The Pauli principle was published early in 1925. .... Well, I had introduced those quantum numbers but, if I had been a good physicist, then I would have noticed already in May 1925 that this implied that the electron possessed spin. But I was not a good physicist and thus I did not realize this... Then Uhlenbeck appears on the scene ... he asked all those questions I had never asked ... When the day came that I had to tell Uhlenbeck about the Pauli principle – of course using my own quantum numbers – then he said to me: 'But don't you see what this implies? It means that there is a fourth degree of freedom for the electron. It means that the electron has a spin, that it rotates'... I asked him: 'What is a degree of freedom?' In any case, when he made his remark, it was luck that I knew all these things about the spectra, and I said: 'That fits precisely in our hydrogen scheme which we wrote about four weeks ago. If one now allows the electron to be magnetic with the appropriate magnetic moment, then one can understand all those complicated Zeeman – effects.'
>
> *Samuel Goudsmit (1971)*

As announced, there was another quantessential treasure hidden in Zeeman's spectral data that caused a great deal of confusion among the early quantum physicists. It is known as the *anomalous Zeeman effect*, and was observed in the spectrum of Sodium, where a line in the absence of an external magnetic field already appeared split: this is because of the coupling between the spin and orbit magnetic moments. When Zeeman turned on the field, he found further splittings in an even number of lines as indi-

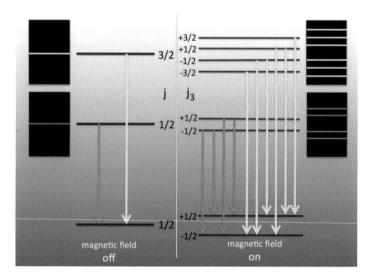

Figure I.4.11: *The discovery of* spin *(and the* qubit*).* This shows the anomalous Zeeman effect discovered in 1898, the same year that Planck introduced his constant. The line spectrum of Sodium, corresponding to the arrows in the figure, was split due to the spin of $1/2$ of the electron. Without the magnetic field, the level l split up into levels with total spin $j = l \pm \frac{1}{2}$ (on the left). Turning on a weak magnetic field he observed the *hyperfine structure* because the spin degeneracy was lifted.

cated in Figure I.4.11. These splittings implied that quantum theory would somehow also admit half-integral values for the angular momentum (as $2j + 1$ is only even if j is half-integral).

In 1925 the resolution was proposed by two young Dutchmen, Samuel Goudsmit and George Uhlenbeck who were still graduate students at Leiden University. They came up with the bold proposal that the electron was spinning around its axis and that that 'spin' would account for the so-called hyperfine splittings observed in the anomalous Zeeman effect. It may remind you of the good old solar system with the Earth rotating about its axis while orbiting the Sun! The idea implied that the observations had nothing to do with an extra feature of the atom as a whole, but rather with a totally new feature of the electron itself.

 Behind the scenes. Wolfgang Pauli had already come across this problem in 1925 and had understood that the quantum numbers of atomic states were basically related to the radial and the angular motions of the electron. Indeed, three dimensions gave rise to three quantum numbers: $n = 1, 2, \ldots$ for the radial direction, and $l = 0, 1, \ldots, n-1$ and $-l \leq m \leq +l$ for the angular motions. But he also noted that to get things right he needed a fourth quantum number which he somewhat desperately called *Zweideutigkeit*, meaning something like 'double valuedness'. The story of how the all-important discovery of spin unfolded is a kind of amusing, but for the young researchers involved in fact rather traumatic.

Goudsmit and Uhlenbeck, discussed their spin-idea with their Leiden advisor Paul Ehrenfest, who liked it and proposed that they should write it up. They did so and showed their work to the grand old Leiden professor Lorentz who had earlier developed a sophisticated theory of the electron, but entirely within the classical framework. A thing he could do well was to calculate the rotational speed the electron would need to have in order to produce the magnetic moment corresponding to $(1/2)\hbar$, and that turned out to exceed the speed of light by orders of magnitude. This in clear contradiction with the theory of relativity. Understandably, this argument knocked down the the confidence of the students and they went back to Ehrenfest to humbly withdraw their paper that contained this incredible stupidity. Alas, it turned out that Ehrenfest had already submitted the paper, and didn't seem to take it too seriously, making the consoling remark: *'Sie beiden sind jung genug sich eine Dummheit leisten zu können.'* ('The two of you are still young enough that you can afford yourself such a stupidity'). Actually it seems that Bohr when he heard about the proposal liked it and Einstein also apparently judged it rather mildly.

It actually turned out that somewhat before that time, a young American physicist, Ralph de Laer Kronig, had also thought of the electron spin (amusingly, I took my first quantum mechanics course with Kronig in Delft in 1966). To his misfortune, he happened to show the idea to Wolfgang Pauli, who instantly demolished it, so that Kronig ended up not working on it any further. The issue of who should and who should not be credited with the discovery/invention of spin remains hidden in darkness. It is this strange story with a touch of tragedy that may explain why a Nobel prize was never awarded for the discovery of the quantessential property of spin as an intrinsic property of particles. It also shows that the advice of even the greatest 'advisors' should sometimes be taken with the necessary pinch of salt. □

The electron possessed a new property called *spin*! It could only exist in a spinning state with intrinsic angular momentum values $s = 1/2$ in units of $\hbar$. In Figure I.4.11 we show how this conjecture did in a rather spectacular way resolve the special properties of those particular 'D-lines' in the spectrum of Sodium. The idea was to think of a new *total* angular momentum quantum number denoted $j = l \pm 1/2$, basically expressing that the spin would either be aligned or anti-aligned with the orbital angular momentum. In that case the component along the field of j denoted as j_3 could run from $-j \leq j_3 \leq +j$. Hence the $2j + 1$ energy levels of the right-hand side of Figure I.4.11 is an even number since $j = 1/2$ and $3/2$ respectively. And that does the job if you assumed in addition that the transitions could only take place if they obeyed the rule $\Delta j_3 = -1, 0, 1$, that followed naturally if you took into account that the outgoing photon itself had spin one.

Let us conclude with a comment on the splittings of the energy levels. If we would have refined our model to include the interaction of the magnetic electron spin degree of freedom with the magnetic moment due to the orbital motion of the electron, the so-called *spin-obit coupling*, we would have found the *fine splitting* of the left column in Figure I.4.11. Furthermore if we would have included the interaction of the electron spin with the nuclear magnetic moment, we would have found the hyperfine splittings, on the right of the figure.

Fermions and bosons

There are many macroscopic phenomena that can only be understood from underlying quantum principles of matter. One of the quantum principles which has a tremendous explanatory power is Wolfgang Pauli's exclusion principle: it decrees that two electrons cannot occupy the same quantum state. This exclusion property is instrumental, for example for understanding the atomic structure of the elements and the magnificent chemical diversity that derives from it. Not all particles obey the principle though: the particles that have half-integral spin do obey and are called fermions, while the particles that have integral spin do not and are called bosons.

Having made a strong plea for the microscopic domain as the realm where the laws of quantum theory are indispensable, I should hasten to correct myself. This is a severe understatement. Quantum theory manifests itself on all scales, but could only be discovered on the microscopic level where it is omnipresent, manifest and inescapable. Once that is recognized, however, it turns out that there is a host of macroscopic phenomena that cannot be explained without a deep understanding of quantum theory. This is so because macroscopic systems are made up of large numbers of microscopic quantum particles. One might expect that there are particular proper-

Figure I.4.12: *The exclusion principle.* The exclusion principle applied in the game called *musical chairs*. (Source: wikiHow)

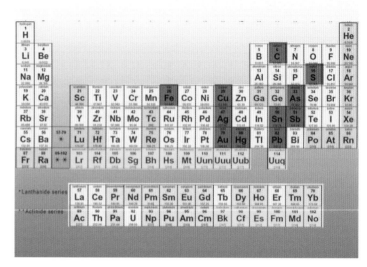

Figure I.4.13: *The struggle to unravel structure.* Mendeleev's periodic table of chemical elements in a historical perspective. The dark red color indicates the elements which were known already in antiquity. Adding the light pink entries you arrive at Mendeleev's table. Including the blue colored elements brings us up to 1945 (Seaborg's table) and the yellow elements were discovered after that. Many entries are thus post-Mendelevian. (Source: Sandbi - Wikimedia Commons)

ties of the microscopic constituents, which are specifically quantum mechanical and have a strong bearing on interactions between the particles, and therefore also on their collective behavior. Consequently there are many macroscopic phenomena which are not obviously quantum, but nevertheless can only be understood if one takes the underlying quantum physics into account.

Going from the microscopic to the macroscopic domain does not necessarily erase all quantum traces. A striking example is the property of spin and the *exclusion principle* of Pauli that – as we mentioned – decrees on the quantum level that particles with half-integral spin cannot occupy the same quantum state. We will have much more to say about this in Chapter II.5 of Volume II , but for the moment we will state the basic facts about it. Whereas the photon is a boson, the electron is a fermion and so are the proton and neutron. So, fermions don't like each other, they like to claim territory and chase away intruders, and they not only try but *have* to avoid each other. In spite of having no genes they certainly come across as rather selfish! Fermions are permanently involved in playing a kind of mu-

sical chairs (see Figure I.4.12). For bosons the behavior is the opposite, if the system is at very low temperature and there is no energy to excite the bosons, they love to join each other, and all settle in the same ground state. They will form what is called a *condensate*, a *Bose-condensate* to be specific. These are macroscopically coherent collective quantum states which may exhibit spectacular properties. This form of quantum coherence manifests itself in for example a laser beam, but also in phenomena like superfluidity and superconductivity. We will return to these properties in Chapter III.3 of Volume III.

Figure I.4.14: *The left step Janet periodic table.* This is a logical representation of the periodic table in direct correspondence with the quantum classification of atomic states, as depicted in Figure I.4.9. Starting from the right each block corresponds to an increasing integer value of the angular momentum as is indicated in the left column, where letters are used with $l = 0 \leftrightarrow s, 1 \leftrightarrow p, 2 \leftrightarrow d, 3 \leftrightarrow f$. And each block contains $2(2l+1)$ states, i.e. $2, 6, 10, 14, \ldots$. In comparison with the standard Mendeleev representation of Figure I.4.2(a), one sees that the extra rows added (of the Lanthanides and the Actinides) at the bottom of the Mendeleev table get a natural place as $l = 3$ blocks in the Janet table.

Atoms: the building blocks of chemistry

The connection between Mendeleev's periodic table of the chemical elements depicted in Figure I.4.13, and the systematics of atomic states of Figure I.4.9 is not immediate. This is so because the Mendeleev table was conceived prior to quantum mechanics. This begs for alternative representations of the periodic table in which the underlying quantum structure is manifest.

The rich structure of the periodic table of atomic elements underlying all the structural diversity of chemistry is a direct consequence of the fermionic nature of the electron. Because in an atom with more than a single electron, not all the electrons can sit in the lowest possible state, they have to successively fill the higher energy states of for example Figure I.4.6. And as the chemical properties of the elements are mostly determined by the outer electrons, they will be different because the charge distributions associated with the states of the outer electrons may have quite different shapes, as we saw in Figure I.4.9.

With our knowledge of quantum theory we might prefer to draw the periodic table differently, for example following Janet as we did in Figure I.4.14. In that non-standard visualization there is a direct correspondence with the way the atomic quantum states are labeled as we depicted in Figure I.4.9. The quantum states at a given energy E_n are organized into *shells* labeled by the angular momentum quantum number l that runs from 0 to $n - 1$. Quantum theory tells us how things work on the microscopic scale but as a consequence thereof it leaves indelible marks on much larger scales in fields like chemistry and material science. We will have to say a lot more on chemistry and condensed matter in Volume III.

Nuclear structure

Nuclei consist of a certain number of protons and neutrons that are kept together by the strong nuclear force. Nuclei that occur in nature are relatively stable for the excellent reason that they wouldn't be there otherwise, but not all nuclei we find in nature are stable. There are many metastable isotopes that can decay in a variety of ways, either by the emission of protons, neutrons, α particles, or by $\beta^{\pm}$ or γ radiation. Many of these occur spontaneously in nature and have important applications, for example in the context of carbon dating. Short-lived β^+ radiators are for example used as radioactive tracers for PET scanning purposes.

An atom consists of a positively charged massive nucleus in the core and a number of electrons 'orbiting' around it, making the overall charge of the atom zero. The natural next step in the quest for fundamental building blocks was to proceed to the structure of the nucleus itself. As always in science, if one observes regularities in structure, one tries to figure out an underlying mechanism that explains those regularities. Here it was not different. The question was open ended in the early days of quantum theory, and it might have happened that one entered a realm where even quantum theory would fail. How exciting! But alas, that didn't happen, physics in the nuclear domain appeared to fully obey the quantum laws. The mechanism underlying nuclear binding is similar to that of the atom in some aspects, but different in others.

Nucleons: Protons and neutrons. Nuclear fission experiments demonstrated that nuclei are composed of particles called *nucleons*, of two types, the *proton* or the *neutron*. From Table B.4 at the end of the book about the discoveries of fundamental particles, we learn that the neutron was discovered by James Chadwick as late as 1932, for which he received the Physics Nobel prize in 1935. but remarkably we also learn nothing about the discovery of

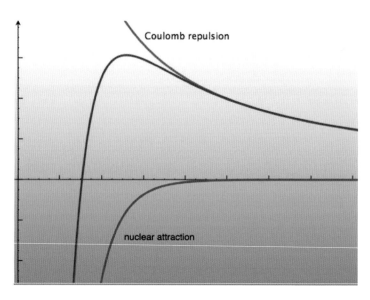

Figure I.4.15: *The nuclear potential between protons as a function of their distance.* The potential is given by the purple curve, which is the sum of a long-range electromagnetic repulsion (in red) and a short-range attractive part due to the strong nuclear force (in blue). Once the particles get close enough they are strongly bound.

the proton as such. That discovery was implicitly made with the discovery of the atomic nucleus by Rutherford in 1911, where the proton is defined as the nucleus of the simplest atom, hydrogen. Rutherford, the great physicist and chemist from New Zealand who spent most of his active research years in Canada and Britain, is often called the 'father of nuclear physics.' He was awarded the Nobel prize for Chemistry in 1908, 'for his investigations into the disintegration of the elements, and the chemistry of radioactive substances.' The neutron was discovered relatively late, presumably because it is unstable as a free particle: it decays under emission of an electron (and an invisible (anti-)neutrino) into a proton! This process was at the root of all radioactive β decay processes of nuclei, discovered by Henri Becquerel as early as 1896 and dramatically expanded by Marie and Pierre Curie. If nuclei are made of protons and neutrons, the first question that comes to mind is: how can positively charged protons stick together so closely in a tiny nucleus if they all carry the same positive charge? Equal charges repel and repel more strongly if they get closer to each other, because the Coulomb force is inversely proportional to their squared distance. So, how come nuclei don't fly apart? What keeps them together?

A looming crisis leading to a considerable number of gifted Desperado's in search of new physics! A simple but bold idea would be to bluntly postulate a new *strong 'nuclear' force* that would be stronger than the electromagnetic force so that it could overcome the electromagnetic repulsion and cause a net attraction. If we in addition assume that this strong nuclear force works equally strongly on protons and neutrons, this could in principle explain the nuclear binding. And indeed, that is the way it worked out!

The picture looks like Figure I.4.15, where we have plotted the interaction energy of two protons as a function of their distance. It is important to note that there are two contributions, one from the electromagnetic repulsion (the red curve), which is long range and typically falls inversely proportional to the distance, and one from the attractive nuclear force (the blue curve), which is strong but acts only over a short range. These two contributions add up to the interaction energy corresponding to the purple curve where one sees that the repulsion dominates for large distances. Compare these curves for the nuclear binding energy with those we gave for the atomic binding in Figure I.4.5, where the ingredients are similar but work out very differently; in the atomic case the attraction dominates the long distance behavior.

Of course also the instability of neutrons had to be included into this picture as well, and that involves postulating yet another force, the so-called *weak nuclear force*, which will be discussed on page 196.

Isotopes and nuclear decay modes

Isotopes are nuclei that differ from their standard stable composition by having more or less neutrons. This means that these are metastable under various forms of emission. Some are short-lived, and some are long-lived. Nuclear isotopes have important applications.

Isotopes. Nuclei are characterized by two labels, one is the *atomic number* (basically the nuclear charge in units of the elementary charge e) and the other is the *mass number*. These labels can be easily converted into the number of protons, n_p, and the number of neutrons, n_n, in the nucleus, as follows

$$\text{atomic number} = n_p \qquad (I.4.9)$$

$$\text{mass number} = n_p + n_n \qquad (I.4.10)$$

The basic question was to understand the stability of the well-known atomic nuclei corresponding to the chemical elements. It turned out to be a matter of striking balances. For a chemical element the atomic number in the periodic table is clearly identified with the number of protons in the nucleus. In principle one would expect that, given the electric charge ($\sim n_p$), there could be different numbers of neutrons and therefore one could expect different atomic weights for a given element. This is indeed the case and we speak of different *isotopes* of the element, where the atomic number is the same but the mass number differs. As their charge configuration would be the same, their chemistry would also be, because that is basically governed by the electronic states around the nucleus. Well-known examples of isotopes are *deuterium* and *tritium*, the heavy forms of hydrogen. In addition to the proton, they have one and two neutrons respectively, and are therefore often denoted as ^{2}H and ^{3}H as to distinguish them from ordinary hydrogen, H = ^{1}H.

Another important isotope is the carbon isotope ^{14}C, to

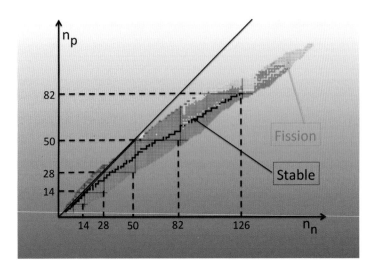

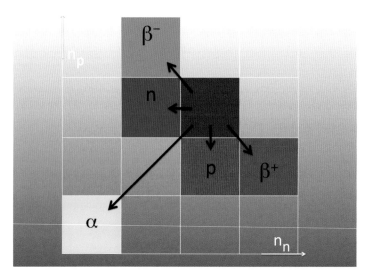

Figure I.4.16: *Stable and unstable isotopes.* The array of nucleotides or nuclear isotopes with on the horizontal axis the number of neutrons and on the vertical one the number of protons. The narrow black band in the middle of the colored region marks the stable nuclei. The other colors refer to nuclear decay types explained in the next figure.

Figure I.4.17: *Nuclear decay modes.* The basic decay modes of nuclei correspond to moves in the diagram: β^- decay corresponds to the emission of an electron, β^+ to the emission of a positron. α-radiation corresponds to the emission of a $^4\mathrm{He}$ nucleus consisting of two protons and two neutrons.

be distinguished from the stable isotope $^{12}\mathrm{C}$. The former occurs naturally but is unstable, due to the decay-process into nitrogen-14,

$$^{14}\mathrm{C} \Rightarrow {}^{14}\mathrm{N} + e^- + \bar{\nu}, \qquad (\mathrm{I.4.11})$$

where it emits an electron and an anti-neutrino. This decay is very slow with a half-life $\tau_{1/2}$ of 5730 years. It is this slow decay that is put to use in *carbon-14 dating* methods to determine the age of sediments, fossils and antique art objects. How nice, a nuclear instability that renders an important service to society, as it helps to unambiguously separate real from fake when it comes to providing quantitative, archeological, historical and anthropological evidence about the age of objects.

In Figure I.4.16 we display the array of isotopes, with the number of neutrons on the horizontal axis and the number of protons (i.e. atomic number) on the vertical one. The

stable nuclei form the black curve through the center of the colored band, below and above is a band of unstable nuclei that may or may not occur in nature. Note that the line of stable elements is below the $n_p = n_n$ line, which indicates that ever more neutrons are needed to stabilize the nucleus with increasing charge. The line of stable elements ends, indicating that beyond a certain atomic number all isotopes become unstable (around $n_p = 82$).

Nuclear decay modes. At any point in the chart of isotopes there are a number of conceivable instabilities corresponding to moving to neighboring spots as indicated in Figure I.4.17. The nearest neighbors, found by moving, down or sideways in the chart, correspond to adding or getting rid of a single neutron or proton. But we may also think of other so-called *transmutation modes*; for example the nucleus may emit α-radiation, which just means that it emits a (stable) $^4\mathrm{He}$ nucleus consisting of two protons and two neutrons. In our diagram this implies that the nucleus moves two steps to the left and two steps down. Another possibility is that a neutron in the nucleus decays by β^- decay into a proton and emits an electron (and an anti-neutrino) in which case we move one step up and one to the left. This is because the net charge increases by one unit, meaning that the nucleus would move one step up in our chart, but at the same time it moves one step to the left as the number of neutrons is decreased by one.

For each isotope the dominant decay mode is color coded in the chart of Figure I.4.16, and as expected the dominant decay tends to move the isotope to the black line of stable elements.

The chart shows that away from the stable nuclei marked as black, we have a rather broad band of metastable nucleotides or isotopes, but that band is bounded. On the very right of the table we get into a region where the would-be elements have no stable isotopes at all. These are compounds that do not occur in nature. But that didn't keep physicists like Glenn Seaborg at Berkeley from cooking them up in the lab. And as you see the nuclear physicists have filled out the periodic table up to an atomic number of about 120 by now. The new elements carry legendary names like *Einsteinium, Curium, Bohrium,* and so on. An ironic footnote is, that, while named after scientists whose names may well live forever, the corresponding elements themselves are only extremely short-lived.

Half-lives count. We mentioned already in passing the quantessential notion of a half-life or a decay time usually denoted as τ and it may deserve some explanation. If we take for example a number of N of the of metastable ^{14}C nuclei which have a certain probability to decay, then the number of nuclei that will decay will be proportional to N. This statement can easily be translated in an equation for the decay rate per unit time dN/dt:

$$\frac{dN}{dt} = -N/\tau.\qquad(I.4.12)$$

The solution (see also the *Math Excursion* on page 612 of

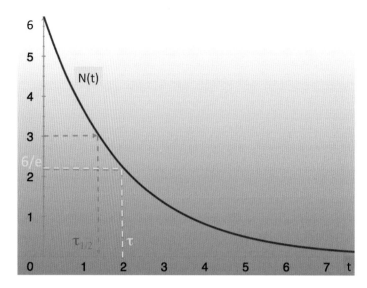

Figure I.4.18: *Half-life versus decay time.* In the case of exponential decay, the half-life $\tau_{1/2}$ is the time needed for half of the initial number N_0 particles to have decayed. After a decay time τ, (which chose equal 2) only N_0/e are left. In the figure we have chosen a scale $N_0 = 6 \times 10^{large}$.

Volume III) can be written as

$$N(t) = N(0)e^{-t/\tau},\qquad(I.4.13)$$

where $N(t)$ is the number of ^{14}C nuclei at time t. You see that the decay is exponential, and the rate equals $1/\tau$. The reader may be more familiar with the notion of a *half-life* $\tau_{1/2}$, the relation is simply $\tau_{1/2} = \tau \ln 2$. This makes the decay go like $2^{-t/\tau_{1/2}}$. so that after time $t = \tau_{1/2}$ only half the number of nuclei are left. In Figure I.4.18 this relation is visualized. What is remarkable about nuclear decays is that their half-lifes can be immense, even as big as the lifetime of the universe! How can a microscopic mechanism with very short characteristic timescales like inside the nucleus produce such incredibly slow processes. Thinking quantum mechanically you would expect a ground state of a certain energy E_0 to typically oscillate with a frequency of order $\nu = h/E_0$, and for a nucleus $E_0 = 1$ keV which yields a frequency of 10^{17} Hz or an oscillation time of order 10^{-18} s. This value has to be contrasted with the decay time of order 10^{11} s for carbon for example. That is a factor of about 10^{29}!

Imagine: you are an electron and want to get out and you only succeed after banging on the door 10^{29} times! Indeed it is exponentially hard to escape because there is a high potential barrier that wants to keep you inside, the decay is exponentially suppressed, because it proceeds via a process called *quantum tunneling*, a fully quantessential mechanism that has no classical analog at all. Classically the electron would have to climb over the mountain, but it has not enough energy to do that, and there is no escape possible. But quantum mechanically it is more subtle because there is a 'certain uncertainty' in the energy of the particle thanks to Heisenberg. This means that a version of the uncertainty relations applies, reading $\Delta E \cdot \Delta t \geq \hbar/2$. You may loosely paraphrase it by saying that the particle can 'borrow' energy for a brief period of time. It's like magic, if you do the trick fast enough nobody will notice and miracles are possible! Anyhow this means that there is a small probability that the electron will have sufficient energy to get away. That probability is exponentially small though, and depends on the height and width of the barrier. And that explains the enormous factor 10^{-29}. We will say more about quantum tunneling in Part II of the book.

Positron-emission tomography (PET)

Positron-emission tomography is a medical imaging technique for diagnostic purposes. In particular to learn about the functioning of organs. It makes use of specific radioactive isotopes that are injected into the patient. The scanner then traces how the radioactive component is transported through the body.

With the use of isotopes in the medical arena one certainly wants to reduce the exposure of patients to poten-

tially harmful radiation and therefore the isotopes needed for this purpose are typically short-lived positron (β^+) emitters. So here it is anti-matter that matters! If a positron is emitted, it will run into an electron in the detector, and together they will annihilated into a pair of high-energy photons that move out back-to-back. These photons get detected and from their momenta one can reconstruct where the positron was located.

The suitable radio isotopes are thus to be found in the orange region under the black line of stable nuclei in Figure I.4.16. Typical isotopes with short half-lives are carbon-11 ($\tau_{1/2} \sim 20$ min), nitrogen-13 ($\tau_{1/2} \sim 10$ min), oxygen-15 ($\tau_{1/2} \sim 2$ min), or fluorine-18 ($\tau_{1/2} \sim 110$ min). These so-called *tracers* are added to compounds the body uses normally, such as sugars, water and sometimes just the air we breath (oxygen-15).

Transmutation: Fission and fusion

> Nuclei aren't good or bad, it's what people do with them we have to worry about.

We discuss the basics of nuclear fission and fusion processes, emphasizing their peaceful applications. This includes the large global initiative, ITER, to construct a working net energy producing fusion reactor.

In Figure I.4.19 we show the binding energy per nucleon as a function of atomic mass number. The natural tendency is to minimize the energy: the system will minimize its total binding energy assuming there are no unsurmountable energy barriers that block access to that minimal energy configuration. The graph clearly shows the remarkable and important fact that elements of low mass number tend to lower their binding energy through *fusion* into heavier nuclei, whereas on the other side we see that at high mass number, nuclei can lower their binding energy

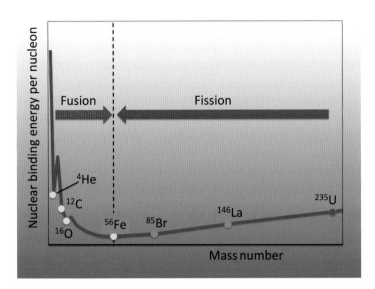

Figure I.4.19: *Fusion and fission.* The binding energy per nucleon inside a nucleus as a function of its mass number. Favored processes are those where this binding energy per nucleon decreases. The light elements tend to fuse, while the heavy ones tend to break up.

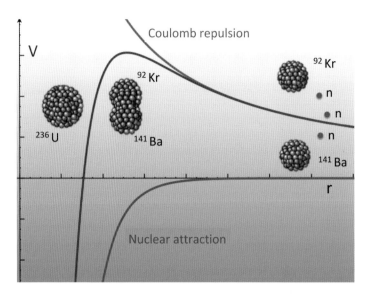

Figure I.4.20: *Fission of uranium,* By absorbing a neutron the ^{235}U isotope changes to the unstable uranium isotope ^{236}U that splits into a ^{141}Ba and a ^{92}Kr nucleus plus three neutrons.

by decaying or *fission* into lighter nuclei. Note also that interestingly the elements ^{4}He, ^{12}C and ^{16}O are relatively stable. In the following subsections we will focus first on fission and then on fusion.

Fission.

> The fundamental point in fabricating a chain reacting machine is of course to see to it that each fission produces a certain number of neutrons and some of these neutrons will again produce fission.
>
> *Enrico Fermi*

The heavy elements on the right of Figure I.4.19 with a high binding energy per nucleon are typically unstable with respect to *decay* or *fission* processes. In these processes the total mass number $(n_p + n_n)$ has to be conserved. We start with fission because it was easier to achieve than fusion – not only in reactors, but also in rather singularly dra-

matic experiments – like the making of nuclear bombs. In applications, whether it is in the deplorable nuclear weapon industry, or in fission reactors, or in hospitals, one always needs nuclei that are 'fissible'. 'Good fissibility' means that their fission after absorbing a neutron will also produce, apart from the heavy fission products, additional neutrons that can then destabilize neighboring nuclei. This way one can start a chain reaction. And clearly if that is not extremely well-controlled it will turn into an exponentially growing decay process, a meltdown or nuclear explosion, depending on the circumstances. History bears witness to quite a few of such cataclysmic events, and nuclear safety and disarmament should remain a primary concern for all of us. We have to find a responsible balance between profitability and safety and the price is high if we don't get it right.

In Figure I.4.20 we have illustrated the fission of a uranium-235 nucleus after the absorption of a neutron into the nuclei of barium-141 and krypton-91 plus three neutrons. The nuclear process is given by the following reaction equation:[3]

$$_0^1 n + _{92}^{235}U \rightarrow \ _{55}^{141}Ba + _{36}^{92}Kr + 3\,_0^1 n \, . \qquad (I.4.14)$$

It is clear that the emitted neutrons can ignite other uranium nuclei and this will keep the process going, provided that there is a sufficient concentration of uranium-235.

Natural uranium is found in ore deposits in many places around the world. It is predominantly a mixture of the two isotopes uranium 238 (99.27%) and uranium 235 (0.72%), and therefore to make nuclear fuel that can be used in reactors, one has to increase the 235 fraction by an 'enriching' process, for example by using centrifuges to get rid of the heavier 238 isotope. In a fission reactor the process is moderated by neutron absorbing materials such as graphite, water or heavy water (where the hydrogen is replaced by deuterium). The uranium-235 itself has a natural half-lifetime of 703,800,000 years, so no wonder there is still a lot left from the original amount stocked in the Earth crust. It naturally decays by emitting an α particle, producing a thorium-231 which in turn then decays rapidly in protactinium-231 and so on. It winds up in a long chain of successive reactions of which some are fast and others slow, with half-lives of thousands of years. The reaction chain of uranium-235 ends with the element lead-207 $\left(_{82}^{207}Pb\right)$, which is stable. However, if we get the uranium-235 to absorb a neutron, it turns into a uranium-236, and that is unstable so it breaks up in krypton and Barium plus three neutrons, and that can keep a chain reaction going.

Fusion. Going back to the binding energy curve of Figure I.4.19 we now turn to the left side, where we see that energy can be gained if we manage to *fuse* light nuclei (like hydrogen) into a stable nucleus with higher atomic number (like helium-4). This is not so simple because one has to 'overcome' the electromagnetic Coulomb repulsion

---

[3]We use the notation $_Z^A X$ with X= chemical element, A= mass number and Z= atomic number.

between for example two protons. Now in an accelerator this certainly could be done but to do this on a larger scale one has to achieve physical conditions which are quite extreme. So, to get fusion going has turned out to be very, very difficult. In spite of numerous experts who have been raising expectations, the timescales for achieving fusion have been repeatedly extended by decades. To go from 'scientific feasibility' to 'successful technology' sometimes takes a long time and may be hard to estimate. This leads to the familiar situation where either the optimists or the pessimists are ridiculed!

The Lawson criterion. How extreme the conditions are that have to be met in order to get fusion to work can be

Chrysopoeia: transmutation into gold?

> There was a lot more to magic, as Harry quickly found out, than waving your wand and saying a few funny words.
> *J.K. Rowling, Harry Potter and the Philosopher's Stone.*

Making gold is the alchemist's dream! In alchemy, the term *chrysopoeia* means transmutation into gold. It comes from the Greek words χρμσοσ, khrusos, meaning 'gold,' and ποιειν, poiëin, meaning 'to make.' The term refers to the creation of the *stone of wisdom* or the *philosopher's stone*. In the early days of alchemy, in Egypt and Greece there was a serious quest for the stone, as it would allow you to turn any metal into gold. It apparently led to a kind of primordial gold rush. For example, Zosima's *formula of the crab*, supposedly constituted a kind of recipe to brew gold out of copper and zinc. If only copper, zinc and a *Bunsen* burner would do! This 'recipe' would instantly turn any 'nitwit' into a billionaire, for as long as they managed to keep it secret of course! In Egyptian antiquity there must have been loads of books on alchemy, and – from a historical point of view – unfortunately, almost all of them have been lost. It was an 'executive order' by the Roman Emperor Diocletian in AD 296, which decreed that all alchemy books on making gold had to be burned. Anyway, we all know that the true heirs of alchemy are of course our friends the stockbrokers. Or should I say the Silicon Valley tech-billionaires who turn doom scrolling addictions into gold!

Now you ask, can nuclear physics revive the old gold-plated dream in a more mundane way? The answer is a clear 'yes!' Gold was first synthesized from mercury by neutron bombardment in 1941, but the isotopes of gold produced were all radioactive, so the gold produced had an expiration date, and that is precisely what you don't want. You don't want a fragile 'bread and butter' like commodity to be your gold standard. Actually there is only one stable gold isotope, ^{197}Au, so to produce desirable gold, nuclear reactions must create this isotope.

It can be done, but unfortunately it is way more expensive than just buying gold. Gold can actually be manufactured in a nuclear reactor by irradiation of mercury with neutrons. For this to work you need the mercury isotope ^{196}Hg, which occurs with a frequency of 0.15% in natural mercury. That isotope can be converted into gold, by first absorbing a neutron and then through electron capture decaying into ^{197}Au with some slow neutrons. I think we can be sure that, all those painfully negotiated and maintained nuclear nonproliferation agreements are not made out of fear that bad people might embark on breeding a nuclear goose producing golden eggs *ad infinitum*. □

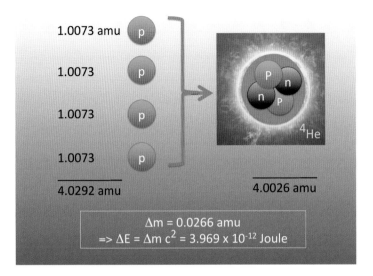

Figure I.4.21: *Energy gain by fusion.* The net energy gain from a fusion of four protons into a ^4He nucleus, as it happens in the Sun. One *atomic mass unit* or amu corresponds to $931.5\ \mathrm{MeV/c^2} = 1.661 \times 10^{-27}$ kg $\leftrightarrow 1.492_10^-10$ joule.

expressed by the so-called Lawson criterion. John Lawson, a young engineer working on nuclear fusion, decided in 1955 to work out exactly how hard it is to achieve fusion. Although his colleagues were quite optimistic about their prospects, he wanted to prove it to himself. He found that the conditions for fusion power relied on three vital factors. By calculating the requirements for more energy to be created in the plasma than is put in, he came up with a dependence on three quantities: temperature (T), density (n) and confinement time (τ). He derived a lower bound on the triple product, $L \equiv n\,\tau\,T$ which would depend on the type of process and the type of machine. For the deuterium-tritium fusion one typically needs $L \geq 10^{21}\ \mathrm{keV\ s/m^3}$ and that is what the international fusion project ITER in France is expected to achieve. The technological promise of a fusion reactor based on the Tokamak concept, where an extremely hot nuclear plasma is confined to a toroidal reaction chamber by very strong magnetic fields, has been clearly established. So far no stable, net energy producing fusion device has been constructed,

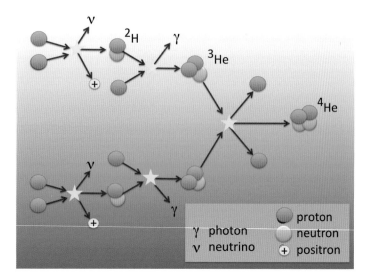

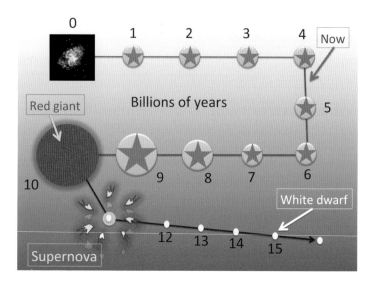

Figure I.4.22: *Fusion in the Sun.* This is the chain of nuclear fusion processes that takes place in the core of the Sun. It is a three step process, leading from protons via deuterium and helium-3 to the stable helium-4 nuclei. The net result is that four protons are converted into a single helium-4 nucleus.

Figure I.4.23: *The life cycle of the Sun.* An average star like the Sun has sufficient hydrogen to burn by fusion so as to keep shining for about 10 billion years. It will then form a red giant after which the core collapses to a white dwarf about the size of the Earth.

but we will discuss the ITER project shortly. It is a sobering thought that it is not us who invented fusion, of course nature did. And we have learned a lot from studying and understanding the energy production in the Sun which basically is a gigantic nuclear fusion reactor.

Let the Sun shine.

> ... No more falsehoods or derisions
> Golden living dreams of visions
> Mystic crystal revelation
> And the mind's true liberation ...
> Let the sun shine, let the sun shine in!

> *The fifth dimension* in the musical *Hair (1967)*

The extreme pressure caused by the gravitational force in the core of stars turns them into extreme pressure cookers, allowing for all kinds of fusion processes to take place. Every second, our Sun turns 600 million tons of hydrogen into

helium, releasing an enormous amount of energy. Achieving fusion on Earth has required a different approach since we lack a natural pressure cooker to achieve the densities and temperatures needed. The temperature at the Sun's surface is 6,000 degrees, while at its core it is 15 million degrees. Temperature combines with density in the Sun's core to create the conditions necessary for the fusion reaction to occur. The gravitational forces of our stars cannot be recreated here on Earth, and much higher temperatures are necessary in the laboratory to compensate.

The basic process of burning hydrogen to produce helium through the chain of fusion processes is depicted in Figure I.4.22. The hydrogen nuclei are just protons, so, in the first step we make deuterium under emission of a neutrino and a positron. The second step is to have the deuterium and a proton fuse into helium-3 under emission of a photon. Finally two helium nuclei can fuse into the stable

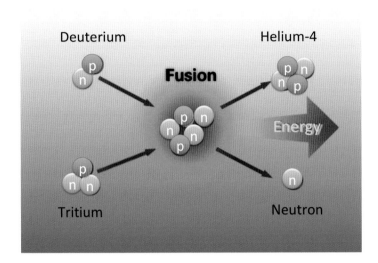

Figure I.4.24: *The basic ITER process.* The basic fusion process: $^2H + ^3H \rightarrow ^4He + n$ is delivering the energy in the ITER fusion reactor. The difference in mass between the total incoming and out-coming nuclei is converted into energy according to Einstein's formula $E = mc^2$.

Figure I.4.25: *ITER.* The international fusion reactor located in France. The reaction chamber contains the plasma which is enclosed in a toroidal magnetic field configuration, where it is heated up to temperatures of a few hundred million degrees so that fusion can take place. (Source: ITER)

helium-4 nucleus under emission of two protons. The net energy delivered in such a process is what is calculated in Figure I.4.21: it amounts to about 4.0×10^{-12} joules per helium-4 nucleus produced. In other words, burning 1 kg of fuel this way would produce about 2.3×10^7 MWh. This is comparable to what a 100 MW energy plant produces in 26 years!

Having analyzed the energy production of the Sun, we have also answered the question whether the Sun will keep shining forever. The answer is a firm 'no', because the Sun will simply run out of fuel at some point. The long-term perspective for life on Earth looks quite dim. In some 5 billion years the Sun will first blow up to form a *red giant* that will swallow the inner planets (including the Earth). The core will then collapse to a compact stellar object called a *white dwarf* while the outer parts will be blown off in space. The life cycle of the Sun is schematically depicted in Figure I.4.23. So, beware: our days are counted!

ITER: the nuclear fusion reactor

ITER will be the first fusion device to produce net energy and it will be the first fusion device to maintain fusion for long periods of time. Futhermore, it will be the first fusion device to test the integrated technologies, materials, and physics regimes necessary to enable a commercial production of fusion-based electricity.

The ITER project comprises a truly global collaboration, where China, the European Union, India, Japan, Korea, Russia and the United States are now engaged in a 35-year project to build and operate the ITER experimental device. The goal of the program is to produce a net gain of energy and deliver a prototype for the fusion power plant of the future. It has been designed to produce 500 MW of output power for 50 MW of input power – or ten times the amount of energy put in. The current record for released fusion power is 16 MW (held by the European JET facility located in Culham in the UK). In the ITER Tokamak, where the plasma is confined by strong magnetic fields into a toroidal reaction chamber, temperatures will reach 150 million degrees, that is ten times the temperature at the core of our Sun!

The 180-hectare ITER site in Saint Paul-Les-Durance, in the south of France, has a 42-hectare platform the size of 60 soccer fields. Building began in August 2010. The hope is that the reactor will be completed around 2030.

Field theory: particle species and forces

A major achievement in quantum physics in the second half of the twentieth century is the development of quantum field theory (QFT). It is a general formalism that encompasses both quantum theory and special relativity, and dramatically shifted our perspective on what particles deep down really are. It made us understand the origins of spin, *and of the* exclusion principle *and its related particle statistics properties. These developments culminated in the Standard Model which comprises precise and explicit new theories that describe the strong and weak nuclear interactions, as well as electrodynamics. Quantum theory opened the door to the microcosmos, and quantum field theory appears to correctly describe all processes down to the smallest scales we have been able to probe so far.*

Our quest to understand nature at ever smaller scales, forced us to study elementary processes at ever higher momenta and energies. This is a direct consequence of Heisenbergs uncertainty relations. Making Δx small requires making Δp and thus p and E large. To achieve such extreme energies one had to build big particle accelerators like CERN near Geneva and Fermilab near Chicago. Imagine, the energy consumption of one such machine is comparable to that of a medium-size city!

When the energies become of the same order as the rest masses of the elementary particles involved, one necessarily has to take special relativity into account. In particular, in view of the equivalence of mass and energy, we have to anticipate processes occurring where energy will be converted into mass and the other way around. On the one hand we expect the production of massive particles out of pure energy, and on the other hand the creation of pure radiation energy out of particle anti-particle annihilation. To make further progress in understanding these processes a theoretical framework that is consistent with both quantum mechanical and (special) relativistic principles was needed. The problem was in fact twofold: one was to find the relativistic generalization(s) of the Schrödinger equation, and the other was to develop a formalism for many particle states, where particles could be created and annihilated and converted into pure energy in the form of photons for example. Implementing these two requirements together gave rise to the (relativistic) *quantum field theory* formalism.

Relativistic wave equations. Let me recall that the classical Maxwell theory is already relativistically invariant. In fact, it was electromagnetism that pointed Einstein the way to relativity because it was hidden in there. You could say that the Maxwell equations are relativistic but not really quantum yet. With the Schrödinger equation the problem is the other way around, it is quantum but not relativistic. It is not, because it is based on the Newtonian – therefore non-relativistic – definitions of energy and momentum. We looked at the basics of the Schrödinger equation in a previous section and constructed the Schrödinger wave equation by means of a substitution where we replaced the classical E and p variables with differential operators, as shown in equation (I.4.2).

That exercise showed that the Schrödinger equation is *not* relativistically invariant. It is a wave equation, but quite different from the electromagnetic wave equation (I.1.47), which features the relativistic wave or 'box' operator, we introduced in equation (I.1.31). Indeed, in the electromagnetic wave equation discussed in Chapter I.1 , space and time are treated on equal footing, and that is not the case for the Schrödinger equation because it has a first-order time derivative, but second-order spatial derivatives.

Naively following the same approach, we could start with the relativistic expression for the particle energy and make the same substitutions:

$$E^2 = \mathbf{p}^2 c^2 + m^2 c^4 \quad \rightarrow \quad (\hbar^2 \Box + m^2 c^2)\phi = 0 . \quad \text{(I.4.15)}$$

Not surprisingly, we now meet again our old friend the relativistic wave operator $\Box$, and in addition a mass term. This seems quite straightforward, and in fact it is. This equation was already written down by Schödinger himself, who discarded it for reasons that we will point out shortly. The resulting equation is called the *Klein – Gordon (KG) equation*, and after all the dust of field theory settled, it turned out to have a consistent interpretation: it describes a scalar particle, or a particle without spin, such as for example the pion.

No ground state, no physics! On the level of a quantum equation for a single particle, interpreting the Klein – Gordon like the Schrödinger equation, gave rise to a real problem with it. Let me digress a little on what that problem was about. If I tell you that $b = 2$ is true, you may say: 'fine, so be it', then I square that equation and say $b^2 = 4$, and again ask you what is b? Well then, if you, once upon a time, had dutifully executed your homework assignments, you would not answer $b = 2$, but $b = +2$ *or* $b = -2$. By squaring the equation, I have smuggled in an extra negative solution. I managed to somehow double the truth! How shrewd, the logic is impeccable but not always reversible. The quadratic equation is less restrictive.

What this means is that the quadratic relation for the energy (and the corresponding wave operator), in the KG equation also introduces negative energy solutions, after all the solutions are $E = \pm\sqrt{\mathbf{p}^2 c^2 + m^2 c^4}$. So we do not add just one, but infinitely many negative energy solutions. Well, nothing wrong with that, if we go back to the bound states in the hydrogen atom. we see that also there we had an infinity of negative energy bound states. The significant difference, however, is that the negative energy values obtained from the Klein-Gordon equation are not bounded from below because the magnitude of the momentum is unlimited. In other words, there would be no ground state, and the particle it describes would be unstable. Unfortunately, no ground state means no physics!

People got stuck in the Klein – Gordon theory, because it seemed impossible to interpret satisfactorily. And indeed to do relativistic quantum mechanics correctly, one had to go beyond writing down a wave equation for a single particle. One would have to go to quantum field theory to resolve the apparent inconsistencies with these equations. Nevertheless, the idea of somehow producing a sensible relativistically invariant first-order equation as a kind of 'square root' of the Klein – Gordon equation was on the table, and the hope was that that would resolve the problems of that equation.

The Dirac equation: matter and anti-matter

Dirac was the strangest man who ever visited my institute. During one of Dirac's visits I asked him what he was doing. He replied that he was trying to take the square-root of a matrix, and I thought to myself what a strange thing for such a brilliant man to be doing. Not long afterwards the proof sheets of his article on the equation arrived, and I saw he had not even told me that he had been trying to take the square root of the unit matrix!

Niels Bohr

(Quoted in Kurt Gottfried, *P.A.M. Dirac and the Discovery of Quantum Mechanics.*)

The remarkable features of the electron, like having an intrinsic angular momentum called spin and being subjected to the mysterious Pauli exclusion principle, all fell into place after Dirac wrote down his beautiful, relativistically invariant, first-order wave equation for the electron. But the biggest surprise was its prediction of the existence of antimatter.

The relativistic equation for the spin one-half electron was published in 1930, and Paul Adrian Maurice Dirac shared the Nobel prize with Erwin Schrödinger three years later. This equation, for the electron and its anti-particle the positron, and the Maxwell equations describing photons, forms the back-bone of a theory called *Quantum Electrodynamics (QED)*, which constituted the first example of a consistent relativistic quantum field theory. With the completion of this theory shortly after the Second World War, a fully relativistic and quantum mechanical treatment of the electromagnetic interactions of electrons, positrons and photons was achieved.

On taking square roots. To get some appreciation for one of the most beautiful equations of physics, it is illuminating to go back to the Klein – Gordon equation as a starting point. We would like to take the positive root, so to say, of the Klein-Gordon, but that is hard. On the mechanics side on the left of (I.4.15), with the algebraic relation it is easy, you just take the root on both sides and only keep the positive root by choosing[4] $E = +\sqrt{\mathbf{p}^2 + m^2}$. But on the Klein-Gordon side of the story, you would have to take the root out of the $\Box$ operator and that is hard to define, because you have to define what you mean by the square root of a derivative. Strictly speaking you could express it as an infinite series of ever higher powers of the momentum operator but that is not what you want, because that would involve taking 'infinite order derivatives' and that makes even strong people quail! What you really would like to have is an expression *linear* in E, p and m that squares

[4]To make the argument and formulas more transparent we choose natural units where $\hbar = c = 1$ in this subsection.

to the Klein-Gordon operator. And that is what Dirac brilliantly achieved by making use of matrices in defining this miraculous 'square root'.

A matrix root: the Weyl equation Let me take one step at a time and first indicate why using matrices dramatically enlarges the space of possibilities for taking a square root.[5] Let us pose 'taking the square root' as a matrix problem. Suppose that instead of the equation $b^2 = 4$, which of course has solutions $b = \pm 2$, I would have considered the matrix equation $B^2 = A$ with A being 4 times the 2×2 unit matrix:

$$A = 4 \cdot \mathbf{1} = \begin{pmatrix} 4 & 0 \\ 0 & 4. \end{pmatrix}$$

If I ask you to solve the equation for B, then you could have come up with 4 independent solutions. If you start with the set $\{X^\mu\}$,

$$X^0 = \begin{pmatrix} 1 & 0 \\ 0 & 1 \end{pmatrix}, X^1 = \begin{pmatrix} 0 & 1 \\ 1 & 0 \end{pmatrix},$$
$$X^2 = \begin{pmatrix} 0 & -i \\ i & 0 \end{pmatrix}, X^3 = \begin{pmatrix} 1 & 0 \\ 0 & -1 \end{pmatrix}, \quad (I.4.16)$$

then 4 independent solutions would be $B^\mu = 2X^\mu$. We may go one step further and check that the much stronger identity holds:

$$(p_0 X^0 + \mathbf{p} \cdot \mathbf{X})(p_0 X^0 - \mathbf{p} \cdot \mathbf{X}) = (p_0^2 - \mathbf{p}^2)\mathbf{1}, \quad (I.4.17)$$

because of the special properties of the set of matrices $\{X^\mu\}$. Multiplying out the left-hand side you get $4^2 = 16$ terms that are quadratic in both the X-matrices and the momentum components p_μ. Equating the coefficients of the six *different* momentum combinations $p_\mu p_\nu$, one obtains six equations that the matrices have to satisfy. Firstly, we have the condition that the symmetric products or *anticommutators* of the matrices have to satisfy $\{X^i, X^j\} \equiv$

[5]This calculation uses a little bit of the material out of the *Math Excursion* on complex numbers at the end of Part III. Here it suffices to know that i denotes the 'imaginary unit' and that it by definition squares to minus one: $i^2 = -1$.

$X^i X^j + X^j X^i = 2\delta^{ij}$. Secondly, we have the condition that the antisymmetric products or *commutators* have to satisfy $[X^0, X^j] \equiv X^0 X^j - X^j X^0 = 0$. And as you may check, the matrices X^μ do exactly that! This special set of matrices, are called the *Pauli-matrices* or *spin-matrices* that are often denoted as σ_μ. The reason they are called the spin-matrices will become clear shortly.

So, we succeeded in writing the four-momentum squared, as a product of two matrices linear in the momentum, that is without using square roots. But this nice construction can be applied to equations as well. If we have a massless relativistic particle, its momentum satisfies $p_\mu p^\mu = 0$, leading to a massless Klein-Gordon equation for a (spin zero) scalar field of the type $\Box \psi(x^\nu) = 0$. However, with what we just learned one could also introduce a linear first order matrix equation. This is just the so-called Weyl equation, named after the German mathematician, theoretical physicist and philosopher Hermann Weyl, who wrote this relativistic wave equation down in 1929:

$$(iX^\mu \partial_\mu)\, \Psi(x_\nu) = 0, \qquad (I.4.18)$$

where Ψ is a two-component, so-called *spinor*, on which the matrices work. The wave-like solutions are of the form:

$$\Psi \sim u(p) e^{-ip_\mu \cdot x^\mu}, \qquad (I.4.19)$$

with $u(p)$ a spinor. Substituting this in the Weyl equation we get an algebraic equation for the two-component spinor $u(p)$:

$$(X \cdot p)\, u(p) = 0 \quad \rightarrow \quad \mathbf{X} \cdot \mathbf{p}\, u(p) = p_0\, u(p). \quad (I.4.20)$$

This is an eigenvalue equation with two independent solutions $u(p) = \eta^\pm(p)$ and eigenvalues $p_0 = E_\pm = \pm|p|$:

$$\mathbf{X} \cdot \mathbf{p}\, \eta^\pm = E_\pm\, \eta^\pm. \qquad (I.4.21)$$

This positive energy η^+ mode describes a massless particle with spin one-half, with its spin polarized parallel to its momentum. It is a particle with a fixed positive *helicity* which therefore is also called a *right-handed* particle.

The negative energy η^--component describes the corresponding *anti-particle* which necessarily has the opposite helicity.

The first factor on the left-hand side of equation (I.4.17), also describes a two-component spinor which can be obtained from the one we just discussed by flipping the sign of the energy p_0, so it will describe a left-handed or negative-helicity particle, and its anti-particle.

The first thing we have to conclude is that the Weyl equation describes a relativistic spin one-half particle. We did however not get rid of the negative energy solutions, but presumably these have to be interpreted as describing an anti-particle. We will return to this picture shortly.

For a long time it was believed that neutrinos would be massless, left-handed particles described by a Weyl equation, but we have in the meantime learned that neutrinos have a small mass after all. They therefore have to be described by a Dirac equation where the two chiralities get coupled through the mass term.

The Dirac matrices and algebra. Dirac managed to do something similar for a massive particle. He started with the quadratic relativistic energy-momentum relation (times the unit matrix), and wrote it as a product of two matrix factors linear in the momentum. To succeed he needed to introduce four 4×4 matrix coefficients γ^μ. Using the standard, very convenient, 'slash' notation $\displaystyle{\not{p} \equiv p_\mu \gamma^\mu}$ (introduced by Feynman), we may write:

$$(\not{p} + m\mathbf{1})(\not{p} - m\mathbf{1}) = (E^2 - \mathbf{p}^2 - m^2)\mathbf{1}. \qquad (I.4.22)$$

Again, multiplying out the left-hand side out you get $4^2 = 16$ terms that are quadratic in both the gamma matrices and the momentum components. To satisfy the equation, the diagonal terms require $(\gamma^0)^2 = \mathbf{1}$ and $(\gamma^i)^2 = -\mathbf{1}$, while the six terms with a product of two *different* momentum components should all vanish. The matrix coefficients correspond to the *anti-commutator* of the corresponding gamma-matrices:

$$\{\gamma^\mu, \gamma^\nu\} \equiv \gamma^\mu \gamma^\nu + \gamma^\nu \gamma^\mu. \qquad (I.4.23)$$

The upshot is that conditions on the gamma matrices that follow from the requirement that equation (I.4.22) is satisfied are summarized by the equation:

$$\{\gamma^\mu, \gamma^\nu\} = 2\eta^{\mu\nu}\mathbf{1}, \qquad (I.4.24)$$

where $\eta^{\mu\nu} = \mathrm{diag}(1, -1, -1, -1)$ is the relativistic Lorentzian space-time metric we encountered before. Matrices satisfying an algebraic relation like the one above form a so-called *Dirac or Clifford algebra*.

The Dirac equation. We are ready to tackle the four-component Dirac equation which in its most compact and elegant form can be written as:

$$(i\partial\!\!\!/ - m\mathbf{1})\psi(x^\mu) = 0, \qquad (I.4.25)$$

This first-order system is relativistically invariant, because one can show that the matrices do indeed also transform like a four-vector. It has wave-like solutions multiplied by a four-component *spinor* $u(p)$. The 4×4 γ matrices act on the components of the spinor. For positive energy ($E > 0$) the solutions look like:

$$\psi(x^\mu) \sim u(p)e^{-ip_\mu x^\mu}, \qquad (I.4.26)$$

substituting this in the Dirac equation yields the algebraic equation for $u(p)$:

$$(p\!\!\!/ - m\mathbf{1})u(p) = 0. \qquad (I.4.27)$$

The negative energy solutions can be written in a similar way as:

$$\psi(x^\mu) \sim v(p)e^{+ip_\mu x^\mu} \qquad (I.4.28)$$

and it yields an equation for the spinor $v(p)$:

$$(p\!\!\!/ + m\mathbf{1})v(p) = 0. \qquad (I.4.29)$$

Comparing these equations we see that the Klein – Gordon equation factorizes into a product of two first-order equations. These two equations are then combined again in the single four-component Dirac equation, which admits positive and negative energy solutions: the former correspond to the electron and the latter to the *hole* (or positron) degrees of freedom respectively.

It is important to remark that the four components of the wavefunction *not* form a four-vector; they form a four-component *spinor* which transforms differently under Lorentz transformations. Another way to say this is, that of the four components, two states correspond to an electron with its two spin states, while the other two would correspond to a positron with its two spin states. But as the gamma-matrices are not diagonal the equation mixes all components. There is a lot of beautiful and important mathematics hidden in the Dirac equation that we will not address here at all. Our goal was to get to know the magnificent equation that provided such a deep understanding of quantessential properties of matter like spin, the exclusion principle and the necessity of anti-matter. ■

The spectrum. Let us first look at the energy spectrum of the free Dirac particle as depicted on the left in Figure I.4.26. The first thing that strikes us in this picture is that the negative energy states have not disappeared. So, again it looks like there is no lowest energy state, and taking the square root of the equation has *not* eliminated the negative energy states in any obvious way. Consequently one would think that this feature would make the model inconsistent and useless. But, no! Dirac brilliantly argued that because his particles necessarily have spin one-half, they would have to satisfy the exclusion principle. But if that is the case, he could decree that all negative energy states would be filled, and there would be no problem. There would be a lowest energy state for the next electron to come in. So Pauli's exclusion principle acts like a *deus ex machina* here.

The second point to observe is that there is an *energy-gap* of $\Delta E = 2mc^2$ between the highest negative energy state

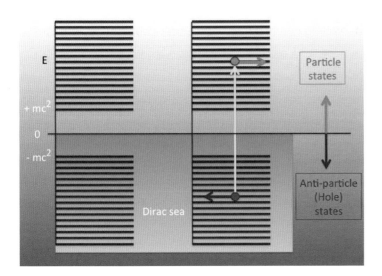

Figure I.4.26: *The spectrum of the Dirac field.* The energy spectrum of the Dirac equation for a spin 1/2 particle of mass m. It has positive and negative energy states. The negative energy states are all filled and form the 'Dirac sea.' A high-energy photon ($E \geq 2mc^2$) can excite an electron out of the sea into a positive energy *particle* state, and the hole that stays behind is just an *anti-particle* with opposite charge and opposite momentum.

Figure I.4.27: *Pair creation.* This is bubble chamber picture of a high-energy photon which enters from the left, and is not visible because it has no charge). It knocks out an electron thereby also creating a relatively low energy pair. Later the photon produces a second pair with more energy. A strong magnetic field is applied perpendicular to the page, which causes the particle trajectories to curve depending on their charge and energy. A perfect way to split the electron and positron tracks therefore.

and the lowest positive energy state. In the field theory context this means that exciting an electron from a negative energy state to a positive state would cost at least $2mc^2$, and effectively produce both a *particle and* a '*hole*'. There is no such thing as only creating a particle. The 'hole' is nothing but the *anti-particle* or *positron*, having the same mass and the opposite charge. So from the 'vacuum' state, corresponding to the completely filled 'Dirac sea' of negative energy states, one may create particle antiparticle (electron-positron) or particle-hole pairs. This is indicated on the right-hand side of the Figure I.4.26. A bubble chamber shown in Figure I.4.27 clearly shows the successive creation of two pairs from a high-energy photon. Understanding of the Dirac equation leads therefore inevitably to the prediction and discovery of anti-matter.[6]

Condensed matter. It is quite gratifying to see that 80 years after Dirac wrote his equation down, it is still alive and kicking. This equation is there to stay! Apparently Dirac himself once quipped that the equation was far more intelligent than its author. And indeed, it has found many important and fundamental applications. Firstly, the equation or variants thereof not only describe the electron, but in fact all elementary constituent particles like the leptons (electrons, muons, neutrinos etc.), and the quarks. Not so surprising as all of them have spin one-half and are fermions. Secondly, the Dirac equation and the field theoretic concepts that come with it are also extremely relevant

---

[6]Dirac himself hoped initially that the positively charged particle

would correspond to the proton, so that the equation would somehow describe the complete hydrogen atom. It was Robert Oppenheimer, then at Princeton University, who pointed out that the oppositely charged particles had to have the same mass and therefore the equation implied a new species of particles, now denoted as *anti-matter*.

in condensed matter physics. This is somewhat surprising because *a priori* that is at low energy and you would not expect excitations to satisfy a relativistic equation. Yet, in a conductor the electrons fill the available energy states up to a level which is called the Fermi level. And there you have a situation which is like the Dirac vacuum, and indeed you can excite an electron which means that you effectively create an particle-hole pair.

Majorana fermions. There are even closer analogies, since quite recently so-called *topological phases of matter* have been predicted in which boundary excitations occur that are effectively behaving like massless Dirac modes, thus behaving like relativistic particles. An example is the so-called Majorana fermion, which is a special case where the particle is its own antiparticle. So it has only two components. The theory of the *Majorana fermion* goes back to thirties of the twentieth century, to a brilliant young Italian physicist who proposed the model, but then mysteriously disappeared. In fact his disappearance has never been fully resolved or explained. Whereas his person remains a mystery, his equation fortunately does not.

The mathematics of the Dirac operator. Finally, the notion of the *Dirac operator*, which is the first-order differential operator that defines the Dirac equation, plays an important role in pure mathematics. For example the index of the massless Dirac operator on smooth curved manifolds is directly linked to certain topological invariants of that manifold, through the so-called *Atiyah–Singer index theorem*. We will return to the Dirac equation in somewhat more detail in the next Volume.

Quantum Electrodynamics: QED

Quantum Electrodynamics is the first and very successful example of a quantum field theory. We outline some of its basic structure and properties, and mention states, opera-

tors and Feynman diagrams. This theory, starting from first principles, made some impressive, precise predictions that agreed with experiment up to 12 significant digits!

The first milestone in relativistic field theory was the formulation of *Quantum Electrodynamics (QED)*, a completely consistent quantum theory of electrons, positrons, photons and their interactions. The theory was completed just after the Second World War, quite independently, by the American physicists Richard Feynman and Julian Schwinger, as well as the Japanese Sin-Itiro Tomonaga. They jointly received the 1965 Nobel prize in Physics for this work. This success generated further developments in field theory which during 1970s culminated in the formulation of the successful *Standard Model* of all the known elementary particles and the fundamental forces between them.

Particles and force fields. In classical physics there is a clear (ontological) distinction between, on the one hand, constituent particles carrying mass and charge (like electrons and protons), that are often considered 'point-like', and on the other hand the force fields through which they interact like the electromagnetic field, and which spread out over all of space-time. In relativistic quantum field theory this distinction disappears. Particles correspond to ' wavefunctions' or states of quantum fields which can be spread out. But the arrow goes both ways, so classical force fields (like the electromagnetic field) when quantized have particle-like excitations (like the photon). And we say that the forces are carried or mediated by those particles. Particle-wave duality is lifted to a particle-field duality at a higher (or should I say, deeper) level.

So, the electron and its anti-particle the positron are described by a Dirac-type quantum field, as are the neutrinos and the quarks. A state of the electron quantum field may describe any number of electrons and/or positrons. So, there is *one* field for all electrons. In fact, every particle type has its own quantum field. But, also the force fields of the strong and weak interactions have their own quantum fields, whose particle-like quanta we call *gluons* and *W and Z bosons*, respectively. In other words, there is a universal particle-field correspondence on the quantum level if we take relativity into account. Quantum field theory transcends the distinction between particles and forces in an essential way, yet the quantum fields describing constituent particles and force fields have distinctive features, because the constituents are fermions with spin one-half, and the force fields are bosons with spin one.

States and operators. A distinguishing feature of the quantum field theory framework is that it allows for the creation and annihilation of particles. Let me try to give a flavor of how that works. The first important ingredient is the existence of a vacuum or a ground state denoted as the zero state $|0\rangle$, that is the state without any particle in it. The second ingredient is that quantum fields can be expressed in terms of *particle creation and annihilation operators* that can act on the vacuum, or any other state, and create or annihilate a particle in that state. A generic state is in fact a multi-particle state that is labeled by the number of particles present in the state and what their energy, momentum and spin-polarizations are. For example a state,

$$|n_\gamma(\epsilon^\mu, k^\mu), n_e(s, p^\mu), n_p(s', p'^{\,\mu})\rangle$$

would correspond to a state with n_γ photons in a state with four-momentum k^μ and polarization vector ϵ^μ, and so on. The electrons and positrons have spin one-half, and their spin-polarization is encoded in the variables s (s').

Particle creation and annihilation.[7]

The physics we want to describe involves the creation and annihilation of particles and this is implemented by creation and annihilation operators we just mentioned. The

photon field, for example, corresponding to the vector potential $A^\mu(\mathbf{x}, \mathbf{t})$, has a linear expansion in photon creation and annihilation operators, which are denoted $a^\dagger(\epsilon^\sigma, k^\nu)^\dagger$ and $a(\epsilon^\sigma, k^\nu)$. If the creation operator acts on a state, it creates a particle in the corresponding state, so for example:

$$a^\dagger(\epsilon^\sigma, q^\nu)\,|0\rangle = |n_\gamma(\epsilon^\sigma, q^\nu) = 1\rangle$$

Here the creation operator acts on the vacuum and creates a new state in which there is one photon present (n=1), with the specified polarization and energy-momentum. If you apply the annihilation operator to the vacuum, you would simply get zero:

$$a(\epsilon^\sigma, k^\nu)\,|0\rangle = 0\,,$$

because there is no particle to be annihilated. If there had been a particle with the corresponding properties in the state, that particle would be annihilated and we would end up with the vacuum state. But if we act on the vacuum state there is no particle to annihilate and the result is the number zero – the operator 'annihilates the vacuum' is the jargon.

In general one considers rather elementary processes, with a few incoming particles creating an incoming state, then these particles interact with each other (so typically particles will be annihilated and created), and what we want to know is what the possible final states are and what the probabilities are that they occur. To do these calculations, demands a lot of skill, since they tend to be extensive and it takes even the largest computers days to do the job. But the hardest part is also to set up the calculation and figure out in all detail which sub-processes will be there, and how important they are. It involves also an incredible amount of book keeping which of course has to be performed impeccably, and one therefore has to build in all kinds of checks and balances to see whether the extremely rigid laws are completely obeyed at any stage of the computation. Experiments like those at CERN are also at the forefront of all kinds of AI applications, both on the data analysis side

---

[7] I have had the pleasure of running into *creationists* and *nihilists*, but so far not into any *annihilists*.

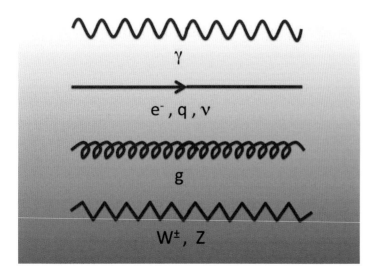

Figure I.4.28: *Propagators.* Particle propagation lines or *propagators* for various particle types. The arrow on the fermion line keeps track of the charge or better of the particle versus antiparticle degrees of freedom of the field.

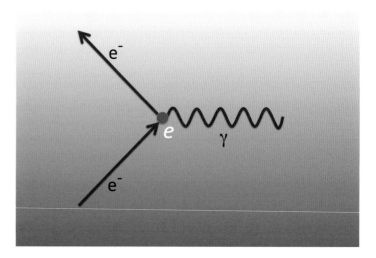

Figure I.4.29: *Interaction vertex.* The unique QED interaction is given by the interaction vertex of a photon with a charged particle, like an electron or quark. The strength of the coupling equals the coupling constant '*e*'.

as on the theoretical, calculational side, where we have to distinguish the numerical methods from the highly automated algebraic manipulation technology.

The language of Feynman diagrams. At this point the diagrammatic language created by Feynman becomes an indispensable tool. Let me give you an impression of how this methodology works. We have mentioned the (in- and out-coming) states, and these are represented as lines entering or leaving the diagram, where each particle type has its own type of 'propagation' line as illustrated in Figure I.4.28. The interactions are represented by diagrams where the particles that interact come together at a *vertex.* For example in Figure I.4.29 we see an electron emitting or absorbing a photon, where the electron moves on but with a different momentum.

The theory is relativistically invariant which means that you can make space-time 'rotations' or Lorentz transformations. This implies that you can also rotate the diagram clockwise

over 90 degrees (as in Figure I.4.30 on the left), and you get the diagram for a photon coming in and an electron coming out and – help – what is that? It looks like an electron moving backwards in time! You may think so, but that is indeed what a positron is. A negative charge (electron) moving backward in time is the same as a positive charge moving forward in time, because that is the way the Dirac equation works. At the vertex – the red dot, the interaction takes place with a strength of the charge e, and in the interaction the energy, momentum and charge have to be conserved. So, what goes in, has in some form to come out again. If you had rotated the diagram counterclockwise instead (as in the same figure on the right), you would have obtained a diagram representing electron-positron annihilation into a photon, and indeed the total charge is zero at all times.

As far as QED is concerned these are roughly the fundamental rules but the diagrams may become arbitrarily complicated.

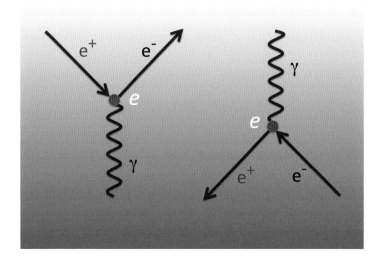

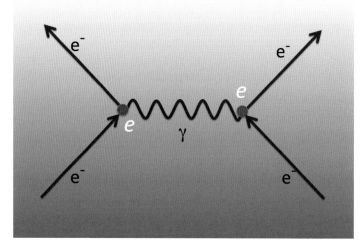

Figure I.4.30: *Interaction vertex.* The rotated diagram gives the coupling for the creation of an electron-positron pair on the left, and the annihilation of an electron-positron pair on the right. The convention is that in the diagram time goes upward. Note that the electron (negative charge) moving backward in time is the same as a positron (positive charge) moving forward in time.

Figure I.4.31: *Photon exchange.* A lowest order photon exchange diagram contributing to the amplitude for electron-electron scattering.

That is the quantessence of the trade: you know what comes in and presumably also what comes out, and then, in principle, you have to construct all possible diagrams that – obeying the rules – can be drawn in between. You can of course order the diagrams by the number of vertices they have and if the coupling is small, then the contribution of higher-order diagrams becomes ever smaller. So, you stop after a few orders and get a sufficiently accurate result. You calculate the diagrams one by one and then add the results to obtain what is called the total quantum *probability amplitude* for the process.

As the word probability amplitude suggests, you have to square this expression to obtain the probability for the process to take place. In Figure I.4.31 we for example give one the (two) leading, lowest order diagrams that contribute to the probability amplitude for electron-electron scattering. What I am trying to convey is that the diagrams fur-

nish a powerful and precise symbolic language which represents an intricate mathematical structure. The Feynman rules give you the unique translation of the diagrams into complicated but very explicit mathematical expressions that then have to be evaluated (mostly by computer) to get the real probabilities out.

Doing precision measurements means doing critical precision tests on theoretical models and that is the core of empirical science. Realistic precision calculations may involve hundreds or thousands of diagrams, and so even the generation of all the allowed diagrams is done by computer. In this field a lot of pioneering work in symbolic manipulation by computers has been done. Nobel laureate Martinus Veltman was the first with his program named '*Schoonschip*' which literally means 'clean ship', though in Dutch it actually means 'cleaning up the mess.' This program has gone through many upgrades and extensions and is still a program used by many practitioners. The most well-known outcome of such physics inspired artificial intelligent systems is the magnificent and versatile symbolic manipulation and graphics platform *Mathematica* developed by Stephen Wolfram.

Figure I.4.32: This work of the Belgian surrealist painter René Magritte is entitled *Les Jeunes Amours* (1963). A more prosaic title, well fitting our sub-nuclear narrative would have been *A Color Triplet of Apple Quarks*. There is even a Dirac sea in the background. (Source: ©'Photothèque Magritte / Adagp Images, Paris)

Subnuclear structure

The Standard Model

The Standard Model is a theoretical model for the basic constituent particles of all ordinary (meaning, not-dark) matter. Think of the leptons *such as the electrons and neutrinos, and the* quarks *that make up the protons and neutrons, but think also of the force-carrying particles that bind the constituents together. The model gives a unified description of three of the four fundamental forces: the electromagnetic, and the weak and strong nuclear forces. Gravity, however, is not included in the Standard Model. The model has made numerous precise predictions that so far have been vindicated by a variety of large-scale experiments in the world's biggest accelerators.*

The Standard Model was completed in the early 1970s. The experimental verification of many of its predictions took another forty years and still continues. A landmark was the discovery of the W and Z bosons at CERN (and somewhat later at Fermilab) in 1983. Another highlight was the discovery of the Higgs particle at CERN as recent as 2012. It was the last missing entry in the particle table of the model. The Higgs particle is a unique ingredient because it provided the explanation for the mass of other particles, in particular the masses of the weak force carrying W and Z particles. The presence of these masses is reflected in the fact that the corresponding interactions are short range as we discussed in the section on nuclear potentials and the Yukawa potential on page 166.

Flavors, colors and families

To understand the structure of the Standard Model, let us look at Figure I.4.35, and explain what information is encoded in the colorful tables. In each of the figures, the top panel contains the force-mediating particles and the Higgs particle, these are all bosons, i.e. they have an integral spin. We shortly describe these in detail but it is more convenient to first turn to the content of the lower panels.

Particle families. The lower panels list the constituent particles: these are all fermions, and have spin one-half. There are three families of constituent particles denoted by three different colors as depicted in Figure I.4.35(b). Only the first family is stable, it consists of the *up* and *down* quarks and the *electron* and its *neutrino*. These are the building blocks that make up all forms of stable (ordinary) matter in our universe. The other families consist of heavier but unstable copies of the light family, and sure enough they also play a crucial, albeit more hidden, role in our universe, such as processes inside stars or in the early universe. We first look more closely at the quarks and thereafter at the leptons.

Quarks: flavors and colors. The first thing to note about quarks is that they carry fractional electric charges. Those in the left column have a charge $+2e/3$, wheras the ones in the right column have $-e/3$, so that the proton which corresponds to two 'ups' and one 'down' has indeed a charge e, while the neutron made up from one 'up' and two 'downs' has zero charge. Besides their spin and charge, we distinguish two other intrinsic properties that were briefly mentioned before: *flavor* and *color*.

Flavors. The so-called *flavor* index corresponds to one of the six letters (u, d, s, c, t, b) ' which in turn refers to their names *up, down, strange, charm, top* and *bottom*.

Besides the lightest nuclear particles or hadrons like the proton, neutron that make up stable matter, there are many nuclear particles that also involve quarks of flavors other than the up and down, but as those quarks are heavier, the particles in which they appear tend to be unstable. By the way, I always found the use of the word 'flavor' in this context a bit strange. What is 'up' or 'down' supposed to taste like, you wonder. The peculiar collection of flavor names for quarks has repeatedly given rise to exotic if not funny, even sexist expressions in titles of articles (involving topless or bottomless particle models etc.), which after submission were of course instantly refused by the editors of the established journals.

Flavor symmetry: the 'eightfold way.' From a historical point of view it is interesting to restrict ourselves to the three-flavour case. It is the case described by Gell-Mann

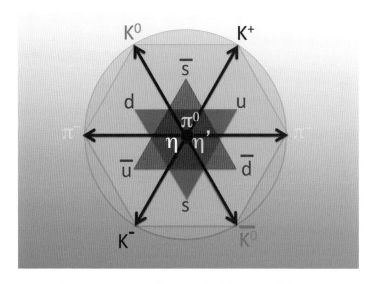

Figure I.4.33: *The $SU(3)$ way.* Gell-Mann's eightfold way is based on the symmetry group that classifies the *flavor* properties of the particles making up the 'particle zoo.' The geometric patterns by which the particles are labeled actually have a three- or sixfold symmetry rather than an eightfold one. The observed particles are the ones on the outer hexagon and the three particles at the origin, together they form the *meson nonet*. The symmetry has two fundamental three-dimensional representations corresponding to the two triangles in the center, which suggested the existence of three quarks (u, d, s) and their antiparticles $(\bar{u}, \bar{d}, \bar{s})$.

in his 'eightfold way', based on a $SU(3)$ flavor symmetry group. To give you a flavor we have depicted some of the geometric representations in which the particles are classified according to this $SU(3)$ scheme in Figure I.4.33. This representation is called the *meson nonet*, referring to the nine possible quark anti-quark combinations of the up, down and strange flavors, which gives $3 \times 3 = 9$ combinations. This representation is one of the examples that makes up the aforementioned 'particle zoo' of nuclear particle states. The fundamental particles form a triplet representation of quarks and an anti-triplet of anti-quarks, and these correspond to the blue and red triangles in the center.

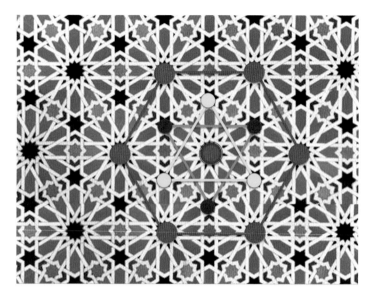

Figure I.4.34: *Quarks and* $SU(3)$. A beautiful early Islamic tiling from the *Real Alcázar* (Royal Palace) in Sevilla in Spain, exhibiting the sixfold symmetry characteristic for the group $SU(3)$. The black stars represent the weight-lattice of states corresponding to the group $SU(3)$ The *representations* correspond to certain triangular or hexagonal subsets of states centered at the origin.

Quarks have never been observed as individual, freely moving particles; they are confined to composites that consisted of quark anti-quark pairs (the mesons) or (anti) quark triples (the baryons). The nonet consists of nine mesons made up of one of the three quarks paired with one of the three anti-quarks in the figure. These scalar (spin zero) particles, are, as you see, siblings of the pions we have mentioned before. The three particles in the center correspond to different linear combinations of the $\bar{u}u$, $\bar{d}d$ and $\bar{s}s$ pairs. Why the 'eightfold way' you are inclined to ask, while the picture clearly exhibits a sixfold symmetry? It turns out that eight of the nine mesons basically form an *octet*, that is a larger irreducible representation of the group, meaning that under the $SU(3)$ transformations those particle states would be transformed into each other. The ninth (η') particle is all by itself and invariant under the symmetry group. In the era when this scheme was proposed all the

observed particles could be catalogued in certain $SU(3)$ representations (like the octet mentioned before), and this of course shifted the quest for fundamental building blocks to the underlying level of the quarks.

If the symmetry was exact, then that would imply that the baryons or mesons that belong to a single representation of the symmetry group should have the same mass; the particles should be degenerate. This turns out not to be the case here, and therefore we say that flavor is only an approximate symmetry. Nevertheless having the symmetry patterns and the observed particles and their masses, Gell-Mann could see that certain particles were missing from the observations, and that way he could make quite precise predictions of their properties and therefore also say where to look for them. An example is the Ω^- particle belonging to the decuplet representation of baryons and discovered in 1964. This is indeed reminiscent of the story of Mendeleev and his periodic table.

It is actually somewhat ironic that the $SU(3)$ or the much larger $SU(6)$ flavor symmetry does not really feature in the Standard Model as we see from the panels in the figure. The flavors are there but they come in pairs, which refers to the weak interactions as we will explain shortly. The 'eightfold way' is completely accidental from the Standard Model perspective. Nevertheless the family structure is very much present and even required for the consistency of the model. But that family structure as such is not *explained* by the model. It is one of the challenges to look for yet more involved schemes.

Color. The second property of quarks refers to what is called their *color*. Each flavor comes in three different 'colors', usually denoted as *red, green* and *blue*. In the figure that is visualized by the stack of three quark panels on top of each other. This 'color' quantum number is some kind of charge to which the strong nuclear force couples, and needless to say, has nothing to do with ordinary color. This nomenclature is at least consistent, which cannot be

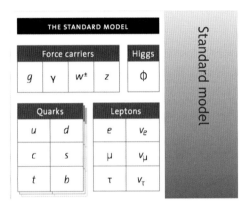

(a) The constituent particles, quarks and leptons are fermions. The particles mediating the forces are bosons, and he Higgs boson generates mass for the particles.

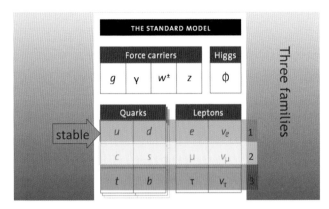

(b) The constituent particles come in three families. All ordinary matter is made of the first family of lightest and therefore stable particles.

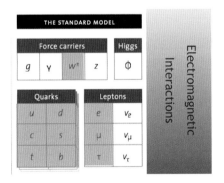

(c) The electromagnetic force mediated by the photon affects all particles that carry electric charge.

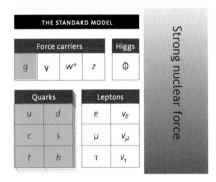

(d) The strong nuclear force only mediates between the three different colors of quarks and does not distinguish flavor. It binds quarks into color neutral nuclear particles.

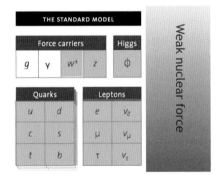

(e) The weak nuclear force affects all constituents, but it does not mix quarks with leptons within a family.

Figure I.4.35: *The standard model.* Constituent particles and how the basic forces act between them.

said of the flavors.

The excellent 'artist impression' of flavor and color properties of quarks is given by the Magritte painting of Figure I.4.32. The painting dates from 1963, one year before
Gell-Mann and Zweig proposed the existence of quarks,
but well before the color property of quarks was postulated,
implying that the quite striking correspondence is entirely
coincidental.

Leptons: electrons and neutrinos. In the bottom panels on the right in Figure I.4.35, we have listed the three
families of leptons: the *electron*, the *muon*, and the *tau*
family, including their respective neutrinos. The neutrinos have pretty ghostly properties in that they have no
charge and were long believed to be massless. It has
quite recently been established, however, that they have
tiny masses. They only interact weakly (and gravitationally), which means that we don't see or feel them, in spite
of the fact that we are permanently bombarded by billions
of these neutrinos per second. They basically fly unhin-
dered through most things, like the Earth for example. The
evidence for their existence was for a long time just based
on their absence, since the amount of missing energy and
momentum in weak-decay processes pointed to the existence of a massless, neutral particle – a neutrino therefore. A tiny brother of the neutron. To catch a few of
them we have to build detectors consisting of an incredible number of steel plates with very special (so-called flat
wire chamber) detectors in between, and that is how after a long time their existence was established in a direct
fashion. The electron neutrino was the first to be discovered in 1956 by Frederick Reines and his collaborators.
He shared the 1995 Nobel prize for Physics for this discovery with Martin Perl who discovered the tau-neutrino
in 1974, quite some time after Leon Lederman, Melvin
Schwartz and Jack Steinberger received the prize for the
muon-neutrino in 1988.

The matching of the lepton and quark panels in the fig-

ures is essential for the consistency of the model. But
it is not known whether the family structure can be explained by some underlying mechanism, where the different family levels are excited levels of some underlying
structure.

Force mediators. In the top panels we see the force mediating particles and the Higgs particle. The force carri-
ers have spin one, which means that they are vectors like
the electromagnetic gauge potentials. The Higgs has spin
zero; it is a *scalar* particle without spin degree of freedom.
To see what interactions these force particles mediate, it
is best to look at the three figures at the bottom. On the
left in Figure I.4.35(c), we have the familiar electromagnetic interaction mediated by the *photon* denoted by γ,
which is described by the QED part of the Standard Model.
Electromagnetism only affects the blue-colored particles,
which are the particles that carry electric charge. Note,
that all constituent particles carry charge except the neutrinos. And that is exactly the reason we can't observe them
very easily. The force particles (including the photon itself)
are electrically neutral except for the $W^{\pm}$ particles which
carry a unit of charge. In the middle figure, we display
the strong nuclear force which only works between quarks
mediated by the *gluons* denoted by g. This brings us to
the theory of the strong interactions to which we now turn.
We will discuss the weak interactions of Figure I.4.35(e) in
more detail thereafter.

The strong interactions

Quantum chromodynamics (QCD). The quantum theory
for the strong nuclear force is called *Quantum Chromodynamics (QCD)*. The strong force is mediated by 8 *gluons*,
which are described by 8 color gauge potentials, that manifest themselves in the presence of 8 'color-electric' and
'color-magnetic fields.'

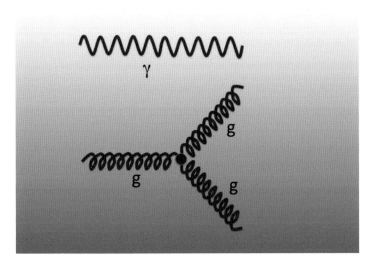

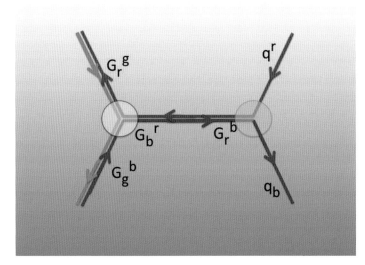

Figure I.4.36: *Self-interaction of gluons.* The photon (γ) has no self-interaction. The gluons (g) have self-interactions, which makes the theory very much nonlinear and much harder to deal with. The three gluon vertex is represented differently on the left of the next figure.

Figure I.4.37: *Color-flow diagram in QCD.* A nice way to visualize the interactions in QCD. Quarks carry a single color line, while gluons carry two (different) lines. In the vertices the color charge is conserved, so, the colors and arrows have to match. Upper index goes into the vertex, lower index goes out.

Self-interactions. A crucial difference with QED is that the gluons themselves also carry color charge like the quarks. This means that they interact with themselves and that understandably leads to complex nonlinear behavior. The reason why electromagnetism is so much simpler is precisely that the photon does not carry electric charge and therefore does not interact with itself. This means that pure electromagnetism without charges and currents is a linear theory and indeed the source-free Maxwell equations are linear as we saw in Chapter I.1. These have simple sinusoidal wave-like solutions, which on a quantum level correspond to freely propagating photons. The essential difference between the non-self-interacting photon and a self-interacting gluon is indicated in Figure I.4.36. In addition, the effective strength of this color coupling is large, so it is hard to make successive approximations to higher order in the coupling. The language of Feynman diagrams loses much of its power because it is an approximation scheme that involves successive powers of the coupling constant.

If that coupling is small the series is expected to converge and it suffices to only keep a limited number of lower order contributions to obtain a meaningful result. If that coupling becomes large the successive contributions keep increasing and one loses the convergence and hence the ability to make meaningful calculations and reliable predictions.

An alternative way to think about gluons, quarks and the way they interact with one another, is given in Figure I.4.37, where the (anti-)quarks are denoted by a single directed color line, and the gluons as an oppositely directed pair of lines. The picture is illuminating in that it shows very clearly what it means to say that color (charge) is locally conserved. The figure is not meant to imply that the gluons are actually made up of (anti-)quarks. Though they can manifest themselves in the same color anti-color 'channel', the gluons represent independent physical degrees of freedom. The fact that strong self-interactions lead to

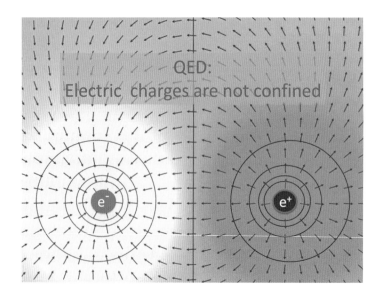

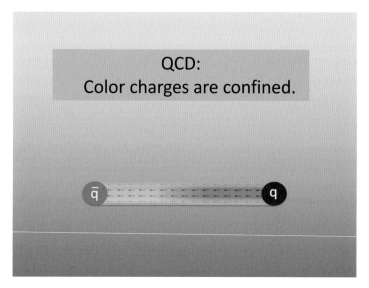

Figure I.4.38: *Free electric charges*. The electric field lines connecting the arrows go from the positron to the electron but they spread out widely over space. The electric charges are therefore not confined and we can observe them as free particles.

Figure I.4.39: *Confined color charges*. In QCD the color electric fields do not spread but are forced into a narrow tube which leads to the *confinement* quarks. It is a consequence of the highly non-trivial nature of the ground state of QCD which behaves like a color magnetic superconductor.

unexpected behavior may not sound unfamiliar to us humans. Anyway, it is this feature in QCD that made it so hard to see from the basic structure of the theory what the resulting physics and phenomenology of quarks and gluons would be.

Confinement. The binding mechanism between two quarks is very different from the attraction between to opposite electric charges. This is illustrated in Figures I.4.38 and I.4.39. In the first figure we see that the electric field between two opposite charges spreads over all of space, reflecting the $1/r^2$ force law. It is as if the field lines repel each other. In this case we can give one of the charges enough energy that the pair breaks up into two free charges. The second figure shows what the color-electric fields between a quark and an anti-quark look like. The field lines are squeezed into a narrow tube that connects the pair. It is as if the field lines attract each another. The energy per unit length of the electric flux tube is constant because the

tube is everywhere the same. This in turn implies that the interaction energy of the pair grows linearly with their separation. It would increase indefinitely if not the energy at a certain point exceeds the energy needed to create a new quark anti-quark pair somewhere in between. Then what we basically have done is to create two pairs out of one pair! We cannot create a separate quark. because as a source it always has to stay connected to a tube.

More in general it turns out that the color force works in such a way that only color neutral composites of quarks, denoted as '*color singlets*,' can exist as free particles. And therefore these are the nuclear particles that we observe in nature. The way this usually is expressed is to say that color is *confined*. The property of color is hidden. Quarks and gluons are for ever *emprisoned*. The simplest singlets are either made-up of three quarks with different colors (these are the *baryons* like the proton and neutron mentioned before), or of color anti-color quark pairs (the *mesons* like the pions). And the same is true for the gluons themselves, because they carry color charge; they only appear in color neutral composites which are called *glue balls*. It is this constraint of color neutrality that explains quarks and gluons are confined and why we cannot observe them as free individual particles like electrons.

The confinement phenomena presents us with a unique, paradoxical situation we did not encounter before. QCD is a theory formulated in terms of fundamental physical degrees of freedom (quarks and gluons) that are not discernible, so that from a philosophical point of view you are tempted to question their very existence. 'To be or not to be, that is the question!'

Asymptotic freedom: how strong becomes weak. What does it mean to say that interactions are strong? In this case it is a relative statement in that it is a force between protons and neutrons, or on a more basic level between quarks, that is strong enough to overcome the Coulomb repulsion so as to make nuclear binding possible. This implies that the coupling strength of the interaction is considerably larger than that of electromagnetism. What we mean to say is that the effective dimensionless number characterizing the strength of the interactions must be much larger, and this amounts to saying that the analogue of the electromagnetic fine-structure constant $\alpha = e^2/(4\pi\hbar c) \simeq 1/137$), which for the strong interactions is called α_s, is of order unity. This tells us that at the relevant nuclear scale of $1 \text{ fermi} = 10^{-15} \text{ m}$ the effective coupling is large.

The confinement picture I.4.39 shows that the color fields emanating from the quark are forced into a narrow tube that terminates at some antiquark. The tube has a cross-section which is typically of the confinement scale, say, one fermi squared. So here is how we should think about this. For distances much larger than one fermi, the quarks are confined, which means that the complicated nonlinear self-interactions of the gluons have collectively created an

effective environment that causes the confinement. However, for distances much smaller than one fermi the quarks are effective moving 'freely,' in the sense that the effects of the self-interactions are negligible. In fact on such scales one could treat the strong interactions more like a type of electromagnetic interactions. The color field lines go radially out of the quark and bend over in the confining tube at a distance of about one fermi. On that small scale one could use the perturbative approach in terms of Feynman diagrams to calculate the dynamics.

It is interesting to look at the result of such intricate calculations of the effective coupling strength as a function of momentum transfer (or inverse distance) both for α (QED) and α_s (QCD). For QED one obtains,

$$\alpha(q^2) = \frac{\alpha}{[1 - (\alpha/3\pi)\ln(q^2/m^2)]} \quad \text{for} \quad q^2 \gg m^2,$$
(I.4.30)

where $\alpha = 1/137$ and m denotes the relevant mass scale one is interested in. For QCD one obtains,

$$\alpha_s(q^2) = \frac{12\pi}{(33 - 2f)\ln(q^2/\Lambda^2)} \quad \text{for} \quad q^2 \geqslant \Lambda^2 \quad (I.4.31)$$

where $f = 6$ equals the number of flavors and Λ sets a mass scale at which one is interested. We have plotted these curves in Figure I.4.40. There are two striking differences between the two curves: (i) the relative difference in strength on the scales we are interested in is indeed big, about a factor of one hundred, and (ii) the strong interaction is decaying substantially for increasing momentum and thus for smaller distances. *The strong interaction gets weak at small distances!* This property is called *asymptotic freedom*. It is of crucial importance because it allows for precise calculations of high-energy scattering processes where you probe very small distances and compare those to the experiments.

So what happens if two quarks collide head-on in a collider? They may strongly scatter and the outgoing quarks or gluons may get a high transverse momentum. These

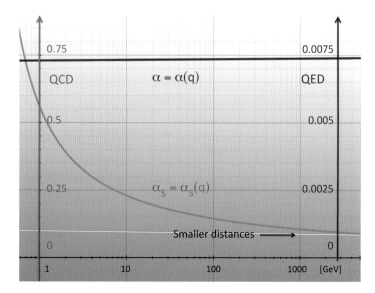

Figure I.4.40: *Asymptotic freedom*. Plots of the effective coupling strength as a function of momentum (or probing distance) for QED and QCD. Note the scales differ by a factor one hundred. The fact that the blue QCD strength becomes weaker at short distances is called *asymptotic freedom*. It means that in the high-energy regime the theory can be studied by the diagrammatic (perturbation theoretic) method.

individually colored particles have to pick up companions to make color singlets at a scale of one fermi and will in the end cause a so-called *jet* of outgoing singlet particles. This highly collimated shower of particles has a total momentum equal to that of the originally scattered quark, so that individual quark momentum is an observable in the above sense.

We can also turn the story around and start at very small distances where the theory is very well behaved and our intuitions make sense because the system is weakly coupled. If we move up in scale towards the infrared the coupling becomes stronger, and when the coupling becomes of order unity the system becomes strongly coupled and our predictive ability breaks down. Now what this quite often means is that something drastic like a phase transition is going to happen. The ground state of the system be-

comes unstable and will change. For example a non-trivial condensate may form, and in fact in a sense the nature of the condensate in QCD is quite well understood and investigated (by computer simulations). The idea is that there is a condensate of magnetic degrees of freedom, monopoles and fluxes, so that the ground state of QCD is very much like a *magnetic superconductor*, a medium which would indeed confine color electric charged particles, like quarks and gluons.

To get some understanding of this mechanism we should look at ordinary (electromagnetic) superconductivity (type II) which will be discussed in Chapter III.3 in Volume III. The ground state of a ordinary superconductor corresponds to a condensate of electron (so-called Cooper) pairs. These cause the so-called *Meissner effect*, which means that magnetic fields are expulsed from the medium. If you turn on a strong magnetic field over a slab of superconducting material, then thin filaments of one unit of flux will penetrate the superconductor. Now imagine that I have magnetic monopoles to play around with and suppose that I drag that monopole into the superconductor, what would happen? Indeed, the magnetic flux of exactly one unit emanating from the monopole would be forced into one such narrow filaments and look for a way out at the boundary of the superconductor where the field would spread out again. But that is nothing but saying that monopoles would be *confined* in such a superconducting medium! And the dual of this mechanism is operative in QCD, a color-magnetic condensate confines the color-electrically charged quarks and gluons.

A final comment on this beautiful theory. Can we not in some way reformulate the theory in what we call a strong coupling regime where one over the coupling constant is the new coupling, which then can be taken to be small. This question was answered by Kenneth Wilson from Cornell University, and it amounted to a formulation of gauge theories on a discrete space-time lattice. in terms of link-variables like the ones we considered on page 35 in Chap-

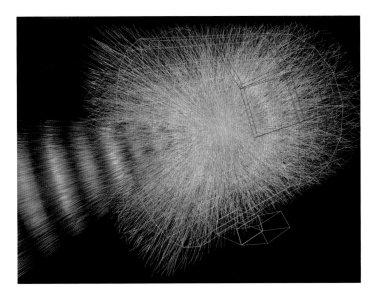

Figure I.4.41: *Lead-ion collisions.* A simulation of a lead-ion collision event for the ALICE detector at CERN, producing an enormous number of particles. To find what you are looking for is far worse than searching for a needle in a haystack! In these experiments one tries to recreate the conditions that were present troughout the universe shortly after the Big Bang.

Figure I.4.42: *The Large Hadron Collider at CERN.* The largest accelerator at this moment is the Large Hadron Collider (LHC) at CERN in Geneva. The protons are accelerated in two oppositely directed circular beams. The circumference of the large ring is 27 km. Pre-acceleration happens in the older Proton Synchroton (PS) and the Super Proton Synchroton (SPS) accelerators.

ter I.2, where we discussed the line integral of a gauge potential. In this formulation one can make a very controlled and systematic strong coupling approximation to QCD, and the most immediate success is that confinement is there right from the start. This means that in this approach the lowest order calculation of the interaction energy between two external quarks yields a linear potential between them, and that is what confinement means. In Figure I.4.39 we see that the field energy per unit length is constant. Then the question became to prove that there was no discontinuity (a phase transition) between the weakly coupled and strongly coupled regimes. This turned out to be the case and with that the lattice approach to QCD has become an indispensable tool in the study of the strong interactions. Wilson was awarded the physics Nobel prize in 1982 for his profound work on phase transitions, which is embodied in his fundamental work on the *renormalization group*,

a very general approach to studying the scaling properties of physical systems that we will return to in Chapter III.4. This work established a deep connection to the work on phase transitions in statistical and condensed matter physics by Michael E. Fisher and Leo Kadanov, and the renormalization program in quantum field theory going back to the early days of QED.

The quark-gluon plasma. If we shoot two protons with very high-energy onto each other, they surely break up, and what comes out are avalanches (called *jets*) of color-singlet particles – nuclear, but also leptons. Indeed in modern experiments the energies are so gigantic that thousands of particles are created in a single collision, as indicated in Figure I.4.41 showing (simulation of) a high energy event in the ALICE detector of CERN. In this experiment the physicists are trying to create a new high den-

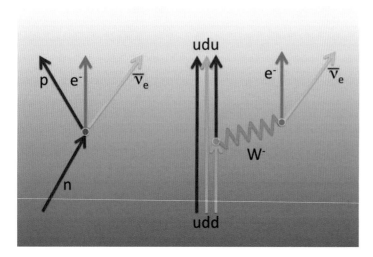

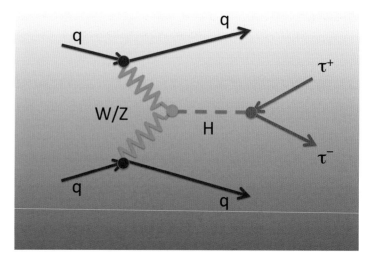

Figure I.4.43: *Beta-decay.* The diagrams for the beta-decay process. On the left a diagram at the level of nuclear physics, and on the right the resolution of the same diagram at the finer scale of the Standard Model. Note that the single vertex on the left corresponds to a pair on the right where the process is involving a W^- particle mediating the weak nuclear force.

Figure I.4.44: *Higgs production.* A standard model diagram representing a particular process by which the Higgs particle is produced from the scattering of two quarks. The experimental signature of this process is provided by the two tau leptons in which Higgs instantly decays.

sity state of matter denoted as the '*quark-gluon plasma*', a state that may have existed in the very early universe directly after the Big Bang. They do that by banging lead-ions with very high energy into each other so that thousands of new particles are created, and for a fraction of a second these form a strongly interacting hot plasma made up of quarks and gluons with striking properties that should resemble the state of matter at the very early stages of the universe.

The electro-weak interactions

The W and Z particles. Let us return to the tables representing the Standard Model and to the elecrtro-weak interactions in particular. In Figure I.4.35(e) we focus on the weak nuclear force, mediated by the charged $W^\pm$ and

neutral Z particles. It affects all constituent particles in an interesting way, the W bosons induce horizontal transitions in the table, because they are electrically charged. Their interaction vertices, allow for fundamental processes like:

$$u + W^- \quad \to \quad d, \qquad (I.4.32)$$

$$e + W^+ \quad \to \quad \nu_e, \qquad (I.4.33)$$

$$\mu + Z \quad \to \quad \mu. \qquad (I.4.34)$$

The horizontal moves stay within the (color)panels, so red quarks to red quarks, electron to its neutrino and so on. A transition from a lepton to a quark is not possible because the W bosons have unit charge and that doesn't match the fractional difference in charge between a quark and a lepton. This in turn implies that the net number of quarks and the net number of leptons are separately conserved in these interactions. Take for example the process of 'β-decay' of the neutron where:

$$n \to p + e + \bar{\nu}_e, \qquad (I.4.35)$$

as depicted on the left in Figure I.4.43. Recalling the compositions $\mathbf{n} = (\mathrm{udd})$ and $\mathbf{p} = (\mathrm{uud})$, the decay process above is in the Standard Model perspective composed of two non-trivial vertices on the constituent level:

$$\mathrm{d} \rightarrow \mathrm{u} + W^- , \qquad (\mathrm{I.4.36})$$

$$W^- \rightarrow \mathrm{e} + \bar{\nu}_e , \qquad (\mathrm{I.4.37})$$

and this process is depicted on the right-hand side of the figure. The 'weakness' of the transitions comes about because the probability of creating an intermediate W and Z particle is very low due to their large mass. That results in an energy barrier which suppresses the transition process.

The Higgs particle. Finally, in Figure I.4.44, we show the complicated diagram of a process that contributes to the production of a Higgs particle (H) in the collision of two protons (or better, two quarks), where these exchange a weak W/Z boson, which can radiate from a Higgs. This Higgs is extremely short-lived and is not directly observed. The signature of the Higgs production in the out-coming state is the presence of two τ leptons. The Higgs was found in 2012 by two large international experimental collaborations: ATLAS and CMS in the Large Hadron Collider (LHC) at CERN.

The Higgs particle is an essential ingredient of the standard model as it is involved in a mechanism by which the masses of the W and Z particles are generated. This is discussed in more detail in Chapter II.6 on symmetries and their breaking.

This concludes our lightning review of what the cherished Standard Model of particle physics is about. In the next section we further explore the unification process in the successive formulations of fundamental physics at the subsequent stages of understanding.

A brief history of unification.

> There are two possible outcomes: if the result confirms the hypothesis, then you've made a measurement. If the result is contrary to the hypothesis, then you've made a discovery.
>
> *Enrico Fermi*

We have so far talked mainly about the fundamental building blocks and that translates into an inventory of what has been observed in experiments up to now. We have also reflected on the models for the interactions between these building blocks that account for the spectrum and the hierarchy of physical states. It is then interesting to step back and look at the history of theories, which is indeed also a history of concepts in theoretical physics. In Figure I.4.45 we have depicted this historical account focussing on the unification concept.

On the bottom line we list the basic classes of physical phenomena concerned, and going upward we also observe how they are linked to the fundamental forces, but we see also a progressing unification in the description of the fundamental physics. The two lines at the top represent theoretical developments which are still considered to be speculative and for which we eagerly await new experimental clues. This figure nicely illustrates the fundamental paradox of how ultimate *reductionism* may well lead to a form of ultimate *holism*!

Returning to the unification aspect, the first example is Newton's theory of gravitation (1687) that unified heavenly and terrestrial mechanics. Another beautiful example is provided by Maxwell's theory of electromagnetism (1865), which clearly unites electric and magnetic phenomena in one framework, but also includes electromagnetic fields and radiation like light, and therefore the subject of optics.

After the Second World War we learned to appreciate and include the quantum principles as in Quantum Electrodynamics (QED), the theory of photons, electrons and their anti-particles the positrons. This highly successful theory motivated theorists to find theories for the weak and strong nuclear forces based on similar principles.

The starting point was an approximate phenomenological model for the weak force proposed by Fermi in 1932. In the late 1960's this was replaced by a consistent unified quantum theory for both the electromagnetic and weak forces. Many names are actually connected to this development, firstly Sheldon Glashow, Abdus Salam and Steven Weinberg, who formulated the theory including the particle content including the weak force mediating particles. For this work they shared the Physics Nobel Prize in 1979.

This model was then augmented with the all-important ingredient of the *Higgs field* by Peter Higgs, Robert Brout and Francois Englert. Brout died in 2011, and therefore Higgs and Englert shared the Physics Nobel prize in 2013, shortly after the particle was discovered at CERN. Finally we should mention the seminal contributions of Gerard 't Hooft and Martinus Veltman, who constructed the consistent mathematical framework which enabled them to prove that the electro-weak theory was *renormalizable*, and which made comparisons of detailed predictions of the electroweak theory with precision experiments possible. They received the 1999 Nobel prize for Physics for this work.

The developments for the strong interactions took place partly at the same time. Chen Ning Yang and Robert Mills proposed in 1954 the fundamental generalization of the Maxwell theory by extending the notion of the electromagnetic gauge invariance from the simple $U(1)$ group to the non-abelian group $SU(2)$. This led to a totally new, very beautiful non-linear system of equations, not surprisingly called the *Yang-Mills equations*. But it took quite some time before it was recognized that these equations formed the basis for the theories of both the strong and weak nuclear

forces. In the section on Gauge symmetries of Chapter II.6, we discuss these symmetries and equations in more detail.

One of the leading scientists in the particle physics developments was the American Murray Gell-Mann who proposed the existence of quarks at the same time as but independently from George Zweig in 1964. Gell-Mann received the Physics Nobel prize for this and other contributions in 1969. After that he also formulated Quantum Chromodynamics (QCD) with his collaborators Heinrich Leutwyler from Switzerland and Harald Fritzsch from Germany in 1973. This theory is based on the Yang-Mills equations for the color gauge group $SU(3)$. The binding mechanism and confinement of quarks was largely proposed by Yoichiro Nambu who received the Nobel prize in 2008. The property of QCD called *asymptotic freedom* made it possible to make sensible predictions for the strong interactions at high energies, This was discovered in 1973 by the American physicists David Gross, David Politzer and Frank Wilczek who received the Nobel prize for their work in 2004. We will say more about this shortly.

Forces of nature, Unite! Let me once more emphasize that the unification in the description of such a wide variety of physical phenomena in the Standard Model was possible because the different components are based on the same conceptual principles. These principles are those of *quantum theory*, those of *special relativity*, and the principle of *local gauge invariance*. The latter principle manifested itself in Maxwell's theory as we discussed in Chapters I.1 and I.2, in Einstein's general theory of relativity, and also in the Yang-Mills equations. Gauge invariance is a key ingredient because it is strongly tied-in with the notion of a force field and completely fixes what the interactions between the forces and particles look like.

In Figure I.4.45 you see that we have added two more rows on top. They express some powerful ideas leading to further unification, ideas that go beyond the Stan-

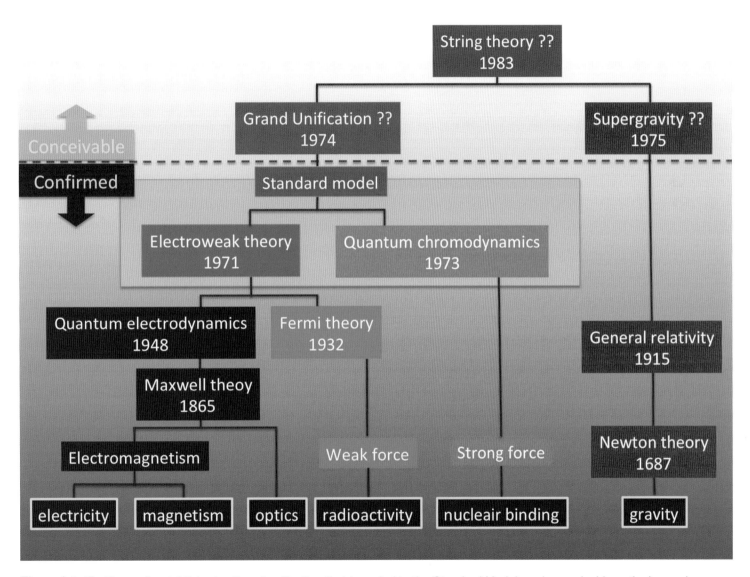

Figure I.4.45: *The well-established paths of unification that have led to the Standard Model, and conceivable paths beyond.*

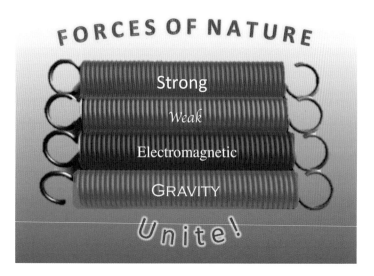

Figure I.4.46: *Forces Unite!* A call for the United Forces of Nature.

dard Model but have not (yet) been vindicated by experiment and should therefore be labeled as speculative. The Standard Model has left us with a number of open questions that strongly hint in the direction of a single overarching quantum gauge theory that comprises the three non-gravitational interactions. Models of such type are called *Grand Unified Theories* or GUTs, but the proposals made so far have not been very successful. An example of such a hint is that the electric charges of proton and electron match perfectly, but within the Standard Model there is no a priori reason that they should have the same magnitude. Except when there would be magnetic monopoles around, but these are not part of the Standard Model; however in GUTs they exist. Another hint is that the family structure is not explained; it may possibly result from some underlying structure.

The theory of gravity remains a case apart. In spite of the tremendous successes of Einstein's theory, it has so far withstood all attempts to make it consistent with the principles of quantum theory. This is a highly non-trivial matter and seems to require a radical change of perspective. On the other hand it should not be too surprising: it is unique because it directly concerns the primary notions of space and time itself.

The line of development starting around 1970 centered around a few additional concepts: the first is the notion of *rigid supersymmetry*, the second was that of local or gauged supersymmetry which gave rise to *supergravity* theories, and finally the basic step from point particles to extended objects like *strings* and so-called *branes*. We close this chapter by a lightning review of some of the salient features of these developments.

Supersymmetry

From bosons to fermions and back. The gauge symmetries we have discussed so far transform certain particle types into each other. The $SU(3)$ color group for example transforms the quarks of different colors into each other. The weak SU(2) transforms up and down quarks or electrons and their neutrinos into each other. But these gauge transformations always transform bosons into bosons and fermions into fermions. Supersymmetry is an intricate symmetry which involves generators which themselves are fermionic with the crucial property that they transform bosons into fermions and back. It entails a drastic extension of the notion of symmetry. Its discovery and early development goes back to the early 1970s. If we call the super charge (or generator of the supersymmetry) Q, it has the following properties:

$$Q^2 = 0$$

$$Q \, |\text{boson}\rangle = |\text{fermion}\rangle \; ; \; Q \, |\text{fermion}\rangle = |\text{boson}\rangle \, .$$

One may add more supercharges, in which case we speak of *extended supersymmetries*. In four dimensions we have a maximum of $\mathcal{N} = 8$ supersymmetries. The more supersymmetry the more constrained the theory will be. Like with other symmetries particle types fall into representations of the various supersymmetry algebras and these representations will contain both bosons and fermions. The smallest representation of $\mathcal{N} = 8$ extended supersymmetry contains a spin-two particle which is a natural candidate for the graviton. So in that sense there is a fundamental link between supersymmetry and gravitation.

The Dirac equation predicted the existence of *anti-matter*, and in a similar way supersymmetry predicts the existence of super mirror images of all the known particles. Bosonic particle species would have fermionic *superpartners* and *vice versa*. These partners are generally denoted as *sparticles*: *squarks* and *sleptons*, while the superpartners of the force particles are called *gauginos*, like the *photino*, the *Winos* etc. The corresponding fields are labeled by the same letters with a tilde on top and we have displayed some of them in Figure I.4.49. In that figure they are depicted as belonging to the massless sector of superstring theory that will be discussed shortly.

A Minimally Supersymmetric Standard Model (MSSM).
One thing we can conclude immediately is that unfortunately the presently observed bosons and fermions (the inhabitants of the Standard Model listed in Figure I.4.35(a)) cannot be each other's superpartners, because the other properties do not match. It is like the situation with the Dirac equation where the proton could not be identified with the anti-electron because they have different masses. The proton (field) has its own Dirac equation. For a superpartner all intrinsic properties are the same except for the spin which differs by half a unit. So to make the world supersymmetric the very minimal thing one may do is construct the simplest $\mathcal{N} = 1$ supersymmetric extension of the Standard Model, and that means just doubling the panels of I.4.35(a) and put tildes on all the particle symbols. This Minimal Supersymmetric Standard Model (MSSM) is actively studied and a lot of effort is devoted to 'hiding' the unwanted partners and finding possible experimental signatures that show up in high-energy experiments. You see that, in particular with extended supersymmetries, one is forced to accommodate large numbers of new particle species. And to break the supersymmetry even more particles have to be added. We will refrain from discussing the MSSM in more detail.

The principal motivation to build the LHC at CERN was to find the Higgs particle, a crucial ingredient of the Standard model that lacked experimental vindication. But the physicists had another deep motivation and that was the hope that the LHC would allow for the much more revolutionary discovery of supersymmetry as an underlying principle of nature. So far there has been no evidence for this. If the 'sparticles' are really there, they would make up a shadow world, which is extremely weakly coupled to our discernible world. Not having seen them up to now means that the supersymmetry would have to be badly broken in our universe, because breaking can give a considerable mass to the super partners. It is a bit like the 'Higgs breaking' mechanism that gives mass to the W and Z particles that mediate the weak interactions in the Standard Model.

Yet, from another perspective it is not inconceivable that supersymmetry is a blessing in disguise. The lightest supersymmetric particle is absolutely stable by construction, and it has been suggested that this lightest supersymmetric particle, for example the *photino* (the super partner of the photon), is a candidate for the elusive particle that makes up dark matter. It couples very weakly, is neutral and massive, and makes a perfect *WIMP*, a *Weakly Interacting Massive Particle*, that is favored in many cold dark matter scenarios. We briefly discussed this in the section on cosmology in Chapter I.2 on page 76. What we may conclude at this point is that the discovery of superpartners in a lab like CERN or Fermilab would be a spectacular discovery in its own right, but would also put string theory (and supergravity) in a far more credible position as these theories predict their existence as a necessary ingredient of nature. We have to wait and see. One of the reasons science is demanding, is that it requires so much patience.

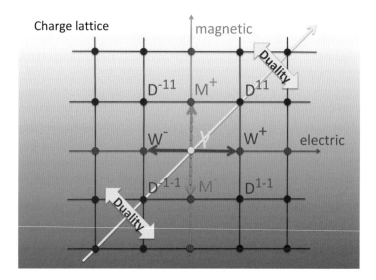

Figure I.4.47: *Montonen-Olive duality.* The electric-magnetic charge lattice of the $\mathcal{N}=4$ supersymmetric $SU(2)$ Yang-Mills theory. This is in the weak coupling regime with on the horizontal axis a triplet of gauge bosons $W^{\pm}$ masses $M_W = ef$ and $W_0 = \gamma$ which remains massless. On the vertical axis there is the same massless photon and two magnetically charged monopole $M^{\pm}$, these are solitons with mass $M_M = 4\pi f/e$. The electric-magnetic Montonen-Olive duality corresponds to mirroring the lattice through the diagonal, interchanging the role of gauge particles and solitons and also interchanging $e \leftrightarrow 4\pi/e$; a strong-weak or S- duality.

To illustrate the power and beauty of supersymmetry, we briefly discuss two further examples: one is the $\mathcal{N}=4$ *supersymmetric Yang-Mills theory*, and the other is *supergravity* which plays a vital role in modern superstring theory.

$\mathcal{N}=4$ **supersymmetric Yang-Mills.** Let me briefly talk about a wonderful, somewhat exceptional class of models, which brings together a number of fundamental concepts that have been taking the stage in theoretical physics from the mid 1970s. The theories I am talking about are $\mathcal{N}=4$ *supersymmetric Yang-Mills theories.*

The marvel is that because of the $\mathcal{N}=4$ supersymme-

try these theories are so constrained that their quantum behavior is well understood, even beyond the perturbative diagrammatic Feynman approach. This also implies that they exhibit an unusual kind of simplicity, which for the theorist makes them an ideal laboratory for testing novel ideas. It is for quantum field theorists what the roundworm C. Elegans is for geneticists so to speak. So it is not the theory on its own that is of particular relevance but its extraordinary properties are of interest

Let us consider the simplest case where the gauge group is $G = SU(2)$. The particle or field content of this $\mathcal{N}=4$ gauge theory consist of a single spin-one super-multiplet that transforms as a triplet or vector representation of the $SU(2)$. Because of the supersymmetry, one can generate a *super-multiplet* by acting with the supersymmetry generators. The fields have the following spin content: there is one spin-1 field (these are the gauge bosons of the theory), there are four spin-$\frac{1}{2}$ and six spin-0, scalar and pseudo scalar fields. All of them transform in the triplet representation of the gauge group.

The scalar fields act like a kind of Higgs field and break the $SU(2)$ gauge symmetry to $U(1)$, which we call electromagnetism in analogy with the electro-weak theory. Because of the symmetry breaking two things happen:
(i) the gauge bosons $W^{\pm}$ acquire a mass $m_W = ef$, and $W^0 = \gamma$ is the massless $U(1)$ 'photon'. The parameter f has dimension $[mass]$ and sets the scale of the breaking. There is also a neutral massless scalar particle that survives in the breaking.
(ii) this theory has non-trivial classical *soliton* solutions, corresponding to the so-called *'t Hooft-Polyakov magnetic monopoles*. These are regular, finite energy classical field configurations that are stable for a topological reason, implying that magnetic charge is also strictly conserved. The monopoles $M^{\pm}$ have a magnetic charge $g = \pm 4\pi/e$ (twice the minimally allowed Dirac value) and have a mass (= energy of the classical field configuration) equal to $m_M = gf = 4\pi f/e$. Note that these magnetic monopoles are a

necessary ingredient of this theory, and you are not free to leave them out. They represent magnetically charged 'particle like' objects in the theory and what one may show is that upon quantization these monopoles also form spin-one supersymmetric representations.

Electromagnetic duality regained. What is striking in this theory is that on the quantum level it exhibits a dual symmetry between the electric and magnetic sectors of this theory. This is the non-abelian analog of the electric-magnetic duality of the source-free Maxwell equations that we mentioned in Chapter I.1, and is called the *Montonen-Olive duality.* We have depicted the duality transformation on the electric-magnetic charge lattice in Figure I.4.47, which shows the electrically charged gauge bosons $W^{\pm}$ and the charge neutral (self-dual) photon in the origin, as well as the magnetic monopoles $M^{\pm}$ on the vertical axis. The spectrum also allows for dually charged sectors called *dyonic* labeled D(n,m). This remarkable symmetry is a *strong-weak* or so-called *S-duality.* Indeed if we take the electric coupling weak ($e < 1$), then the magnetic coupling is strong ($g = 4\pi/e > 1$). So, this theory is like the pure Maxwell theory *self-dual*; it maps one to one onto itself under the duality transformation. The upshot is that we have two fully equivalent formulations of the same physics, one as the standard 'electric' gauge theory with massive $W^{\pm}$-bosons, a massless photon, and gauge coupling e, and the other as a 'magnetic' gauge theory with gauge bosons $M^{\pm}$, a massless photon and a gauge coupling $g \sim 1/e$.

Imagine what this means, if you turn up the coupling parameter e then you expect the strongly coupled theory to no longer be controllable and predictable. But in this case we have an alternative, not an alternative reality because there is only one reality, but an alternative perspective or description where that would-be violent and uncontrollable reality is very well behaved, completely calculable and predictable.

This special property derives from the fact that the theory is not only supersymmetric but also has *confomal symmetry.* This implies that the charges do not renormalize, and they do *not* develop a momentum dependence, like in the case of 'asymptotic freedom' of Figure I.4.40. The fact that the coupling constant has no dependence on momentum or distance means that this quantum theory is *scale invariant* ($r \rightarrow \lambda r$) and in fact *conformally invariant* because it is also invariant under inversion ($r \rightarrow 1/r$). It is a *superconformal gauge theory*.

There is one more point about this *superconformal gauge theory* which makes it even more exceptional. Remember that we mentioned that in addition to the massless photon we have also a massless scalar particle in the theory. This particle mediates an attractive force between the other particles with a coupling strength equal to the gauge coupling (the only coupling constant in the theory). Imagine we have two identical monopoles then we expect there to be a Coulomb repulsion due to the photon, but now there is the attractive scalar force which is exactly equal but opposite. And as you may have guessed, these two forces cancel each other out and that is truly remarkable. So, if you bring two monopoles together very slowly, they don't feel any force pushing them apart. The mass of a multiply charged monopole with charge mg scales exactly linearly: $M_{mg} = mM_g$. This implies that also the masses are not renormalized, and the classical mass formulas turn out to be exact. But adding a monopole with opposite magnetic charge is another story, because now the two forces add and the anti-pole feels an attractive force that is twice as strong. It is an unstable configuration, a monopole anti-monopole pair would annihilate and be converted into pure energy. And by the way for the charged particles like the W^+ the same story holds.

So, that's the marvel: a supersymmetric , gauge and conformally invariant quantum field theory! A remarkable outlier, and indeed, some theorist feel tempted to quote Dirac's 1931 monopole paper, saying 'One would be surprised if

Nature wouldn't have made use of it.'

We will see that if not nature, then at least the string theorists have made use of it in a marvel called the AdS/CFT holographic correspondence that we will discuss later on.

Local supersymmetry: supergravity. A first important and profound generalization of Einstein's theory is a theory called *supergravity*, proposed in 1976 by Daniel Friedman, Sergio Ferrara and Peter van Nieuwenhuizen. Supergravity theories are invariant under *local* supersymmetry (or extended supersymmetry) transformations, and this means that the *supersymmetry is gauged*. It contains the Einstein theory but in addition to the *graviton* it predicts the existence of a fermionic partner called the *gravitino* with spin 3/2. These ideas have been worked out and extended in great detail ever since by a sizeable community of devoted theoretical physicists. Extended supergravity theories would also encompass gauge symmetries of the Grand Unified type and were considered as candidates for a Theory of Everything. The maximally extended supergravity in four dimensions, which features 8 supercharges, is related to a unique supergravity theory in 11 dimensions, which was constructed by Eugène Cremmer, Bernard Julia and Joël Scherk working at the Ecole Normale Supérieure in Paris. The non-gauged $\mathcal{N} = 8$ theory in four dimensions can be obtained from the eleven dimensional one by compactifying seven dimensions on a seven-dimensional torus.

The sobering fact is that there was no support from the phenomenological side (no super symmetric partners ever showed up in experiments), and there is a myriad of extra particles that have to be accommodated (or better, eliminated) somehow. Moreover, the ultraviolet behavior of these theories of gravity kept causing problems. It turned out that they are not renormalizable, because of unwanted infinities that kept showing up in certain calculations. And this was resolved until much later, when around 1995 it was recognized that supergravity was the low energy approximation to a theory called *M-theory* living in eleven dimensions. This Meta theory, is the Mother of all ten-dimensional superstring theories which we will talk about shortly.

A Theory of Everything?

> Even if there is only one possible unified theory, it is just a set of rules and equations. What is it that breaths fire into the equations and makes a universe for them to describe? The usual approach of science of constructing a mathematical model cannot answer the questions of why there should be a universe for the model to describe. Why does the universe go to all the bother of existing?
>
> Stephen Hawking, *A Brief History of Time* (1988)

Let us recapitulate the big steps we have discussed in this chapter: we started with classical particles and classical fields like the electromagnetic field. Then we introduced the quantum theory, where we described basically a single particle in a fixed external force field and that produced an extremely successful model for the atom with electrons in orbits around the nucleus. Then we moved on to include the kinematics of special relativity and that brought us to quantum field theory where the distinction between force fields and particles was lifted, since both are described by quantum fields whose spectrum consists of states with an arbitrary number of particles of the type described by that field. This program culminated in the highly unified Standard Model. In their quest for an all-overarching *Theory of Everything (TOE)*, that would also include gravity, the physicists took one step further and started moving in various directions, all of which led up to the study of superstrings.

What if ....? The unification Figure I.4.45 at least suggests that a *Theory of Everything* is certainly not excluded. Hitherto a physical or logical veto that would prohibit such an overarching theory has not been disclosed. The term 'everything' is unfortunate, because it is not the pretension that such a theory would explain all observable physical phenomena, rather it would specify all the necessary and sufficient ingredients on a fundamental level, which would suffice to make a universe like ours. Still, you might wonder what it means, if such a Theory of Everything (or TOE) exists.

Most people think of it as a set of principles from which everything we do and do not know about nature would uniquely follow. We would take nothing for granted, not the existence of light nor certain particles, or even the existence of space and time. But maybe the starting point could be the notion of energy or information or of oberservability. As I said, *everything* is a lot, and practitioners aim a little lower. A TOE marks the end point of the quest for ever more fundamental and basic building blocks that are the subject of this chapter.

The discovery of a (or should I say *the*) TOE would mark the closure of basic physics. This would be both an impressive and a surprising achievement. Nature would have a true bottom so to speak. Yet, from a practical point of view such a completion is not such a big deal really. It probably would make physics a more boring place to be. Particle physics would at best become some kind of tourist trap, which one might want to avoid because the interesting characters lived there a long time ago. A monument for intelligence! And beauty, yes of course! Lots to admire and enjoy. But adventure? Alas, no!

But now I am talking like the physicists at the end of the nineteenth century who thought that the completion of basic physics was imminent. And it certainly was not! Quite the opposite, the twentieth century turned out to be one of the most revolutionary, inspiring and successful eras in physics ever. A century of relativity (geometry), of information and of quantum, as we argued in Chapter I.2.

Around 1980 it became clear that theories of 1-dimensional

extended objects called *strings* provided a drastically different perspective on the problem of gravity. They have been center stage from 1984 onwards, but these theories have so far not been able to impress with resolving existing problems or with predictions that were confirmed by experiment. The relevance of string theory as a theoretical laboratory is fully recognized as a powerful extension of quantum field theory, and it has helped us to understand such elusive concepts as quantum black holes and quantum phase transitions. And superstring theory keeps alive the hope for a Theory of Everything, a Holy Grail of particle physics. Therefore we will conclude this chapter with a section on this topic which is still very much in a state of flux. As will become clear once more: beauty has its price.

Superstrings

And so we face a contradiction between quantum field theory and general relativity similar to the contradictions that led to quantum mechanics. Many physicists believe that this contradiction contains the seeds of an upheaval as profound in its own way as the discovery of quantum mechanics and relativity

Edward Witten, *Nature* (1996)

String theories in their present formulation are quantum theories of extended objects, like strings, and (mem)branes of different dimensions. Mathematical consistency of the this theory requires two conditions to be fulfilled, (i) the theory should be supersymmetric, and (ii) the theory lives in ten or eleven dimensions. A closed formulation of the theory that may exist in eleven dimensions, and for some mysterious reason is called M-theory, is not available, but a small set of ten-dimensional limiting descriptions of that theory are known, and these correspond to the five different superstring theories.

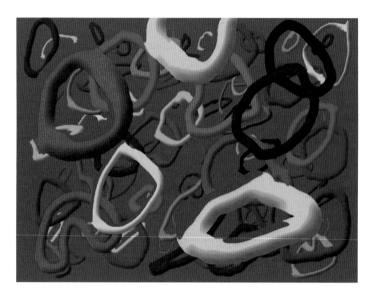

Figure I.4.48: *String worlds.* What the world might look like at $\simeq 10^{-35}$ m .

Just like a single quantum field describes an arbitrary number of particles of a given type, the basic property of the fundamental (super)string is that it describes an infinite number of fields, or particle types! Most of them correspond to extremely massive particles that cannot be produced in our accelerators. Crucial for phenomenology and falsifiability are the 'massless' fields that the theory predicts.

The one outstanding fact is that the theory includes gravity. The gravitational field obeys an equation to which Einstein's equations are an approximation. This makes the theory a serious candidate for a quantum theory of all fundamental particles and interactions including gravity. An important – quantessential – step forward, but many hurdles still have to be overcome. Most importantly, it is still not known how the beloved Standard Model fits in, though all the ingredients appear to be there. The problem so far is that the theory describes more than we need.

Understanding gravity. Our understanding and interpretation of gravity has through history made dramatic turns. Of course it started with the idea of a force leading to the

whole Newtonian dynamical framework including his 'universal law of gravitation'. The second grand turning point came with Einstein's theory of General Relativity, where it was shown that the gravitational force was just a manifestation of the curvature of space-time. Further searches were driven by the strongly perceived necessity to bridge the gap between quantum theory and general relativity.

This turned into the elaborate field-theoretical edifice of supergravity in all its diversity. That approach turned out to have serious shortcomings and at some point seemed doomed, but then it gave way to superstring theory in which supergravity again found a safe haven.

String theory, as a possible overarching quantum theory of all interactions including gravity, has passed through some major revolutions after its inception dating from the early 1970s. It is customary to distinguish three eras of superstring theory:

1st era (...–> 1984): String theory as an attempt to describe the strong interactions (Veneziano, ...).
2nd era (1984-1995): Superstring theory as a theory of quantum gravity (Scherk et al, Schwartz, Green, Witten, ...).
3rd era (1995-present): Extended objects or D-branes, M-theory and the holographic AdS/CFT correspondence (Polchinski, Witten, 't Hooft, Susskind, Maldacena, Strominger, Vafa,...).

We see that string theory, as a would-be unified theory of all fundamental interactions including gravity, was launched in 1984. In that theory the gravitational field equations are derived from imposing conformal invariance on the underlying string degrees of freedom that live on the world-sheet of the string. In that perspective gravity is an effective long-distance description of an underlying string dynamics and in that sense is an emergent phenomena.

However, in spite of its intrinsic beauty and elegance, string theory did not quite deliver. It forced us to accept many hard to swallow extras like supersymmetry, a 10-dimensional space-time, and quite some extra degrees of freedom, of which no hint showed up in experiments. A deluge of extra degrees of freedom that 'nobody had ordered' so to speak. But moreover it appeared that string theory had no direct answers in store concerning very important questions like how to treat *realistic* black holes quantum mechanically, and how to address the even more urgent questions concerning the direct experimental evidence for dark matter and dark energy.

And that takes us to the present engagement of string theory, in particular with the idea of holography which culminated in Juan Maldecena's rather stunning *Anti-de-Sitter/-Conformal-Field-Theory (AdS/CFT) correspondence.* This radical proposal was published in 1997 in a paper which is considered one of the most influential of the present era. It is often referred to as the *gauge/gravity duality* or *Maldacena duality*.

The gauge/gravity duality refers to a rather specific setting of the Anti de Sitter space-time (in various dimensions), but suggests a profound and generic aspect of string theory. The canonical example refers to the situation of string theory in the 5-dimensional *Anti de Sitter (AdS) space-time.* This space-time has a cosmic boundary, which is a flat 4-dimensional Minkowski space-time. On that boundary lives a four-dimensional conformal quantum field theory (CFT), which is a large N copy of the $\mathcal{N} = 4$ $SU(N)$ gauge theory that we discussed in the previous section. The duality says that the full string theory in the AdS background is exactly dual to the CFT on the boundary. Thus the theories are fully equivalent; they describe the same physical reality in two different perspectives. So for example if we have the formation and subsequent evaporation of a black hole in the Anti de Sitter universe, this process could be completely understood as some unitary time evolution in that boundary conformal quantum field theory.

If you want, you can read the AdS/CFT correspondence in an even more – literally – 'outlandish' way, namely, that gravity and space-time are elevated to a holographic illusion! If we know everything about the conformal theory on the d-dimensional boundary, we would be able to reconstruct all conceivable (gravitational) physics in the (d+1)-dimensional space. This prompts the interpretation that gravity as such doesn't really exist as a fundamental force. How elusive can reality be? If it doesn't really exist, then it certainly wouldn't have to be quantized. The quantum behaviour is emulated in a quantum field theory living on the boundary of space-time. Let me paraphrase this ironic state of the universe as an ironic state of mind: or *we* are an illusion, or the theory that claims that we are an illusion is an illusion.

Strings: all fields in one?

What is a string? Let us start with the most elementary type of string which directly connects with our intuition. A string is like an idealized one-dimensional tiny piece of a rubber band that moves through ordinary space and time. The motion of a string can be broken down into the motion of its center of mass, and a relative internal motion. For *closed strings* the relative motion corresponds to waves moving in either direction *along* the string. But you can also have *open strings* that have to satisfy certain boundary conditions, which basically say that its endpoints have to move with the velocity of light or that they have to be attached to some higher dimensional physical object called a D-(mem)brane. These boundary conditions ensure that the string has a certain tension which is an energy per unit length. This tension makes these strings very much like the strings on a violin that have oscillatory modes, known as standing waves that correspond to its basic, harmonic overtones.

It is not hard to imagine how a string model is supposed to

represent particles, if we are far away – we cannot resolve the internal structure of the string, and we see the string as a point-like object with a certain mass and momentum and there may be other internal quantum numbers like charge or spin. Therefore strings manifests themselves as particles at large scales and low energies. The apparent mass of that particle corresponds to the energy of the internal (relative) oscillations of the string.

$$E^2 = (P^{com})^2 + \Sigma_k (p_k^{rel})^2 \simeq P^2 + \Sigma_k m_k^2. \qquad (I.4.38)$$

Clearly, the different oscillatory modes (labeled by k) have to correspond to different particle species, but the mass scale of the masses m_k would be humongous. If the string is tiny, say of the order of the Planck length, then its internal modes are extremely hard to excite. You need an energy of the order of the Planck mass which we introduced in Chapter I.3, i.e. $m_k \simeq 10^{19}$ proton masses! We have to conclude that all the particles we know and love should correspond to different modes in the lowest energy or *massless sector* of the string. It is here that the superstring is important because it has a huge internal symmetry group which means that the massless sector is also extended, containing all spin values starting at two (the graviton) all the way down to zero. The zero mass sector of superstrings corresponds to the particle content of certain supergravity theories.

The take home message at this point is merely that a single string carries an infinite number of different particle degrees of freedom, of which only the massless sector is of phenomenological importance. So, one type of superstring may represent all different particle types and their superpartners as we have indicated in Figure I.4.49. So you should think of all the fields related to the particle types we have been discussing previously, corresponding to different modes of a single type of superstring. The higher mass modes are crucial to ensure that the theory is mathematically consistent, they help in making the theory well behaved at high energies. And that makes sensible calculations on the quantum level possible.

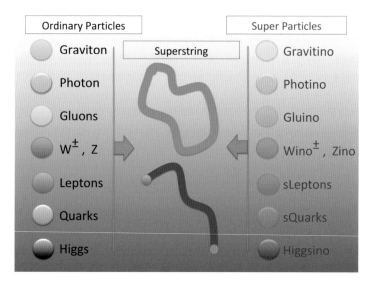

Figure I.4.49: *Superstrings.* All known particle types plus many more such as the superpartners or *sparticles* should correspond to different lowest energy modes of a superstring. These particle types were already ingredients of the earlier supergravity theories.

The world-sheet. If a point particle moves through space-time, we call its trajectory a *world-line*. Similarly if a string moves along in space-time, it traces out a two-dimensional surface embedded in space-time, a surface which is called a *world-sheet*. The world-sheet has one space-like dimension along the string and one time-like dimension to allow the propagation of the string.

There are two related geometries in the formulation of string theory: one is the two-dimensional intrinsic geometry of the world-sheet and the other is the geometry of the background space-time also called the target-space in which the string is moving. The world-sheet is parametrized by its space- and time-like coordinate (σ, τ) and its geometry is determined by a world-sheet metric $g_{\alpha\beta}(\sigma, \tau)$. This world-sheet is embedded in a ten-dimensional space-time with coordinates $(X^\mu; \mu = 0, ..., 9)$ with its own metric $g^{\mu\nu}(X^\lambda)$. The world-sheet is therefore described by its embedding,

$X^\mu = X^\mu(\sigma, \tau)$, that specifies its position in space and time. If you give me a point (σ_0, τ_0) on the world-sheet, the embedding yields a corresponding point $X_0^\mu = X^\mu(\sigma_0, \tau_0)$ in space-time. A three-dimensional impression of what that looks like is given in Figure I.4.51. The embedding provides a relation between the two geometries in the sense that the embedding induces a metric on the world-sheet from the space-time metric. Just like we can construct the metric on the surface of a sphere by inducing it from the metric of the $\mathbb{R}^3$ in which we embedded the sphere, as we did in Chapter I.2.

The modelling of a string propagating in space-time involves an action (or Hamiltonian) that has all the required invariances and couplings, and loosely speaking it corresponds to the 'area' of world-sheet. This is not too surprising if you remember that the string has a tension and therefore wants to minimize its length and therefore energy (energy = length × tension).

What I want to get across here is that the expression for the 'area' of the world sheet involves the induced metric on the world-sheet which is an expression that in turn depends on the σ and τ derivatives of the space-time coordinates $X^\mu(\sigma, \tau)$. What this means is that in this formulation of string theory, the string dynamics is like a quantum field theory defined on the world-sheet, where the space time coördinates X^μ play the role of a set of $(d+1)$ scalar fields. So, yes, we are indeed quantizing space-time in the sense that we quantize the coordinates. For superstrings the story is similar, a superstring moves in super-space which has also fermionic coordinates, and those provide fermionic field degrees of freedom on the world-sheet.

The string action has to be a scalar quantity and therefore will also involve the space-time metric $g_{\mu\nu}$, which depends on the space-time coordinates and makes the action highly nonlinear in the scalar fields. But let us for a moment assume we study the string in flat space-time then with $g_{\mu\nu} = \eta_{\mu\nu}$ is constant. Then the action will be invariant under space-time translations and Lorentz-transformations, and therefore we expect that the spectrum of the theory will reflect that and can be interpreted as representations of the Lorentz group and these label the space-time fields that the string theory produces. And that is for example how the graviton, as a massless spin-two representation, shows up in the spectrum of the string.

Background dependence. String theory goes fundamentally beyond General Relativity, because according to this theory space-time itself is supposedly made up of strings. In the actual formulation of superstring theory we have to deal with this paradox that on the one hand the strings propagate in a given background space-time, and on the other the actual background space-time is made up of strings. The background should be the outcome of the theory, it has to be predicted. This leads to certain consistency requirements. Space-time, as we experience it, is a manifestation of the collective behavior of strings, a kind of background or ground state. It would imply that space and maybe even time are 'emergent', an idea that would have tremendous philosophical implications as well.

In the massless sector of superstring theory we also find spin-one-half fermionic constituent particles, as well as the known spin-one force fields. Moreover these fields would couple in the correct way because the gauge symmetry principles that underly both the Standard Model and Einsteins gravity theory are naturally built into string theory. In a sense, string models have too much symmetry and therefore predict many extra particle types. We do not want these particles because we do not see them in nature; this implies that certain sectors of the theory have to be suppressed or even removed. To do that in a consistent way is a challenge.

As I have mentioned, for string theory to make sense two strong theoretical constraints have to be met. Number one is the existence of supersymmetry and number two a stringent condition on the dimensionality of space-time. For superstrings the space-time dimension is ten. Indeed these conditions seem quite unnatural and make you worry, because neither supersymmetry nor ten-dimensional space-time have been observed. Yet from a mathematical consistency point of view there is no doubt about the necessity of imposing them from the start.

String interactions. In field theory the basic interactions are represented by interaction vertices where three or more particle lines meet and there is a coupling constant associated with each vertex. As strings represent all particle types their interactions should somehow take care of all particle interactions. In Figure I.4.50 it is clear that for the closed strings there is only one type of interaction vertex which corresponds to the joining and splitting of two strings and henceforth there is only one string coupling constant, called λ. The external legs of the string diagram, which represent the incoming and outgoing particles, are taken to be in the desired particle modes. This is how the different modes get coupled together and the complicated bookkeeping of labels is in some sense implicitly done by simply drawing the corresponding string diagram. A higher order string diagram with a number of incoming and outgoing strings is depicted in Figure I.4.51 .

String quantization.

Optimal paths. If you use Google maps it helps you find the shortest route. It offers you the choice between the shortest route in distance or the shortest route in time. What do particles do? If we take a photon, it will move from A to B along a path of minimal action, but what does that mean? The photon will certainly move along a straight line but that is the shortest in both time and distance. To really find out we have to do one more step. We know that in a medium like water or glass light moves slower than in vacuum or air. So, if A is under water and B above water the photons do *not* move along a straight line from A to B, they take a route that consists of two straight sections that

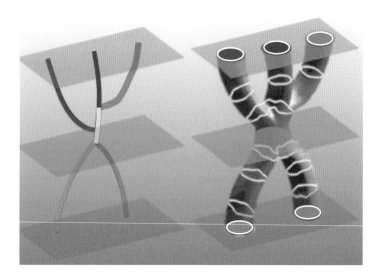

Figure I.4.50: *String interactions.* Strings have only one fundamental interaction vertex consisting of breaking or joining strings. So all different particle interaction diagrams of a given topology can be represented by a single string diagram.

make an angle at the surface. This is the problem we discussed in detail at the end of Chapter I.1 on page 18. The angle depends on the refraction indices in the two media, which are inverses of their velocities. The path that takes the shortest time is not the straight line from A to B, but rather a line that is broken at the surface. So the classical trajectories are optimal in the sense that they are minimal action trajectories, they correspond to local minima of the action.

That raises the interesting question that all school kids ask: How does a photon know which path to take? It can't do the necessary calculations, can it? No it can't! So it does not use Google's algorithm, which amounts to calculating most of the nearby paths in a restricted domain and choosing the optimal one. The photon, being a quantum particle does in fact a quantum computation it takes all paths simultaneously let them interfere and what comes out is weighted sum over possible paths the photon could have

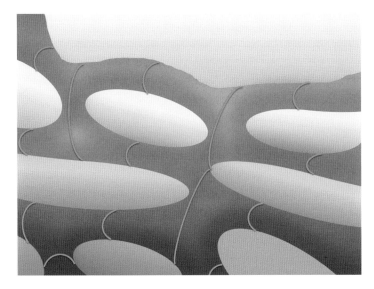

Figure I.4.51: *Joining and splitting strings.* Artist impression of strings moving in space-time and interacting by joining and splitting. It illustrates the geometric nature of string interactions. This string *world-sheet* has holes (handles) and closed boundaries which represent the incoming and outgoing closed strings.

taken. In short the photon performs a *path integral*.

The path integral. If we make the step to the quantum description of the particle, then we have to include all possible paths from A to B. The quantum propagation is now a weighted sum over paths, which is the famous Feynman path-integral. The probability amplitude to go from A to B is a superposition of amplitudes, the contribution of each path is weighted by an exponential phase factor where the phase is exactly the classical action of the path divided by $\hbar$.

So indeed in quantum mechanics these contributions can reinforce each other if they are in phase at B or dampen each other if they are out of phase; quantum particles interfere with themselves!

Going Euclidean. Here is another interesting aspect of path-integrals. In general they involve paths or config-

urations in space-time, which has a Lorentzian and not a Euclidean signature. However, what physicist often do when calculating or defining these integrals is to 'deform' them to Euclidean space, hence the term *Euclidean path-integral*. We calculate the Euclidean action of the paths and those with high action are exponentially suppressed with an exponent that equals *minus* the action divided by $\hbar$. One interesting consequence of this is that if we take the Euclidian action of a (d+1) dimensional physical system, we are summing over spatial configurations in a (d+1)-dimensional Euclidean space. But, as we argued in Chapter I.1 this is very much like doing statistical mechanics in (d+1) dimensions, where we for example calculated the partition function of the system as a sum of all possible configurations weighted by the Boltzmann factor which was also an exponential of minus the energy divided by kT. This correspondence expresses a profound relation between calculations in quantum field theory in d spatial and 1 time dimensions and calculations in statistical physics in (d+1) spatial dimensions. We will return to this connection in Chapter III.4.

From particles to strings. I tell you this particle story, because it helps to understand how string theory can be formulated as a generalization of a theory of point particles to a theory of one-dimensional extended objects. A classical path would typically correspond to a minimal action configuration of the world-sheet which corresponds to an extremal ('optimal') area of the word-sheet. The Euclidean equivalent for a closed string world sheet would be a soap bubble surface between two solid rings. And we know that a real soap bubble chooses the 'minimal energy' surface. It also showed what the fluctuations about the minimal energy configuration (the straight cylinder) look like: the string moves at intermediate times about its equilibrium position. There could also be wiggles running transversely – meaning along the string – but those have higher energy and unfortunately could not be excited with the soap-bubble kit I gave my daughter for her birthday in a failed attempt to make her study physics a long time ago.

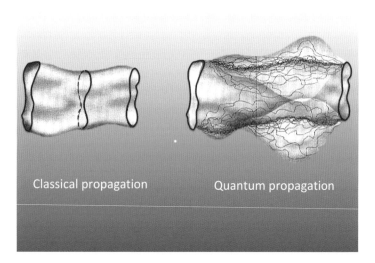

Figure I.4.52: *String propagator.* On the left the classical propagation of a string in space-time corresponding to the minimal action world-sheet bounded by the initial and final state. On the right the quantum propagation as a weighted sum over all string *world sheet configurations* bounded by the initial and final states. On the left there is a unique intermediate state, while on the right we have a superposition of many.

Figure I.4.53: *Euclidean world-sheet.* Woman keeping up the Euclidean appearance of 'vacuum bubble,' a contribution to the vacuum-to-vacuum amplitude for a closed string. (Source: Atelier bulles geantes)

A string amplitude implies summing over all possible world-sheets satisfying the appropriate boundary conditions. This is illustrated in Figure I.4.52, where on the right we have a superposition of configurations that contribute to the propagation from the initial (left) to the final (right) configuration. The action is basically the area, which depends on the metric on the world-sheet. The problem then boils down to the construction of a correct and well-defined measure for doing this integral over the 'space of all metrics', without leaving metrics out, but at the same time not overcounting. This is a complicated mathematical problem because of the huge symmetries in the problem.

This basically concludes my ham-handed introduction to the quantization of strings including small world-sheet fluctuations.

Weakly and strongly coupled strings. An important question at this point is, what are the world-sheet configurations that matter most, and will dominate the path-integral. In the figure just mentioned I have clearly limited myself to rather small fluctuations around minimal area classical configuration. So this is what a cheap navigator in your car would do, it misses out on surprising not so obvious shortcuts. You see for example that the topology of the world-sheets I included are all of the trivial cylindrical type. I have apparently not allowed for string interactions, meaning splitting and joining of tubes, and creating holes in the world sheet, like we depicted in Figure I.4.53. What this basically means is that I have assumed that the string interactions are *weak*. The stronger the string interaction are, the easier (more probable) the excitation these complicated surfaces of high genus will be.

A full string amplitude requires summing over *all* possible world-sheets that satisfy the appropriate boundary conditions, which means that you end up with a sum over *genera* (the number of holes) that label the topological class of the world sheet, and for any given genus you have to sum over all compatible metrics.

So as a relevant example let us consider the vacuum-to-vacuum amplitude for closed strings, This involves summing over all closed (no boundary) two-dimensional surfaces of arbitrary genus: these are called *Riemann surfaces*. They are embedded in (d+1)-dimensional Euclidean space and weighted by the negative exponential of their area. One such configuration with some holes features in Figure I.4.53 .[8] So this particular amplitude is now equivalent to an interesting problem in statistical physics: the calculation of the partition sum of random 2-dimensional surfaces in a d-dimensional space.

What these considerations make clear is that our naive intuitions about string theory really only apply to the case of weak string coupling, and nobody knows what a strongly coupled string theorie actually means. That is to say, up to about 1995 nobody understood, but after the so-called second string revolution in the present era of string theory, we know much better what's going on. We will discuss some of this shortly.

Five superstring theories. You would maybe hope that with such outlandish requirements string theory would be highly unique, after all how could a Theory of Everything not be unique! But this appeared not to be the case. There are five different superstring theories in ten dimensions, which differ very much by the symmetries they have. Let us list these theories without further going into detail about their specific features: we distinguish: *Type I, Type IIA, Type IIB, Heterotic* $E8 \times E8$, and *Heterotic* $SO(32)$. We have depicted these superstring theories and how they are connected to each other and with M-theory, to be discussed shortly, in Figure I.4.60 .

So, either these theories are wrong, or we have to work very hard to understand how our not-so-supersymmetric, not-so-ten-dimensional world can be interpreted as a not-so-simple solution to the equations that govern string theory. In that sense the theory does make very strong predictions, which at least in principle are falsifiable. This implies that we cannot just go out and do a decisive experiment, however, Predictions that have spent ages in waiting rooms are not uncommon in science, and this now also applies *a fortiori* to the very fundamentals of the quantum gravity world.

So far we have discussed (extended) supersymmetry as a distinguishing feature of supersymmetric gauge theories and super gravity theories. The next question is what the additional requirement that space-time be ten-dimensional means.

Ten-dimensional space-time? The second consistency condition of string theory is that space-time has to be 10-dimensional; this is in strong contrast to the 4-dimensional version we are all familiar with. At first this requirement sounds too outrageous to be true, and is all day convincingly falsified by our daily experience! But for theorists nothing is unsurmountable, they bear in mind Einstein's consoling words: 'Subtle is the Lord but malicious He is not.' And they have cooked up scenarios of how to get rid of six of those ten dimensions by a procedure called *compactification*. This amounts to tightly 'rolling up' the extra dimensions into a variety of compact manifolds like spheres or tori or combinations thereof.

Kaluza – Klein theory. This way of effectively reducing the dimension of space has a long history, and goes back to the first quarter of the twentieth century. Theodor Kaluza and Oskar Klein independently proposed a geometrical unification of the gravitational and electromagnetic forces, by looking at General Relativity in five dimensions, where they assumed that the fifth dimension would be curled up into a tiny circle. Interestingly, the extra components of

---

[8]A not-so-nice colleague suggested that this was part of a job application ceremony.

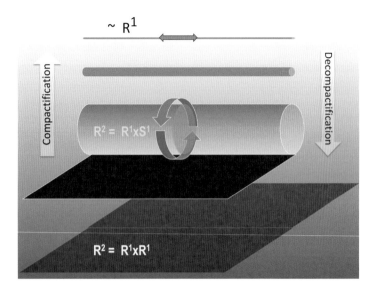

Figure I.4.54: *Compactification.* Here we give an idea how one spatial dimension can be compactified to a circle. The rotational U(1) symmetry of the circle results in the existence of U(1) gauge field in the large dimension. The relative coupling to the matter fields is inversely proportional to the radius R of the internal circle. In this perspective taking a weak coupling limit is like opening up an extra dimension ($R \rightarrow \infty$). This is the original dimensional compactification scheme of Kaluza and Klein, which plays also a role in going from 11-dimensional M-theory to 10-dimensional superstring theories.

the curvature tensor you get in going from four to five dimension would correspond to the degrees of freedom of the electromagnetic field in four dimensions (and an extra scalar field). The extra components of the metric would be '$g_{\mu5} = g_{5\mu}$.' These generically correspond to the gauge potential A_μ, with g_{55} being an extra scalar field. Furthermore, the whole 5-dimensional system of Einstein's equations, after compactification, correctly reproduces the coupled Maxwell-Einstein equations in four dimensions. The momentum component in the fifth dimension of a moving particle basically corresponds to its electric charge. Einstein actually liked the idea but it was hard to reconcile with quantum theory and therefore slid into decline.

In science, attractive ideas that don't quite work can be

safely stored away in a kind of fridge. This fridge consists foremost of the collective memory of the scientific community, and the written records of course. Ideas can hibernate for years or even for a century or so, before getting rediscovered and making a glamorous come-back in a novel context. Compactifying dimensions à la K-K is such an idea. The extra dimensions would probably be too tiny to see with present-day accelerators. To probe such small sizes you need correspondingly small wavelengths, which mean very high energies. So in that way you escape the manifest presence of those dimensions. But there is one feature that would be manifest at low energies. If the compactified space has symmetries – and it usually has – those symmetries after quantization give rise to massless particles that would clearly manifest themselves, also at low energies. It is precisely the rotational symmetry of the circle geometry of the fifth dimension that generates the massless photon in the Kaluza-Klein scenario!

Suppose we compactify one dimension of space into a circle then that has important consequences for the allowed states of a quantum particle. Remember that the spectrum of the momentum or energies for a free particle in flat space is continuous, and the wavefunction for a fixed momentum (p) state corresponds to a sinusoidal wave with the wavelength $\lambda = \hbar/p$. With the compactified dimension being a circle the particle momenta are quantized exactly as in the old Bohr model we discussed in Chapter I.3 on page 134, because we have the periodicity condition that the wave has to fit on the circle: $n\lambda = 2\pi R$ and therefore (relativistic) $E_n = p_n \sim n/R$. And in the original K-K model this component of the momentum is just the charge of the particle, that charge is thus quantized. The attentive reader now will ask whether here we have a model without monopoles where charge would be quantized. How come? The answer is that in this model topologically stable monopole configurations do exist as solitons much like in the supersymmetric gauge theory we discussed before. So Dirac does not have to turn in his grave!

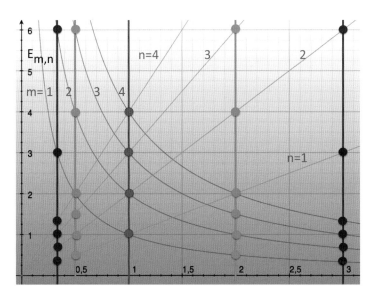

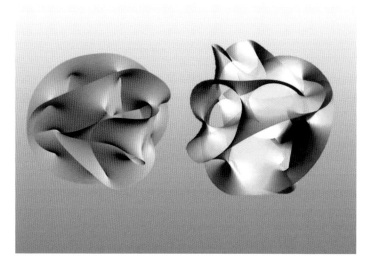

Figure I.4.55: *T-duality.* The non-oscillating modes of a of (bosonic) closed string on a circle with compactification radius R. The energy $E = E_m + E_n \simeq mR + \dfrac{n}{R}$, where m is the (topological) winding number and n the momentum which is also quantized. We have drawn the vertical lines for fixed R, demonstrating that the energy spectrum for radius R and $1/R$ are identical if we interchange m and n, making the spectra identical. Taking the limit $R \to \infty$ is decompactifying, which is like opening up an extra dimension. This means that the topological sector disappears and the momentum becomes continuous.

Figure I.4.56: *Compactification, the story of six inner dimensions.* Compactification means that space-time has four large and six compact or internal dimensions. Here we show two three-dimensional projections of possible six-dimensional compactifying spaces. It is evident that these so-called Calabi-Yau spaces have intricate geometries. (Source: Polytope24)

T-duality. If we have a string theory and we compactify one dimension, something interesting happens with the states of a simple string in that dimension. Of course the string can oscillate, but we are not interested in those states at this point. We want to look at the zero-modes. The string can move around the circle and behave like a particle, and that gives the spectrum we just discussed $E_n \sim p \sim n/R$, but for a string there are distinct topological sectors as the (closed) string can wind an integer number m times around the circle with radius R. This gives a contribution to the energy of the string proportional to its length so that gives a topological contribution $E_m \sim mR$. So, for a string we arrive (choosing appropriate units) at a simple formula for the energy spectrum of the

non-oscillatory modes: $E = E_n + E_m = n/R + mR$. This spectrum is remarkable because it has an exact symmetry under the inversion $R \to 1/R$, as is shown graphically in Figure I.4.55.

And as the circle is part of the space-time, the target space in which the string moves, this symmetry or map is called '*T-duality*' or *target space duality*. Here we showed the elementary example where the duality was actually a symmetry, a self-duality, but the duality as a map plays an important role in the mapping of different 10-dimensional superstring theories onto each other as we will see shortly.

Note that we have encountered two types of duality: the first was called 'S-duality' or 'strong-weak duality' which may apply to both supersymmetric particle and string theories. Secondly we have 'T-duality' or 'target space duality', which makes only sense for string theories.

Calabi-Yau compactifications. An interesting quite special class of compact six-dimensional spaces over which the superstring can be compactified is the class of 6-dimensional Calabi-Yau manifolds, used in the compactification from ten to four space-time dimensions. These spaces have a number of very special properties that we will not discuss here. In Figure I.4.56 we exhibit two-dimensional views of three real dimensional cross-sections of these six-dimensional spaces. They are of interest for certain superstring theories, because they ensure that the resulting four-dimensional theory closely resembles a super extension of the Standard Model.

The multiverse. A weakness of the compactification scenarios in string theory is that nobody has been able to show that compactifications – if any – would be generated dynamically by this prospective Theory of Everything. This is a pressing issue because what looked like a unique and universal theory turns out to have an astronomical proliferation of conceivable compactifications. But to each compactification would correspond a different type of four-dimensional universe, with its own cosmic history, particle content and set of forces, in short, its own Not-So-Standard Model! Some of these universes could collapse before anything interesting would happen. Others may expand too fast for stars to form, let alone life to develop. In some of them there would be light, while in others none, or maybe many sorts of light. In fact a mind-boggling universe of universes is opening up, which is called the *multiverse*.

String theory so far is a theory of many possible theories, a theory of a multiverse in which wildly differing types of physics could manifest themselves, even in parallel. And, yes, ours would be just one of them. This is quite orthogonal to the basic motivation of most scientists who search for a unique universal theory of Nature. The common prejudice used to be that the Theory of Everything would come up with our dear universe as the unique or at least strongly favoured solution. We like to think of our

Figure I.4.57: *A multiverse?* An artists impression of the multiverse. A two-dimensional projection of a ten-dimensional compactification scheme. (Source: Forum Futura)

world as the unique expression of the universal principles underlying that theory. It would have left the Creator but one option. It came somewhat as a shock that, after a promising start in that all-overarching direction, string theory moved in fact the opposite way. Maybe it is trying to tell us something contrary to our expectations, and for that science has excellent credentials. After all, the existence of a multiverse is yet another step away from our old anthropocentric dream of us being (in) the center of THE universe. THE universe? What are you talking about? Such a dramatic form of relativism would indeed constitute the ultimate irony of science, or of human existence.

It is not by accident that a strong protagonist of the multiverse, Leonard Susskind of Stanford University who wrote a popular book called *The Multiverse* about it, claims that the proper interpretation and *main prediction* of string theory is precisely that we live in a multiverse. The nasty aspect of this view is that the existence and properties of our own universe become extremely hard to predict from such a premise and in that sense not much progress has been made. It is an example of where contingency and evolutionary thinking enters physics at the most fundamental level. It is analogous but much worse than asking a physicist to precisely predict the number and sizes of the planetary orbits in our solar system from Newton's laws. That can't be done. Newton's equations describe all sorts of planetary systems. And indeed, all observed systems do fit in his framework, but asking to predict them would be many bridges too far. And to be fair we don't expect that because we know that the details of the solar system are the outcome of a highly contingent, non-universal historical process and not simply calculable from first principles. To put it differently, all dogs are animals but not all animals are dogs, that's the problem! The biological conundrum, we know what an animal is and what the species on Earth look like, but predicting them from single-cell organisms using genetics is somewhat harder.

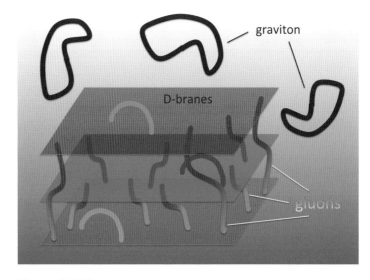

Figure I.4.58: *D-branes and strings.* A stack of three flat D2-branes. Open strings have to end on branes, by connecting them they represent nine $U(3)$ gauge fields living on the branes. This figure is is reminiscent of Figure I.4.37 with the bi-colored lines representing gluons propagating. Closed strings are not connected to branes and correspond to gravitons.

M-theory, D-branes and dualities

> It was believed for many years that there were five possible string theories, prompting the question: if one of these describes our universe, who lives in the other four worlds? But recently it has become clear that those five string theories are limiting cases of one majestic and mysterious theory.
>
> Edward Witten, *Nature* (1996)

D-branes. Whether they liked it or not, string theorists discovered that strings are not enough to make a consistent quantum theory of gravity. In fact 11-dimensional supergravity had a somewhat uncomfortable 'living apart together' relation with the 10-dimensional string theories. This supposedly low energy approximation of string theory lived one dimension up and had features that were lacking in string theory. These were stable soliton like classical solutions called branes, to be thought of as p-dimensional generalizations of membranes. This quite naturally prompted the question what the role of these *p-branes* in string theory would be.

Strings are one-dimensional extended objects, and indeed, a question that came up already early-on was: why if you give up the unique particle notion as the fundamental starting point, stop at one-dimensional extended objects? Why not include membranes and other higher dimensional extended objects? It was part of the second string revolution around 1995 that Joe Polchinski of the Kavli Institute for Theoretical Physics in Santa Barbara had the crucial insight that higher dimensional objects he called *D-branes* had to be included indeed. He intoduced D-branes in string theory as the end points of open strings. They could therefore in principle have dimensions p running from zero to nine. D-branes could be flat of infinite extent, or curled up into compact objects like black holes for example, they could be single or stacked up. Each type of string theory would allow for D-branes of specific dimensions. In superstring theory these p-dimensional D-branes, or Dp-branes, are dynamical objects which in the appropriate supergravity limit correspond with the very heavy soliton-like p-banes.

In Figure I.4.58 we have depicted a stack of three colored D2-branes, and we have also drawn open strings ending on them. Let us discuss this picture in the weak coupling low energy limit of string theory, then it is known that open strings carry a vector representation of supersymmetry algebra. These open string states correspond to fields carrying one space-time index μ in this case running from 0 to $p = 2$, and carry two 'internal' (color) indices labeling the branes to which they are connected, in other words they beg to be identified as gauge fields A_μ^{ab}. In the figure there are nine possible color combinations, making up a three-dimensional $U(3)$ 'color' gauge theory. The picture clearly shows that the gauge theory is attached to the Dp-brane and therefore (p+1)-dimensional. From the branes point of view the strings between them are like excitations of the branes, they describe the brane dynamics. If the D-brane is embedded in a higher dimensional space then we have that the closed strings live in a higher-dimensional $(d > p)$ space then the gauge fields as indicated in the figure. This fact posed yet another conundrum one had to face. One additional comment on the figure, imagine the the D-branes to be so-called *black branes* meaning that they would correspond to some horizon then one could imagine the open strings pairing up to make some closed strings which could then leave the D-brane. The brane would radiate!

M-theory and superstring dualities.

> This theory, which is sometimes called M-theory (according to taste, M stands for magic, mystery, marvel, membrane or matrix), is seen by many as a likely candidate fo a complete description of nature.
> Edward Witten, *Nature* (1996)

In Figure I.4.60 we give a bird-eye's view of the modelling landscape in ten and eleven dimensions. Who is living

Figure I.4.59: *Duality.* In this painting of the Renaissance Milanese painter Guiseppe Arcimbolo (1526 – 1593), we see that a given physical vegetarian reality, this particular painting called *Verdure* or *Vegetables*, has two different interpretations which are dual to each other. In the weak coupling limit it is a vegetable basket, in the – I presume – strong coupling limit it turns into a vegetable face. The transformation is a rotation over an angle of π. (Source: ©Photo Scala, Florence.)

where and how they are related. The precursor of string theory was 11-dimensional supergravity: it did have attractive features like for example classical 2- and 5-brane solutions but seemed to not be fully consistent. In the figure it has moved a bit to the background because it is presently understood to be the low energy approximation of M-theory. The magic theory that remains in many ways a mystery, as there is no explicit formulation available, and we don't even know if such a formulation exists. And therefore the most fundamental principle underlying M-theory may still be hidden as well.

M-theory is known because of its low energy supergravity manifestation and through other limits which manifest themselves as the five superstring theories in ten dimensions. These limits are related to compactification of one

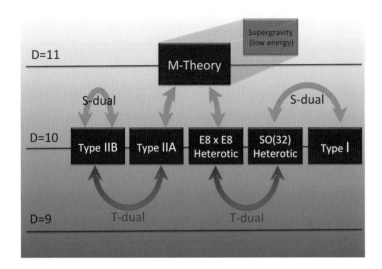

Figure I.4.60: *M-theory.and string dualities.* M-theory is a theory in eleven dimensions. It contains all five 10-dimensional superstring theory types. These ten-dimensional theories can be related through certain S- and T-dualities.

space dimension. For example the low energy limit – supergravity – can be compactified over a circle to ten dimensions, where the supergravity 2-brane is wrapped around that circle, which reduces the 2-brane to a string. And the resulting theory could be identified as the weakly coupled ten-dimensional *Type 2A* string theory. In the strong coupling limit of the string theory the compactified dimension would open up as we have discussed before. Furthermore, in the *Type IIA* string theory one could do a T-duality transformation (like $R \to 1/R$), which turns the theory into the *Type IIB* string theory. So it is in this sense that many connections between the various models were established, and indeed this network of dualities clearly demonstrated that these five theories are basically five different guises of one underlying theory, which has been named M-theory. Quite a mind-boggler!

At this point of the tour we have arrived at the center of the third string era, and I could imagine that if you are a 'freshman' reader, not at all familiar with these ideas,

this narrative will come across as an arcane, brilliant but bizarre endeavor. A type of excursion in domains of the mind that you would not expect in a book about physics, a discipline that stands out for its factual rigour and its exemplary strong empirical basis.

The reason that I include these developments is exactly because this is what the struggle of science at the frontiers of knowledge may look like and should look like. It should be explorative in all conceivable ways, as long as it is not plainly stupid. This holds for the experimental as well as theoretical domain. It was Einstein who in 1934 made the following remark:

> The theoretical scientist is compelled in an increasing degree to be guided by purely mathematical, formal considerations [...]. The theorist who undertakes such a labor should not be carped at as "fanciful"; on the contrary, he should be granted the right to give free rein to his fancy, for there is no other way to the goal.

Let us take this advice to heart and embark on exploring a final set of far reaching ideas that got a spectacular impetus out of string theory.

Holography and the AdS/CFT program

> We would like to advocate here a somewhat extreme point of view. We suspect that there simply are no more degrees of freedom (inside a volume) to talk about than the ones on can draw on its surface as given by $S = A/4$. The situation can be compared with a hologram of a three-dimensional image on a two-dimensional surface. The details of the hologram on the surface are intricate and contain as much information as it is allowed by the finiteness of the wavelength of light–read the Planck length.
>
> Gerard 't Hooft *Salamfestschrift* (1993)

Holography. We are going to discuss a profound novel correspondence that is of interest to physics and mathematics of many sorts. It is the holographic idea, that all the information contained in a space of $(d+1)$ dimensions can be faithfully represented on a holographic screen of d dimensions. In the context of gravity, this conjecture was first put forward in the quantum understanding of black holes by 't Hooft as early as 1993 and taken up shortly after by Susskind in the context of string theory. We have talked about black hole entropy and the information paradox in the section on black holes in the previous chapter on page 139. The current narrative is that information cannot get lost but instead is somehow encoded, 'frozen in', on the horizon. The horizon keeps track of all things that pass by, so to say. This information content corresponds exactly with the Bekenstein-Hawking entropy that is also located on the horizon of the black hole. It would allow for the possibility that the information would ultimately be carried away again as hidden correlations in the Hawking radiation. So the information carried by things that have fallen into a black hole can – in principle at least – be retrieved. In particular in a consistent quantum mechanical description of the black-hole formation and evaporation process this *has* to be the case.

Black hole holography. The study of holography applied to black holes in the context of string theory culminated in a 1997 paper by Juan Maldacena at the Institute for Advanced study in Princeton, in which he made a strong claim of an exact dual relation between a superstring theory in a 5-dimensional Anti de Sitter space denoted as AdS_5, and an $\mathcal{N}=4$ supersymmetric $SU(N)$ gauge theory for large N defined on the boundary of AdS_5, which is equivalent to four-dimensional flat Minkowski space. This exceptional claim has in the meantime been substantiated and extended in many very convincing ways.

It brings together a number of ideas that we have touched upon in this book: the idea of symmetric curved space-times that are solutions to Einstein's equations, the idea

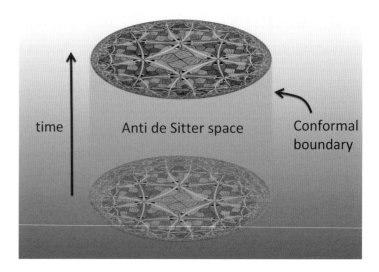

Figure I.4.61: *AdS/CFT correspondence.* The superstring theory compactifed over S^5 to a five-dimensional Anti de Sitter (AdS) space-time, which corresponds to the interior of the cylinder. That space has a 4-d boundary which is a flat Minkowski space (the cylindrical surface) on which a conformal field theory (CFT) lives, which is the hologram, a fancy encoded but faithful representation of the five-dimensional string theory in the interior.

of supersymmetry and supergravity, the $\mathbf{N}=4$ superconformal gauge theories, and the ideas of string theory/supergravity compactification. Indeed a more encompassing confluence of ideas is hard to imagine and it may rekindle dark memories of some horrifying final exam that you once failed. I am sorry!

To be slightly more specific we are discussing the 10-dimensional IIB string and supergravity models, which are defined on a ten-dimensional space-time $\mathbf{M}=AdS_5 \otimes S^5$, then on the AdS space one ends up not with 8 but 4 supersymmetries, the other four get broken by the compactification. Furthermore the background space AdS_5 is a very special space that has a large symmetry group which corresponds with the four-dimensional conformal group, and this yields a space-time theory with a $\mathbf{N}=4$ superconformal symmetry.

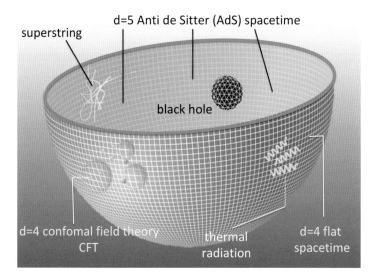

Figure I.4.62: *AdS/CFT correspondence.* An artist's impression of the holographic principle as it is operative in a compactification from ten to five dimensions. The superstring theory lives in a five-dimensional Anti de Sitter (AdS) space-time (inside the bowl). That space has a 4-d boundary which is a flat Minkowski space (the blue bowl) on which a conformal field theory (CFT) lives, which is the hologram, a fancy encoded but faithful representation of the five-dimensional string theory in the interior. (after A.T. Kamajan)

This string theory has actual open and closed strings but also D4-branes and we put a stack of N at the boundary, so producing an $N = 4$ super-conformal SU(N) gauge theory at the boundary. Note that the symmetries of both theories coincide and therefore that will facilitate the identification of string states in the bulk with particular observables in the quantum field theory.

This gauge/gravity duality is a strong-weak type duality, which means that the low energy weakly coupled gravitational theory tells us about the strong coupling behavior of the quantum field theory. And as there is a complete equivalence the converse is also true, so the weakly coupled gauge theory should teach us about strongly interacting string theory.

If you look at the Hilbert space of states or the spectrum of the string theory on AdS_5, you get an impression how involved and surprising this Maldacena correspondence must be. For very low energy the theory of gravity just is the Einstein equations linearized around the background, and the excitations are gravitational waves. If we move to string theory, we get the closed strings which represent the massless supergravity degrees of freedom and if the background has D-branes we will excite open strings attached to branes. After that massive string modes will also be excited. When we go up even further in energy we will enter the regime where D-branes will be created. And if they are sufficiently heavy, they may start to form small black holes. And the more energy we put in the heavier and larger the black holes become. This process can continue until the horizon coincides with the boundary of a very large black hole. To imagine that this great variety of interacting degrees of freedom can be faithfully mapped to a large N super-conformal gauge theory is quite miraculous. What I can tell you is that a great variety of checks has been performed (involving very extensive computations of particular features) and all of these have confirmed the expectations.

However, the real shortcoming of this correspondence is that it only seems to work in this quite exceptional geometry with the serious problem that it involves the *Anti* de Sitter space which has a *negative* cosmological constant. This is in direct contradiction to the well-established fact that our universe has a small but definitely *positive* cosmological constant. This appears to pose a serious challenge to the AdS/CFT programme. The question is whether there is some version of a duality that holds also in De Sitter space.

Emergent gravity. This brings us to a brief description of the still rather controversial idea of 'emergent' or 'entropic gravity' and its protagonists like Erik Verlinde and collaborators. They have addressed the question of what could happen if we move from an Anti de Sitter to a De Sitter background with positive cosmological constant. It is suggested that a rigorous holographic image on the boundary is no longer what happens, instead the speculation is that the entropy will acquire a volume term and spread from the boundary into the space, maybe causing deviations from Newtons laws that look like the effects of dark matter and dark energy. If confirmed by further analysis that would certainly constitute another truly stunning result.

At home in the quantum world

> Before I came here I was confused about this subject. Having listened to your lecture I am still confused. But on a higher level.
>
> *Enrico Fermi*

We have come to the end of the first part of the book. This part was devoted to the basic concepts and contents of quantum theory and its classical roots, as it developed over the last century. We of course always have lived in a quant-essential world, but it is only now dawning upon us what that means. We started by describing the gems of classical physics, which ran into a number of serious troubles that could only be resolved by embracing the quantum principles. In this chapter we described the subsequent successes of applying the quantum principles to ever deeper layers of the microscopic world. A journey that as we saw is by no means completed.

Quantum theory entered our thinking on the atomic scale, say at 10^{-10} meters, and from there it started spreading. We recall that there are two ways to go from there and extend the results. The first is to go to ever smaller scales, and that is the route we have followed in this first part of the book. We went all the way down from the atom, via the nuclear structure to the elementary quarks and leptons, to a scale of about 10^{-20} meters, the scale accessible to modern accelerators like the LHC at CERN.

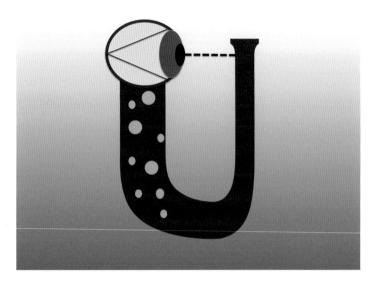

Figure I.4.63: *It fom Bit.* In a famous essay John Archibald Wheeler pondered over the philosophical ramifications of the idea that Information lies at the basis of our universe. Is it possible that All of Nature grew out of information only? The Cosmic Code as an all-embracing Hyper Genetics. This intriguing image also symbolizes evolution, or how Nature seems to be in search of itself, through the human effort of scientific inquiry, which by definition is part of that Nature.

The other way is to go up and apply quantum theory on scales corresponding to chemistry, or the many other forms of condensed matter that we find in nature or create in the lab. We save this part of the quantum story for the final Volume. The next, middle part of the book is called *quantessence*, and is devoted to the more formal aspects of quantum theory. We will expose some of its very rich logical and mathematical structure and comment on it. I think it would be a poor choice to leave it out, exactly because it is a central part of quantum theory. We can't really do without because what makes the theory so attractive is that on a conceptual level it is so counter-intuitive. And where confusion reigns it is vital to keep the language as clean as possible as to be sure about what the questions are and what the answers mean. I don't know of any theory where the mathematical framework is so rich and unambiguous, and at the same time the narratives and interpretations are so paradoxical and hard to grasp. This makes the theory exciting and we will discuss a number of well-known but stupefying paradoxes in the next Volume. We are all set to start climbing the amazing mount quantum.

If the world 'out there' is writhing like a barrel of eels, why do we detect a barrel of concrete when we look? To put the question differently, where is the boundary between the random uncertainty of the quantum world, where particles spring into and out of existence, and the orderly certainty of the classical world, where we live, see, and measure? This question...is as deep as any in modern physics. It drove the years-long debate between Bohr and Einstein. . . . Every physical quantity derives its ultimate significance from bits, binary yes-or-no indications, a conclusion which we epitomize in the phrase, *it from bit.*

John Archibald Wheeler,
Geons, Black Holes & Quantum Foam (1998)

Further reading.
On nuclear physics:

— *Introductory Nuclear Physics*
Kenneth S. Krane
Wiley (1988)

On particle physics:

— *Introduction to Elementary Particle Physics*
Alessandro Bettini
Cambridge University Press (2014)

— *Concepts of Elementary Particle Physics*
Michael E. Peskin
Oxford University Press (2019)

On string theory:

— *The Elegant Universe - Superstrings, Hidden Dimensions, and the Quest for the Ultimate Theory*
Brian Greene
W. W. Norton & Company (2010)

— *The Little Book of String Theory*
Steven S. Gubser
Princeton University Press (2010)

Complementary reading:

— *The Second Creation: Makers of the Revolution in Twentieth-Century Physics*
Robert P. Crease
Page (1991)

Indices

Subject index Volume I

Name index Volume I